2022 Surface Preparation and Cleaning Conference

Chandler, Arizona, USA
17 – 21 October 2022

ISBN: 978-1-7138-6333-5

Printed from e-media with permission by:

Curran Associates, Inc.
57 Morehouse Lane
Red Hook, NY 12571

Some format issues inherent in the e-media version may also appear in this print version.

Printed with permission by Curran Associates, Inc. (2023)

For permission requests, please contact Surface Preparation and Cleaning Conference (SPCC) at the address below.

Surface Preparation and Cleaning Conference (SPCC)
c/o Mark Thirsk
Linx Consulting-PO Box 384
Mendon, MA 01756-0384
USA

Phone: 617-273-8837

mthirsk@linx-consulting.com

Additional copies of this publication are available from:

Curran Associates, Inc.
57 Morehouse Lane
Red Hook, NY 12571 USA
Phone: 845-758-0400
Fax: 845-758-2633
Email: curran@proceedings.com
Web: www.proceedings.com

TABLE OF CONTENTS

Glass wafer backside opaque layer removal on 300mm fabrication tool for advanced packaging

*Ju-Geng Lai, and Efrain Altamirano-Sánchez
Imec, Kapeldreef 75, 3001 Heverlee, Belgium *kenneth.lai@imec.be

Introduction

- Glass wafers are used as carriers for temporary bonding and dies transferring from silicon carrier to tape frame or target wafer for advanced 3D-DTCO.
- An opaquing layer is deposited on the glass-wafers to enable wafer handling and processing in 300 mm tools and downstream integration.
- The glass carrier wafers could suffer opaque frame damage after laser debonding and adhesive layer removal. In this study, we developed a new opaquing layer stack and a removal method on 300 mm glass-wafers.

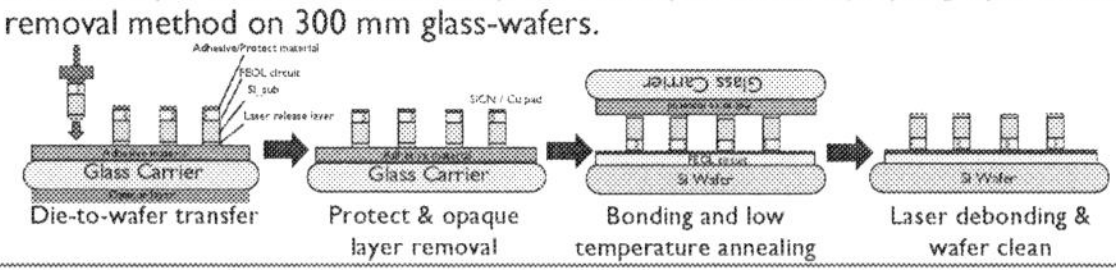

Opaque layer stack on glass wafer

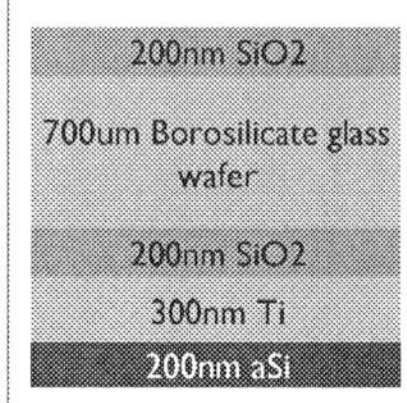

- The borosilicate glass-wafer is encapsulated by a SiO2 layer to protect it from metal contamination and extend the carrier's lifetime for re-using.
- A Ti thin layer is deposited on the backside of the glass carrier wafer as an opaquing layer.
- The aSi layer prevents metal contamination on the wafer handling system in the 300 mm tools and provides certain etch selectivity to the SiO2 sub-layer.

HF/HNO3 etch evaluation for opaque stacks

- The hydrofluoric nitric acid (HF/HNO3) mixture is a chemistry that is generally used for bulk Si etch.
- Visual inspection results demonstrate similar color change and process time dependency for Ti, aSi, and aSi-Ti stack blanket wafer after HF/HNO3 etching.
- These data provide significant evidence that HF/HNO3 can remove protect layer aSi and opaquing layer Ti. Color changes suggest SiO2 sub-layer loss after aSi/Ti removal.

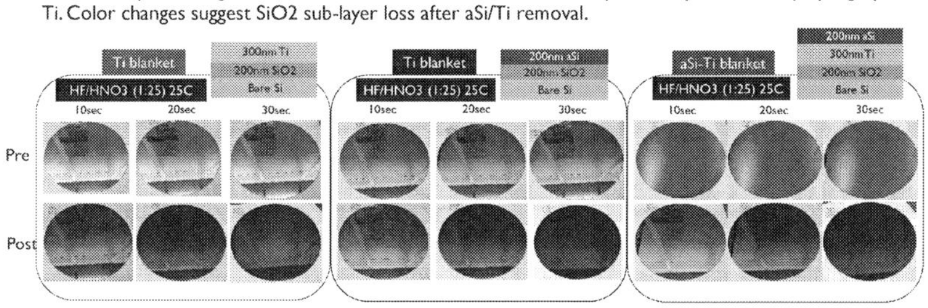

- The interception of SiO2 etching calibration curve indicates both 200nm aSi and 300nm Ti layer are fully removed in the first 4~5sec.
- The 200 nm SiO_2 used as a protection layer provides a good process margin, enabling the de-opaquing and protection of the glass carrier.

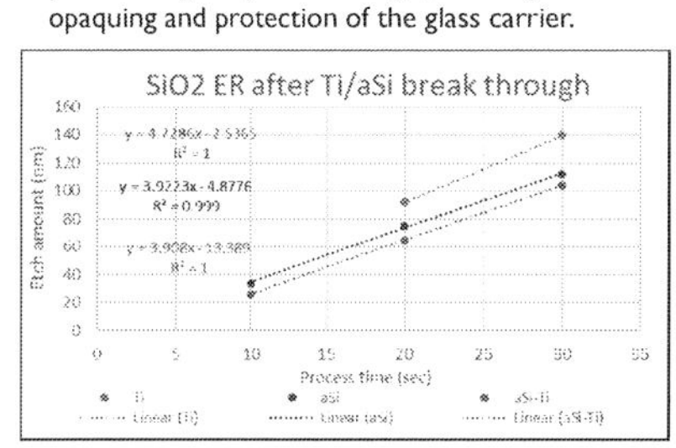

Hardware capabilities for opaque and transparent wafers

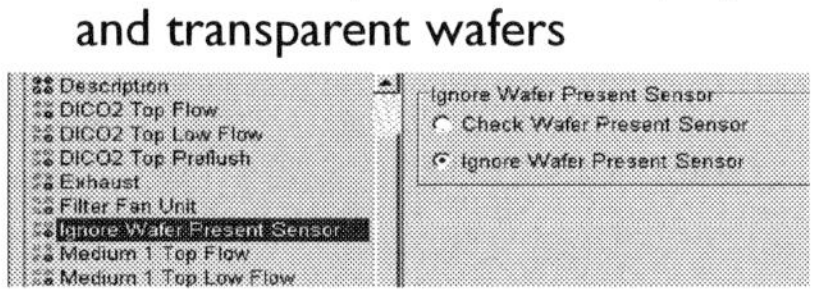

- We carried out the test in a DV-Prime™ from Lam Research, where opaque and transparent wafers can be processed by programming sensor wafers.
- This function can be defined by recipe setting for transparent glass substrate and Si wafer.

Opaque layer removal from glass wafer

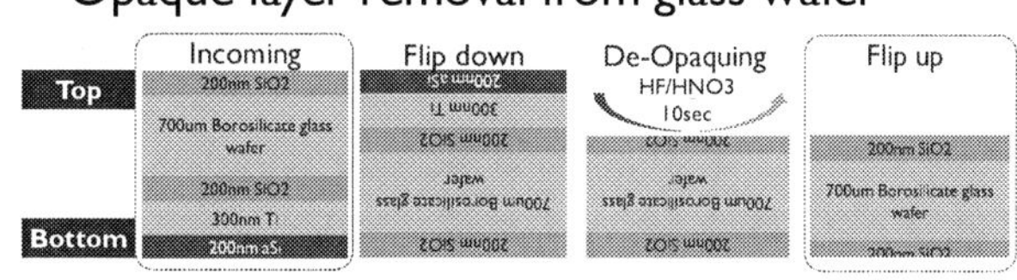

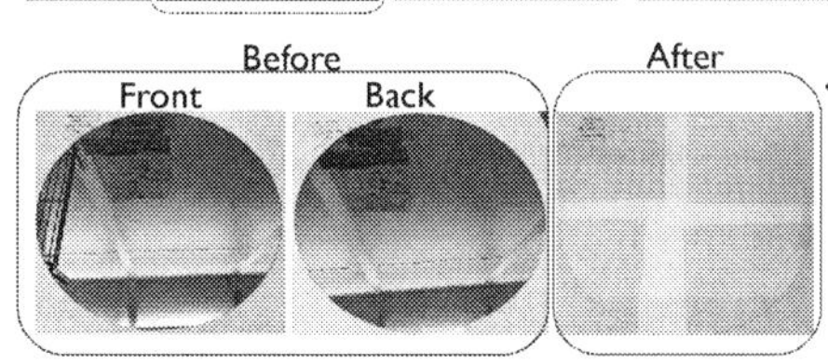

- The backside opaquing stack removal (aSi/Ti) on SiO2/borosilicate glass wafer was carried out on DV-Prime™ which has a wafer flip function that can execute a backside clean/etch process which was upgraded to be able to handle transparent glass carrier wafers.

HF/HNO3 lifetime evaluation

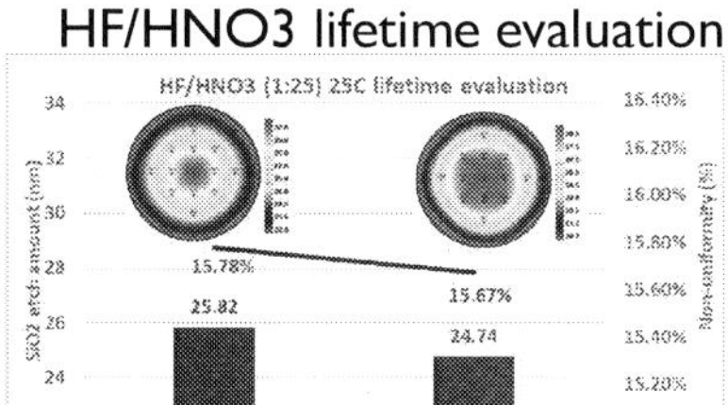

- HF/HNO3 mixture is pre-mixed before processing for better chemistry stability.
- Lifetime test proved steady HF/HNO3 etching in 72hrs.

Full lot process stability test

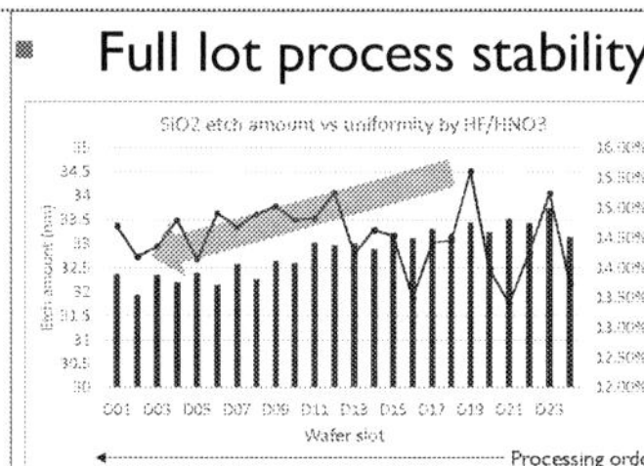

- For chemistry saving, HF/HNO3 will be reclaimed to mixing tank during processing.
- Full lot test show robust WtW process condition.

Non-uniformity	
WiW (average)	14.52%
WtW	2.73%

Formula: (MAX-min)/2Average

Summary

- In this study, we defined opaquing stack and the function of each utilized layer.
- The hydrofluoric nitric acid mixture can remove both amorphous silicon and titanium layers with good selectivity to silicon oxide.
- The opaquing layer (Ti) on the SiO2/glass wafer can be removed on a 300 mm production tool.
- HF/HNO3 lifetime evaluation and full lot test demonstrated stable chemistry and robust process conditions for opaquing layer removal.
- These results provide a method that can be successfully transferred from the lab to the fab environment for advanced 3D integration.

www.imec-int.com

Air Liquide

Surface Nanoparticle Monitoring for Plasma Etching Chamber Components Using Single Particle - ICP-MS

Lisa M Mey -Ami, Fuhe Li
Balazs Nanoanalysis; 46409 Landing Pkwy, Fremont, CA 94538
Lisa.Mey -Ami@airliquide.com

Introduction

- Nanoparticles are defined as particles with at least one dimension in the nano-scale (1-100 nm) range and they are either naturally occurring or engineered.
- Naturally occurring particles are often present as contaminants in all aspects of the chip fabrication process, including etching, lithography, chemical mechanical planarization (CMP), deposition, and implantation.
- **Nanoparticle contaminants are recognized as leading cause of microchip failures for current and next generation semiconductor manufacturing**

BALAZS Nanoanalysis

Why Nanoparticle Analysis is Needed

10-100 nm particles are now critical. Monitoring & controlling single nm and near 1 nm particles will soon be required.

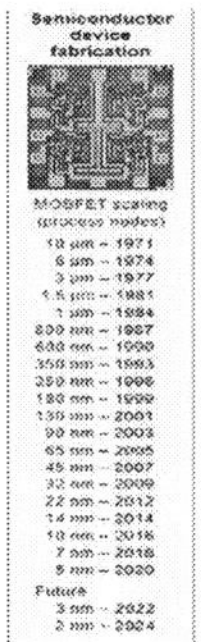

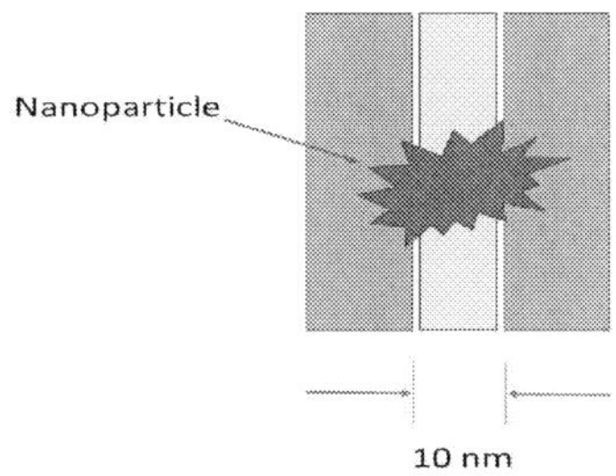

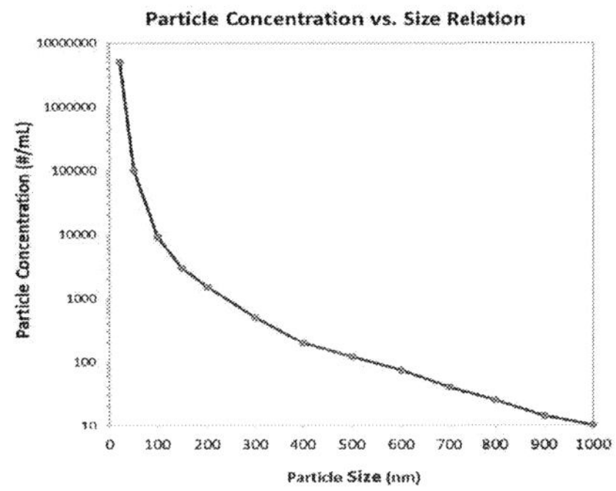

BALAZS nanoanalysis

Plasma Etching

- Etching is a critical circuit-defining step in the modern semiconductor ULSI device fabrication
- Components of an etching chamber are high-purity materials (e.g. quartz, silicon carbide or coated ceramics)
- However, contamination can be caused by surface corrosion due to reactive gases using in etching process (chemical cause) and/or plasma surface ion bombardment or sputtering (physical cause).
- Particles are one of the forms of the surface contamination which can adversely affect the device performance and device fabrication yield (especially the sub-10nm process)

BALAZS nanoanalysis

Novel technique: Application sp -ICP-MS for Particles on Solid Surfaces

- Particles are routinely removed from a solid surface by scrubbing the solid surface by mechanical agitation. The water extracts are analyzed for particles using a laser particle counter (LPC).

- Single Nanoparticle ICP-MS with its greater sensitivity (single nm resolution) than LPC was applied to the part extracts scrubbed by mechanical agitation

- In addition, higher frequency techniques for scrubbing the surface: ultrasonic and megasonic energies were recently explored and the extracts were subjected to sp -ICP-MS analysis

BALAZS nanoanalysis

Typical LPC Results of OEM Parts Post Cleaning:
** No Elemental or NP size (<100nm) info **

Particles/cm ^{2}	> 0.1 – < 0.5 μM **Spec: 10,000**	> 0.5 - < 2 μM **Spec: 1000**	> 2 μM **Spec 100**
Quartz Ring	750 - 900	120 - 130	23 - 54
Aluminum Coupon	70 - 110	13 -20	0 - 1
Ceramic Ring	890 - 920	120 - 170	0 - 4

BALAZS nanoanalysis

Parts Extracts Evaluated by mechanical shaker / sp-ICP-MS

- **Quartz Part**: Used in various plasma etching reactors: liners, electrodes, tubes, wafer boats, and chamber walls. Quartz window is typically positioned directly above wafers in an ICP etching chamber for non-conductors
- **Ceramic Part**: Used in liners on the sidewalls of vacuum processing chambers. In addition, ceramic parts are present on gas distribution plates supplying the process gas to the chamber, baffle plates of a showerhead assembly, wafer inserts, focus or edge rings, plasma screens and plasma windows.
- **Aluminum part**: Aluminum oxide parts which exhibit high corrosion resistance and have insulating properties are used on an inner wall surface of the chamber and on exposed surfaces within a chamber .

BALAZS nanoanalysis

NP Found in Mechanical Shaker Surface Extract of a Quartz Tube Part (Particles/cm^2)

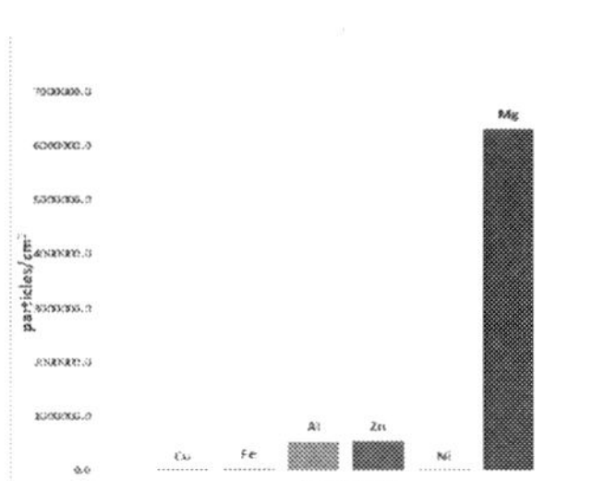

Main NP elements

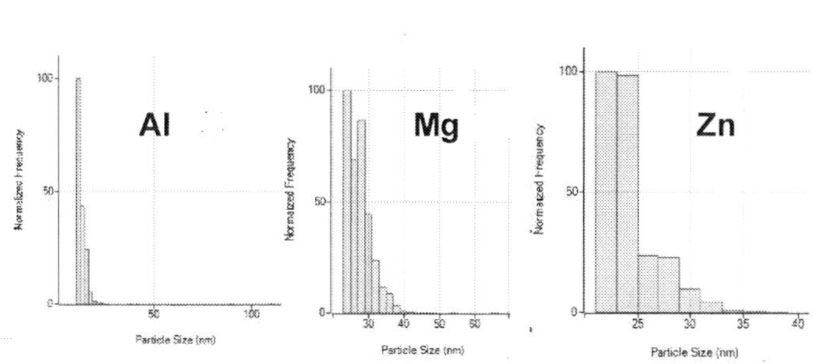

Size distribution curves for main elements

BALAZS nanoanalysis

NP Found in Mechanical Shaker Surface Extract of Ceramic Tube Part (Particles/cm^2)

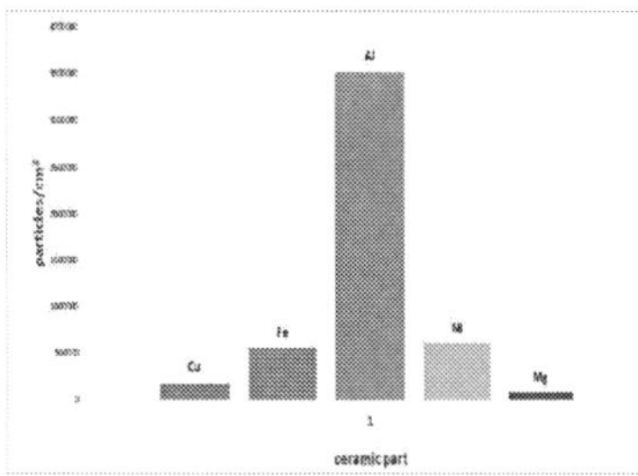

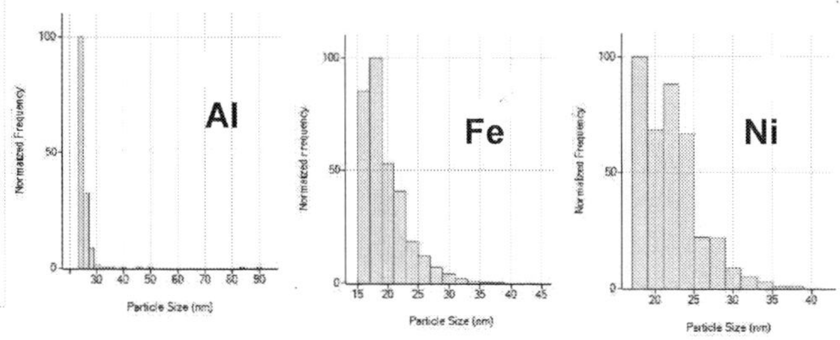

Main NP elements

Size distribution curves for main elements

BALAZS nanoanalysis

NP Found in Mechanical Shaker Surface Extract of Al Coupon Part (Particles/cm^2)

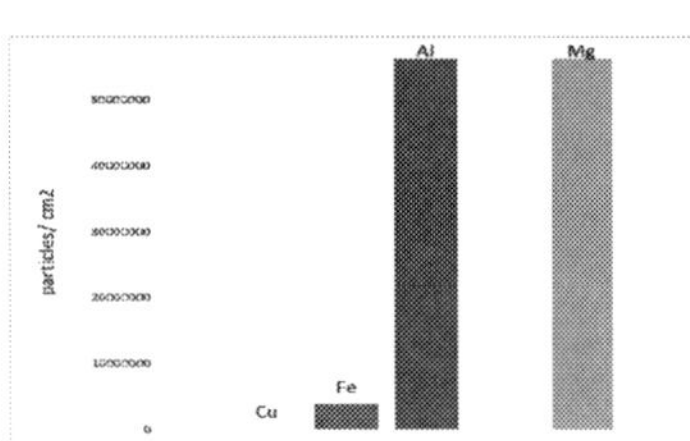

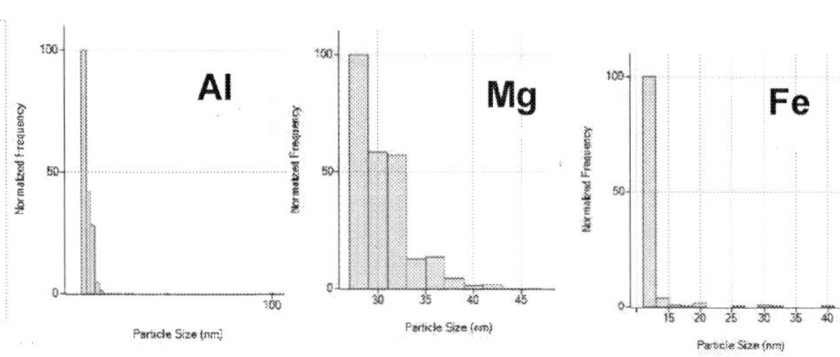

Main NP elements

Size distribution curves for main elements

BALAZS nanoanalysis

Particle Theory: The need for higher frequency scrubbing

- Intensity of Force required to remove particle is proportional to 1/radius of particle. Forces for particles on a substrate to overcome
  - Chemical bonds
  - Ionic or phobic
  - Adhesive
  - Van Der Waals
- Water cleaning using megasonic energy overcomes surface tension of the particle on the substrate

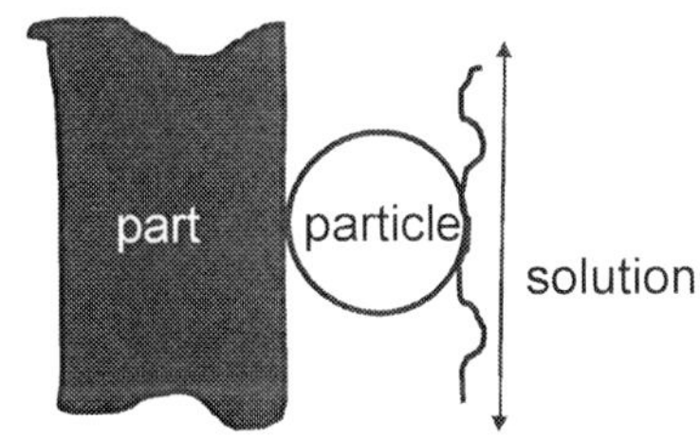

BALAZS nanoanalysis

Mechanical Agitation versus /Ultrasonic or Megasonic Cleaning

- Mechanical shaker uses circular shaking motion requiring a much longer extraction time
- Ultrasonic energy (40- 100 kHz) produces random cavitation
- Megasonic energy (0.7 to 1.2 MHz) produces controlled cavitation resulting in less damage to the parts

BALAZS nanoanalysis

Comparison of Scrubbing Techniques: Al Coupon

Particles/cm ^{2}	Mechanical shaker	Ultrasonic	Megasonic
Mg	ND	ND	ND
Al	3200	40,000	63,000
Cu	ND	ND	ND
Fe	3900	30,000	60,000
Ti	ND	ND	ND

ND = Not Detected

BALAZS nanoanalysis

Comparison of Scrubbing Techniques: Anodized Al Coupon

Particles/cm ^{2}	Mechanical shaker	Ultrasonic	Megasonic
Mg	ND	ND	28,000
Al	3200	310,000	300,000
Cu	ND	ND	28,000
Fe	7000	ND	ND
Ti	ND	13,000	8400

ND = Not Detected

BALAZS nanoanalysis

Ultrasonic and Megasonic Scrubbing Times: Quartz Part

Particles/cm ^{2}	Ultrasonic (X min)	Ultrasonic (3 * X min)	Megasonic (X min)	Megasonic (3 *X min)
Mg	13,000	73,000	19,000	58,000
Zn	ND	28,000	ND	19,000
Al	84,000	194,000	95,000	161,000
Fe	74,000	160,000	69,000	128,000
Ti	16,000	46,000	18,000	36,000

ND = Not Detected

BALAZS nanoanalysis

Conclusions

- Nanoparticle contaminants are recognized as the leading cause of microchip failures
- Control and reduction of NPs from the surface of critical chamber components is critical to the overall yield of microchip fabrication
- Reliable metrology is needed for determining NPs (e.g sp-ICP-MS)
- Ultrasonic and Megasonic Energies offer improvement in removing NPs from the surface of critical chamber components
- Time and frequency of ultrasonic/megasonic NP removal need to be optimized

BALAZS nanoanalysis

Optimization of Dummy Poly-silicon Removal in High-k Metal Gate Process

Xiongfei.Wei[1], Wenjun.Wang[1], Xiaoyan Zhang[1], Jian.Wang[1]

[1] ACM Research (Shanghai), Inc

[a] Email: xiongfei.wei@acmrcsh.com

Smart Megasonix
The Industry's Most Advanced Wafer Cleaning Technologies. Only from ACM.

ACM RESEARCH

Content

- Introduction
  - Gate first high-k metal gate process
- High-k loop wafer etch experiment
  - Chemical etching rate and selectivity
  - Dummy poly-silicon remove and etch stop layer
- Optimization of ADM etch on poly wafer
  - Influence factors of wet etch uniformity
  - Nozzle scan optimization
  - Etch uniformity of high temperature and concentration
- Conclusion

ACM RESEARCH

ACM Research, Inc.

Basic Introduction

Gate first high-k metal gate process

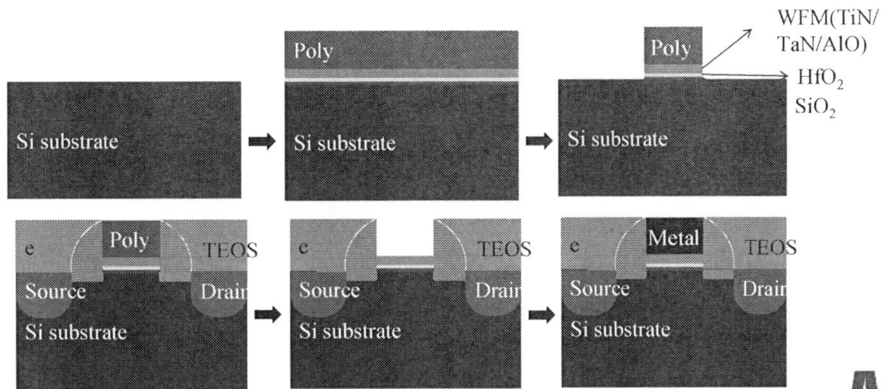

Chemical etching rate and selectivity

- ADM: Ammonia Diluted Mixture, NH_4OH:DIW=1:20;
- SC1: $NH_4OH:H_2O_2:H_2O$=15:1:300

Chemical type	Film type	Process time(s)	ER(A/min)
ADM	Poly	60	606.25
	THOX	60	3.26
	TiN	60	0.3
SC1	Poly	60	30.62
	THOX	60	4.08
	TiN	60	16.85

- High selectivity of ADM on oxide film and poly film
- High etching rate of SC1 on TiN film

SEM of high-k loop film stack

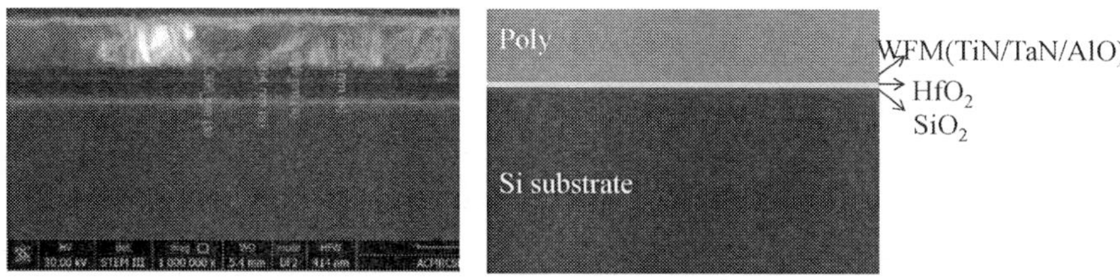

(a) (b)

(a) SEM of high loop film; (b) diagram of film stack

Dummy poly-silicon removal and etch stop layer

Etch mode	Mode 1	Mode 2	Mode 3	Mode 4	Mode 5
Chemical	None	SC1 40s	ADM 40s	ADM 40s SC1 10min	ADM 40s+SC1 10min

(a) (b) (c) (d) (e)

(a) Mode 1, reference; (b)Mode 2, poly-silicon still exists; (c)Mode 3, poly-silicon removal and stop on work function metal; (d)Mode 4, poly-silicon & work function metal removal and stop on hafnium oxide; (e)Mode 5, same result as Mode 4.

Influence factors of wet etch uniformity

Etch rate and uniformity of different ADM temperature

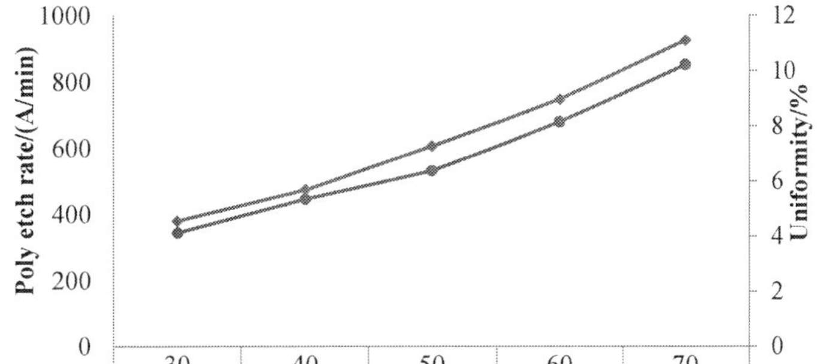

	30	40	50	60	70
Poly ER(A/min)	378.77	473.3	606.25	747.23	925.48
Uniformity (%)	4.12	5.34	6.37	8.15	10.22

ADM process temperature/°C

+ **High ADM temperature causes poor etch uniformity**

ACM RESEARCH

Influence factors of wet etch uniformity

Etch rate and uniformity of different ADM mix ratio

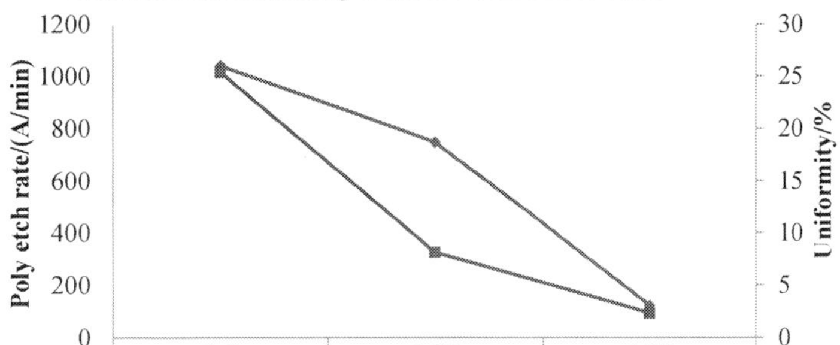

	1:5	1:20	1:50
Poly ER(A/min)	1038.95	747.23	122.65
Uniformity (%)	25.34	8.15	2.33

ADM mix ratio

+ **High ADM concentration causes poor etch uniformity**

ACM RESEARCH

Etching uniformity without nozzle scan

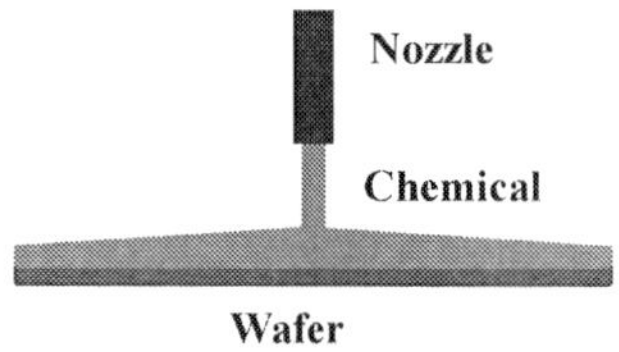

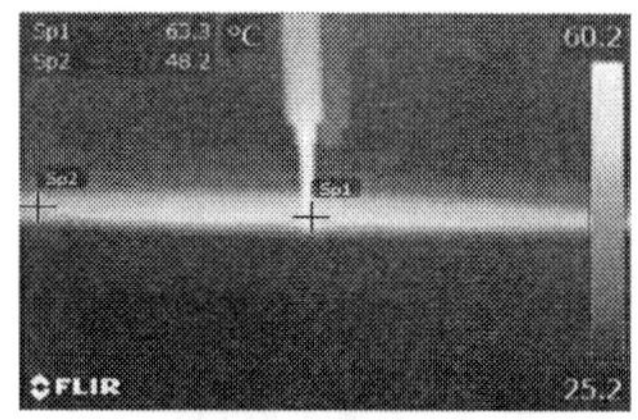

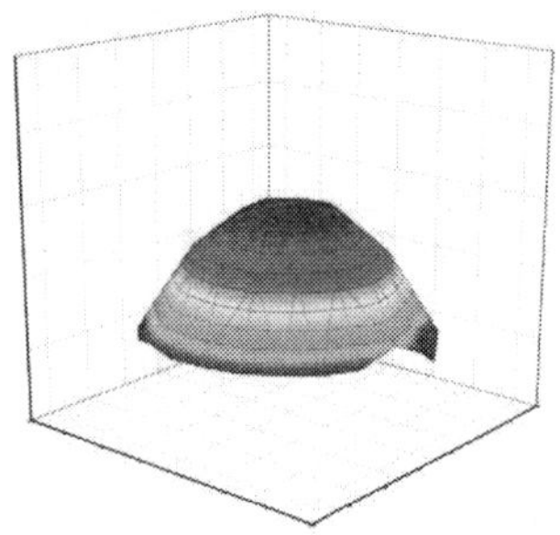

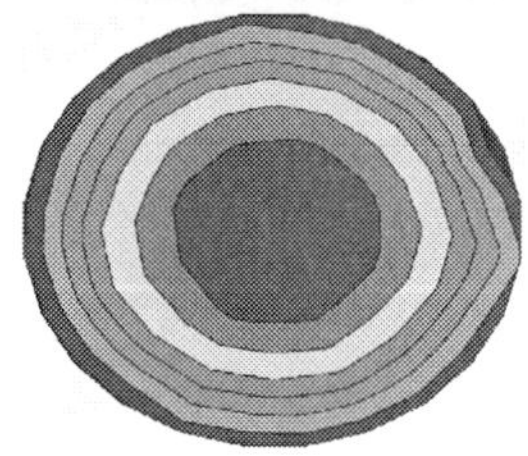

Nozzle scan on process wafer

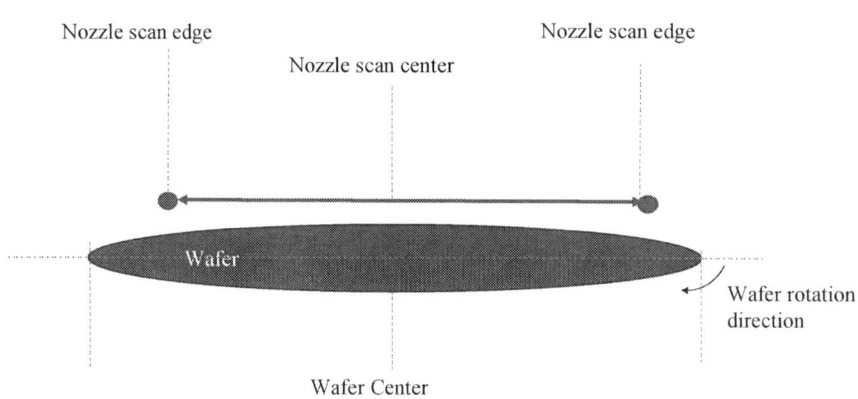

Optimization of nozzle scan

Process mode	Mode 1	Mode 2		Mode 3		
Scan profile	NA(fix in center)	Scan 1	Scan 2	Scan 3	Scan 4	Scan 5
Uniformity (%)	36.02	25.12	15.86	9.51	6.91	3.78

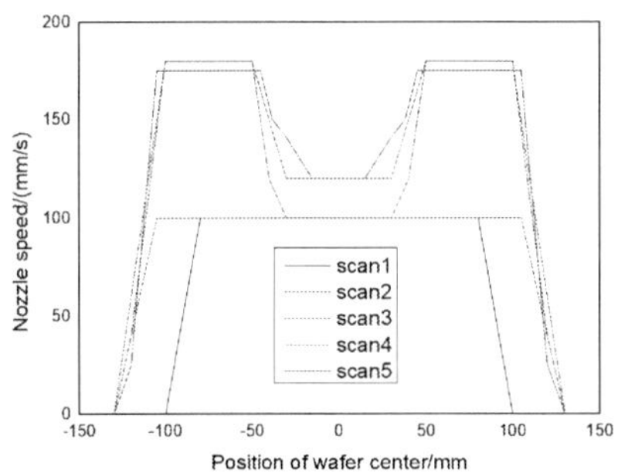

- **Mode1 : no scan, nozzle fix in center;**
- **Mode2 : nozzle scans at a uniform speed and fixed acceleration;**
- **Mode3 : nozzle scans at a variable speed and controllable acceleration**

ACM RESEARCH

ACM Research, Inc.

Optimization of uniformity

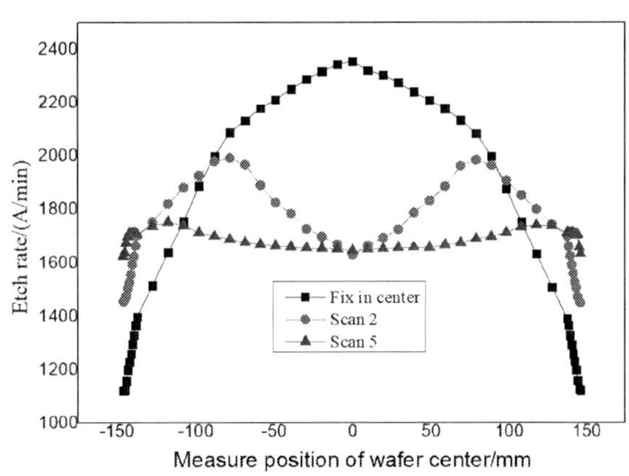

- **70°C and mix ratio 1:5 ADM**

ACM RESEARCH

ACM Research, Inc.

Conclusion

- Dummy poly-silicon can be removed by ADM and work function metal can be removed by SC1
- High-k loop etch stop layer can be controlled by ADM and SC1 combination.
- Etch uniformity of high temperature and concentrated ADM on poly-silicon can be improved from 36% to less than 4% by optimizing chemical nozzle scan profile

ACM RESEARCH

ACM Research, Inc.

Acknowledgements

The author would like to thank Wenjun Wang, Xiaoyan Zhang, Jian Wang and Sally-Ann Henry for discussion on the data for the paper

Also Fujin Jia, Yiping Zhang and Lei Xu for help with the SEMS processing of the wafers

The author would like to thank SPCC for accepting this paper at the conference

ACM RESEARCH

ACM Research, Inc.

Thank You!

Contact Information:
Sally Ann Henry
+43 660 7769721
Sallyann.henry@acmrcsh.com

Xiongfei Wei
+86 18018560821
Xioangfei.wei@acmrcsh.com

ACM Research, Inc.
42307 Osgood Road, Suite I
Fremont, CA 94539
www.acmrcsh.com

***Smart Megasonix*™**
The Industry's Most Advanced Wafer Cleaning Technologies. Only from ACM.

Elimination of Surface Particles with Parallel Streak Signature by Optimizing Post CMP Cleans

Jomel Desamito, Dhiman Bhattacharyya and Mark Conrad
GLOBALFOUNDRIES, Malta, NY

Abstract

Post-CMP cleaning is one of the very important processes that is needed to remove residual particles, residues, and metal particles from CMP processed wafers. Any changes in CMP slurry composition to improve CMP performance brings the challenge of keeping the wafers free from any slurry particles or residues to meet the current defect performance.

Jomel Desamito
GLOBALFOUNDRIES, 400 Stone Break Extension, Malta, NY 12010
Email: jomel.desamito@globalfoundries.com
Phone: 518-769-1856

1

Elimination of Surface Particles with Parallel Streak Signature by Optimizing Post CMP Cleans

If there is a particulate defect that remained on the wafer after this process, it is possible that it can kill the wafer, especially when we have smaller feature semiconductor devices, and the industry is evolving rapidly as time goes on that these large particles dropping on the wafer may kill a die.

The current study investigated the source of a defect that appeared after gate-poly deposition and implemented a solution to eliminate those defects.

Jomel Desamito
GLOBALFOUNDRIES, 400 Stone Break Extension, Malta, NY 12010
Email: jomel.desamito@globalfoundries.com
Phone: 518-769-1856

2

Elimination of Surface Particles with Parallel Streak Signature by Optimizing Post CMP Cleans

These particles manifested as a parallel streak (blue parallel streaks) after gate-poly deposition and was traced back to wet nitride strip process in a batch tool (shown in figure 1, far left map). Then post nitride strip, the wafer processed downstream at RIE and show as incomplete etch (shown right panel top).

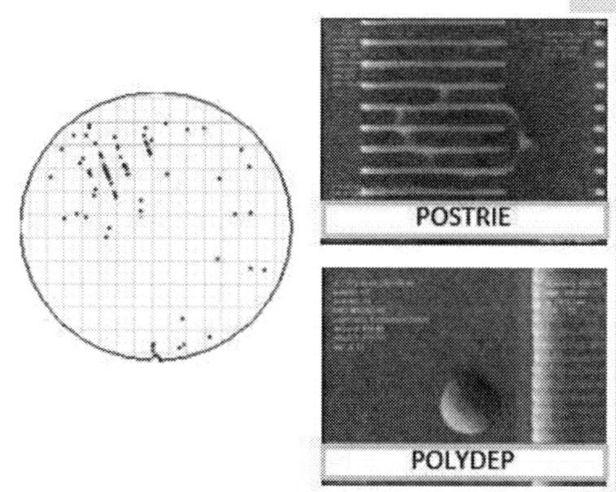

The right panel (bottom) shows a representative image (not this wafer) of embedded defect downstream Post Poly Dep.

Jomel Desamito
GLOBALFOUNDRIES, 400 Stone Break Extension, Malta, NY 12010
Email: jomel.desamito@globalfoundries.com
Phone: 518-769-1856

3

Elimination of Surface Particles with Parallel Streak Signature by Optimizing Post CMP Cleans

The appearance of parallel streak coincided with a change at the CMP process, from Silica based slurry to Ceria based slurry. The POR post-CMP clean process consisting of dilute acid base clean was not able to remove the Ceria based residues/particles, as well as the subsequent cleaning process. The parallel streaking signature was generated on the batch tool during the wet nitride strip process (shown next slide).

Jomel Desamito
GLOBALFOUNDRIES, 400 Stone Break Extension, Malta, NY 12010
Email: jomel.desamito@globalfoundries.com
Phone: 518-769-1856

4

Elimination of Surface Particles with Parallel Streak Signature by Optimizing Post CMP Cleans

The incoming wafers with Ceria residues/particles contaminated the bath in batch wafer clean tool, were accumulated on the tank more particularly at the chemistry surface, hence, cross contaminated the wafers during pull up out of the tank. This image shows a process bath with particle/residues on liquid surface and a wafer pulling up/out of tank.

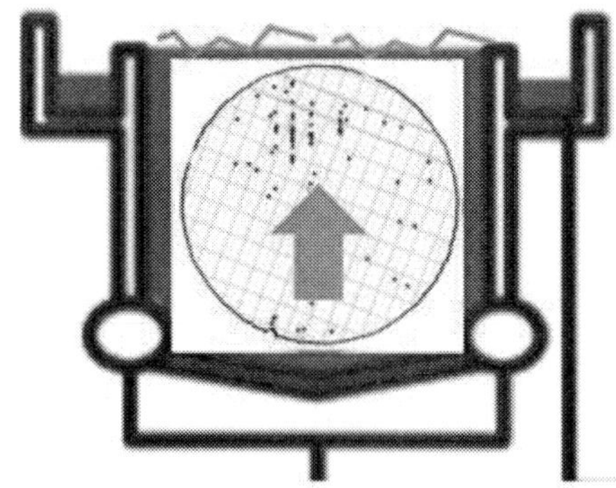

Jomel Desamito
GLOBALFOUNDRIES, 400 Stone Break Extension, Malta, NY 12010
Email: jomel.desamito@globalfoundries.com
Phone: 518-769-1856

5

Elimination of Surface Particles with Parallel Streak Signature by Optimizing Post CMP Cleans

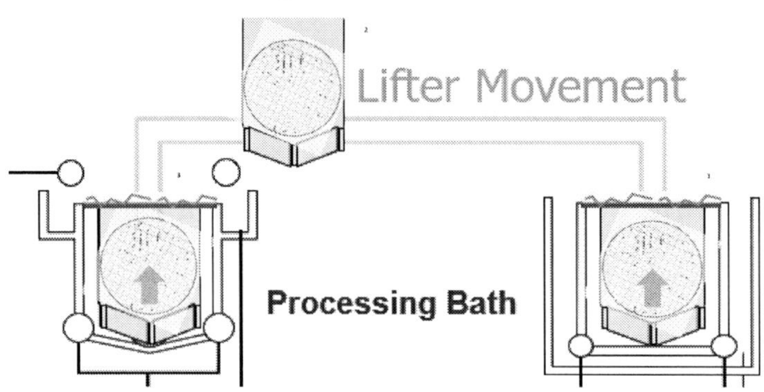

Step 1: Chemical bath processing and pulling up/out of the tank.
Step 2: Wafer transferring from chemical bath to the rinse tank
Step 3: DIW rinse tank to displace the chemical on wafer and pulling up/out of the tank for next step.

Jomel Desamito
GLOBALFOUNDRIES, 400 Stone Break Extension, Malta, NY 12010
Email: jomel.desamito@globalfoundries.com
Phone: 518-769-1856

6

Elimination of Surface Particles with Parallel Streak Signature by Optimizing Post CMP Cleans

The slurry residues/particles on chemical surface transferring back to the wafer during the pull up from tank (orange arrow direction) leaving a trail of streaking defect on the wafers. Even though the recirculation and quick dump rinse already exists on the clean recipe, the defects still managed to re-contaminate the wafers. The current working hypothesis is due to the strong chemical affinity of these slurry ceria residues/particles to oxide films, adhering to it greatly and concurrently there is a weak repulsion of these particles on a low pH cleaning process operation.

Jomel Desamito
GLOBALFOUNDRIES, 400 Stone Break Extension, Malta, NY 12010
Email: jomel.desamito@globalfoundries.com
Phone: 518-769-1856

7

Elimination of Surface Particles with Parallel Streak Signature by Optimizing Post CMP Cleans

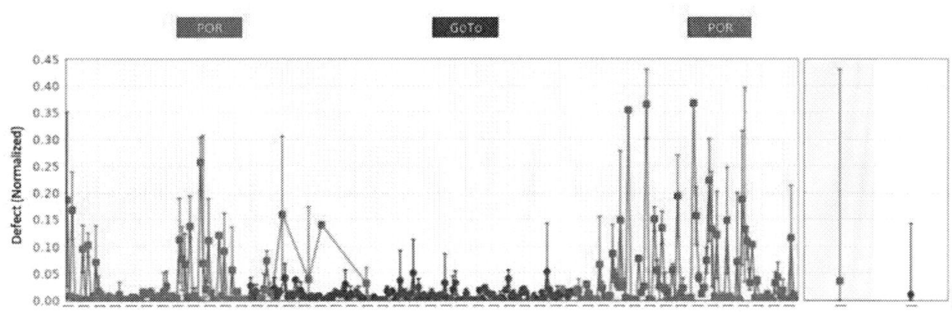

In order to eliminate these Ceria particles, a new clean process was evaluated for post-CMP clean. Above shows the trend of embedded defects significantly reduced when the new recipe was used.

Jomel Desamito
GLOBALFOUNDRIES, 400 Stone Break Extension, Malta, NY 12010
Email: jomel.desamito@globalfoundries.com
Phone: 518-769-1856

8

Elimination of Surface Particles with Parallel Streak Signature by Optimizing Post CMP Cleans

Jomel Desamito, Dhiman Bhattacharyya and Mark Conrad
GLOBALFOUNDRIES, Malta, NY

Summary

Based from the collected data, a significant reduction on embedded defects in the baseline was achieved by identifying the root cause and implementing a new cleaning process to remove the residues/particles on the wafer.

Jomel Desamito
GLOBALFOUNDRIES, 400 Stone Break Extension, Malta, NY 12010
Email: jomel.desamito@globalfoundries.com
Phone: 518-769-1856

9

SINGLE WAFER PATTERN COLLAPSE EVALUATIONS

XIUMEI XU, ZHENG TAO, MOHAMED SAIB, FARID SEBAAI, MURAT PAK, CHRISTIE DELVAUX, EUN BI NAM, JEROEN VAN DE KERKHOVE, YUSUKE ONIKI, PALLAVI PUTTARAME GOWDA

SPCC, OCT 17-18, 2022

PUBLIC

KEY Qs

1) Stability criteria for different dimensions, profiles, stacks...
2) How to prevent pattern collapse in a cost-effective way

FUNDAMENTALS

Original → Driving force → Adhesion

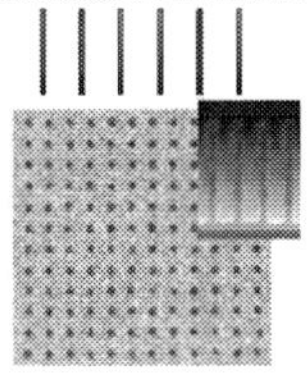

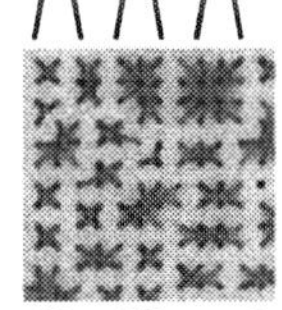

- **Capillary force**
- Stress/strain
- Electrostatic

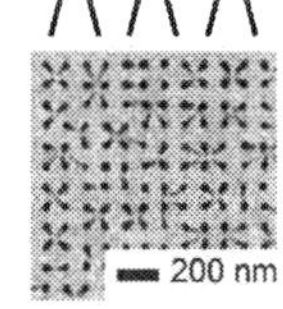

- Wet adhesion
- Dry adhesion

SOLUTION

RT IPA, hot IPA, flash drying, SMT

design change (MESH, FS...)

scCO2, freeze drying, sublimation,

Applications

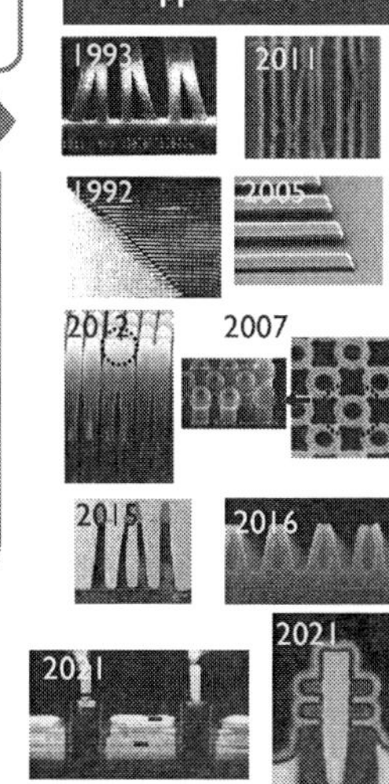

OUTLINE -- SW PATTERN COLLAPSE EVALUATION PLATFORM

Test structure

Si nanopillars

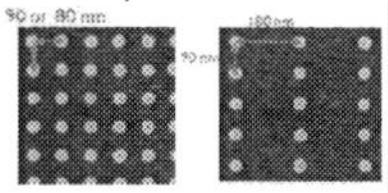

Various heights

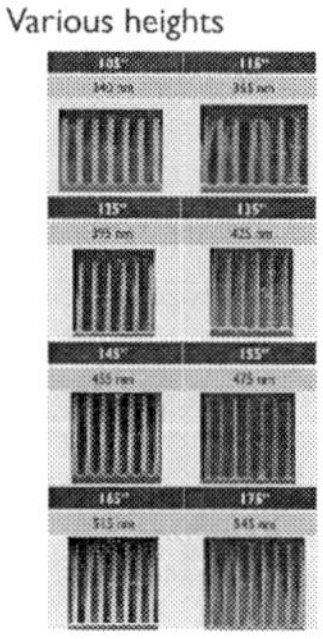

Metrology

Correlation of collapse rates with bending stiffness:

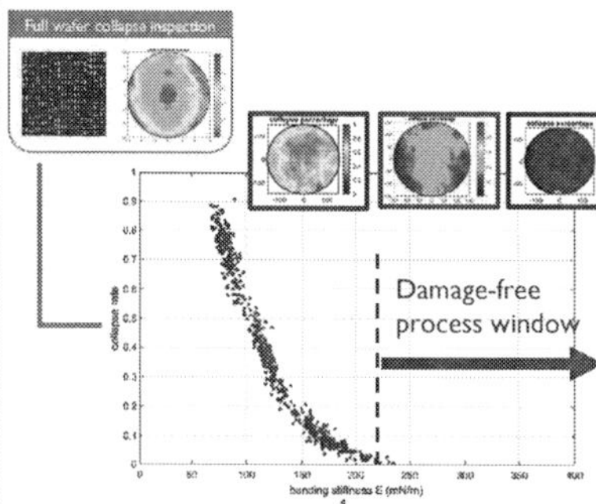

Bending stiffness:

$$S_{pillar} = \frac{3\pi E d^4}{64 h^3}$$

E: Young's modulus, d: diameter

h: height

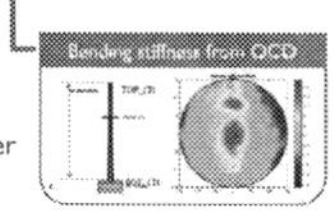

SW process evaluation

Process window: hot IPA > RT IPA > DIW

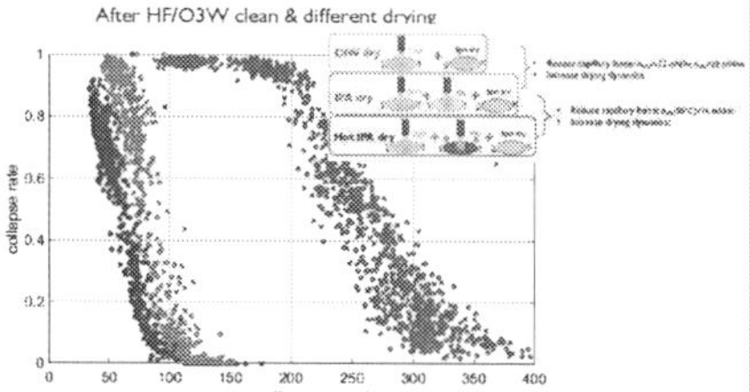

Center to edge uniformity in different drying process

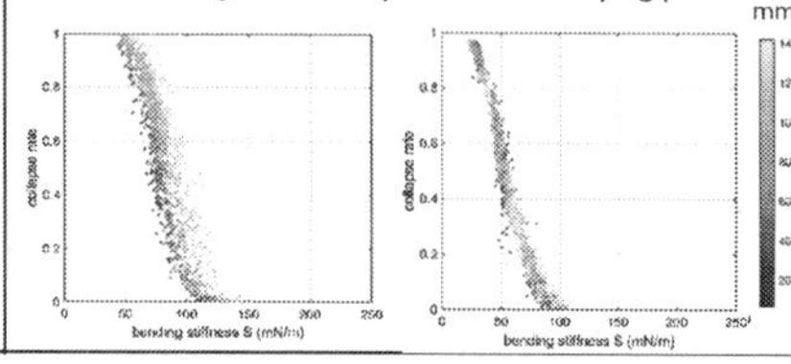

imec

STANDARD TEST VEHICLE FOR PATTERN COLLAPSE EVALUATIONS

300 mm wafer patterned with silicon nanopillars

- Simple patterning scheme

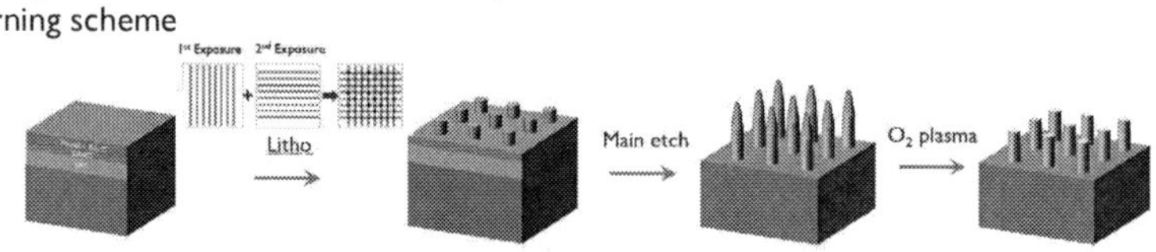

- Square packing (P90 nm or P80 nm), or rectangular packing (P90 x P180 nm)

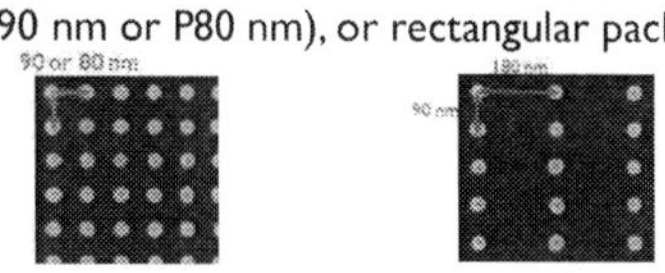

- Silicon nanopillars CD 25 ~30 nm, with various heights (H ~ 300 – 600 nm)

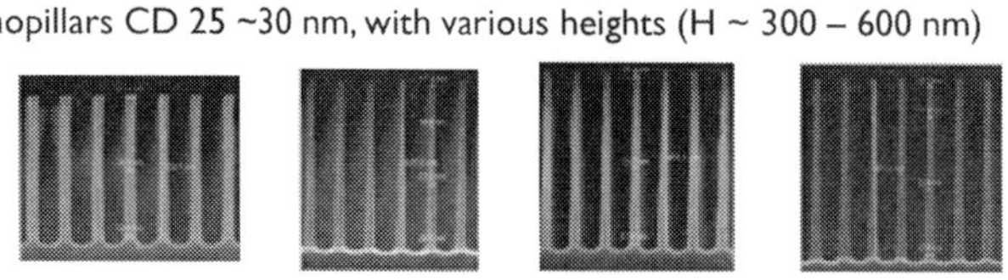

imec

Xu, Solid State Phenom. (2018, 2021)

CHARACTERIZATION – STANDARD METHODS

Bending stiffness of pillar with cylindrical profile:

$$S = \frac{3\pi E d^4}{64h^3}$$

E: Young's modulus
d: diameter;
h: height;

X-SEM

Center

Mid

Edge

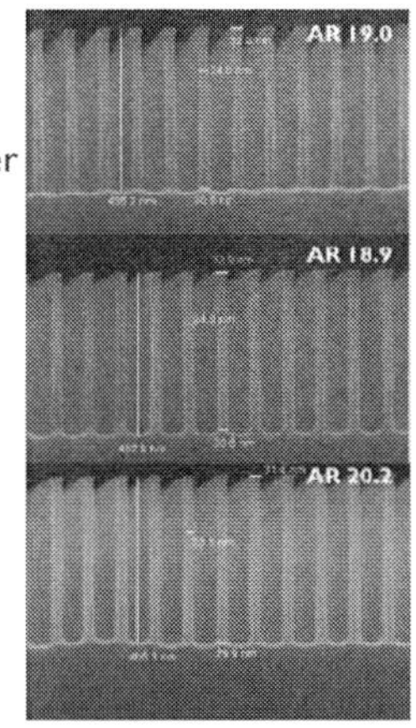

CD-SEM

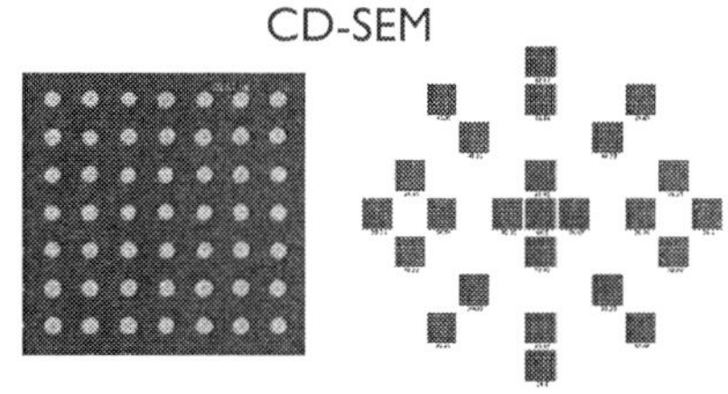

CDSEM: CD and CDU

- Does not provide 3D profile and height;

XSEM: profile and height

- Destructive technique;
- A couple of inspections per wafer;

imec

DEFECT INSPECTION AND ANALYSIS

❑ Full wafer SEM inspection: FOV 3um

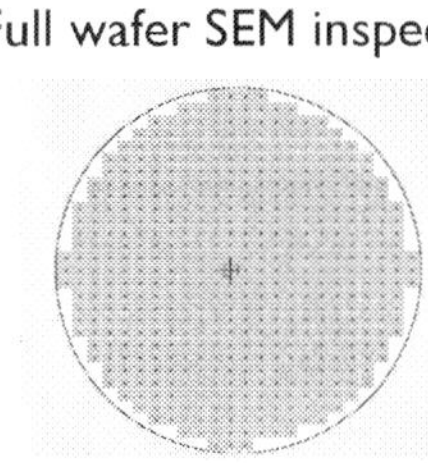

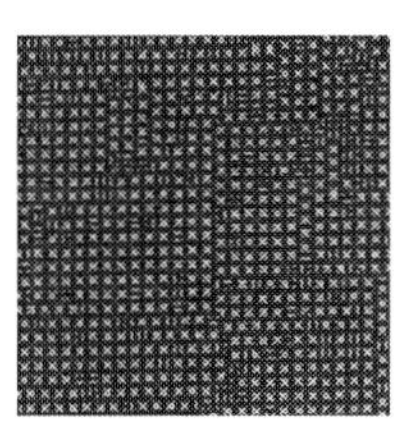

~ 500 Dies per wafer

❑ In-house developed image processing software for full wafer analysis of collapse rates

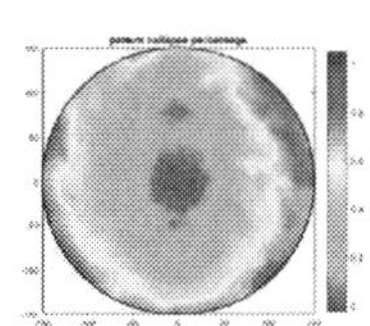

imec

CORRELATIONS OF COLLAPSE RATES WITH STIFFNESS

BIG ERROR BARS DUE TO LIMITED XSEM INSPECTIONS

Full wafer collapse inspection

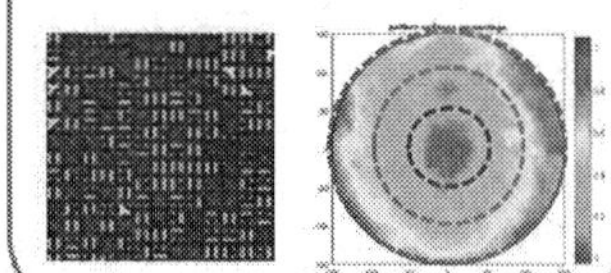

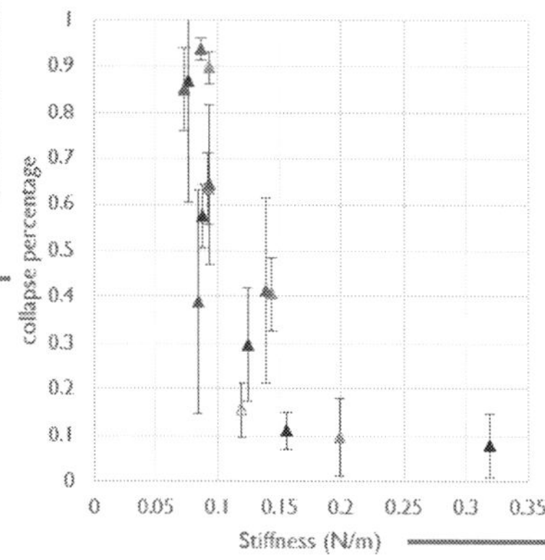

XSEM

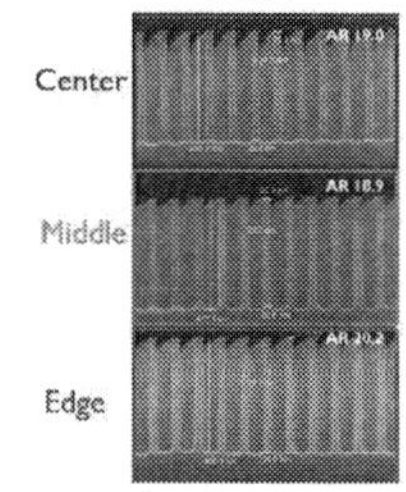

Bending stiffness

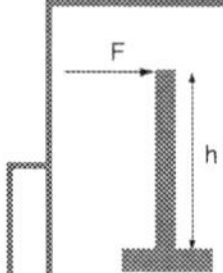

$$S_{pillar} = \frac{3\pi E d^4}{64 h^3}$$

E: Young's modulus
d: diameter
h: height

imec

NON-UNIFORMITY AND NON-REPRODUCIBILITY

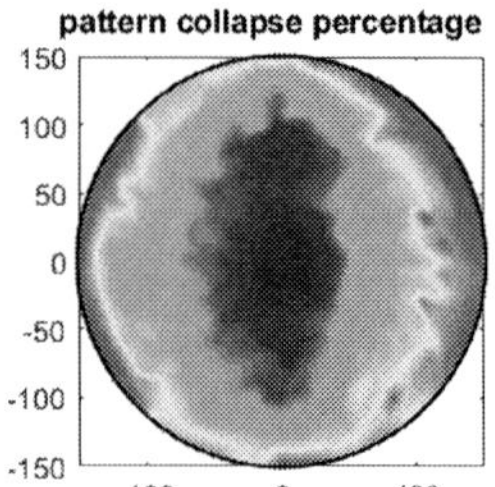

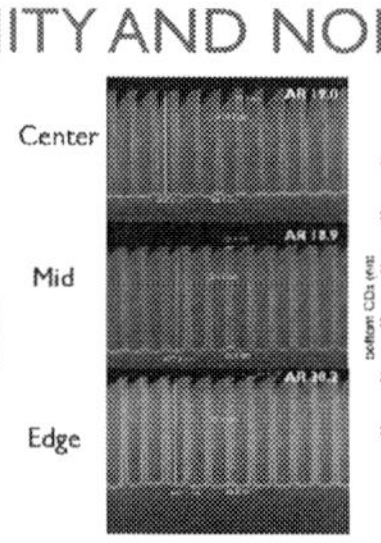

CD

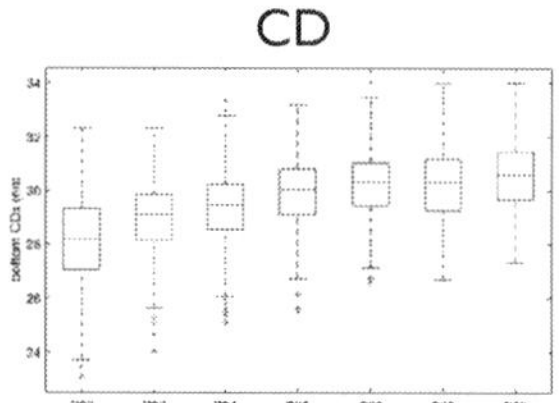

Height

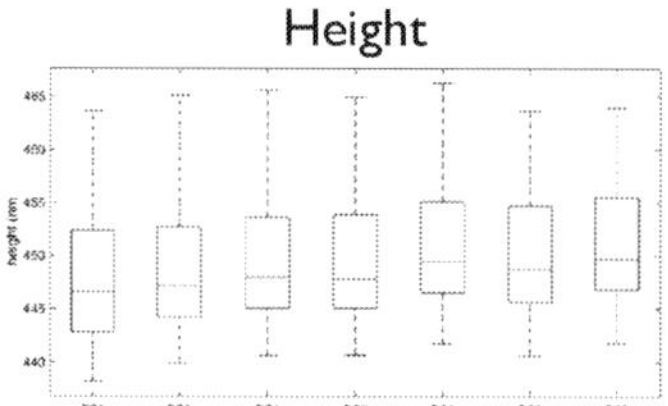

Error propagation in bending stiffness: $S_{pillar} \sim \frac{3\pi E d^4}{64 h^3}$

d (nm)	h (nm)	S (N/m)	Δd (nm)	Δh (nm)	ΔS (N/m)	ΔS/S
30	445	0.23	±2	0	±0.061	±27%
30	445	0.23	0	±30	0.016	±7%

As CD scales down, very small CD variation can affect bending stiffness significantly.

imec

SCATTEROMETRY FOR 3D PROFILE CHARACTERIZATION

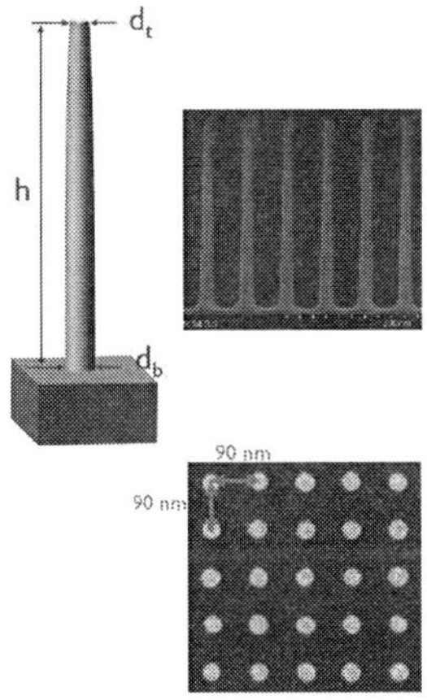

- ❑ Non-destructive optical based measurement;
- ❑ High throughput enables full wafer characterization;
- ❑ Average pillar dimensions (diameter, height, tapering angle etc) over ~50μm spot size;

Reproducible correlation curves unique to wet clean/drying process

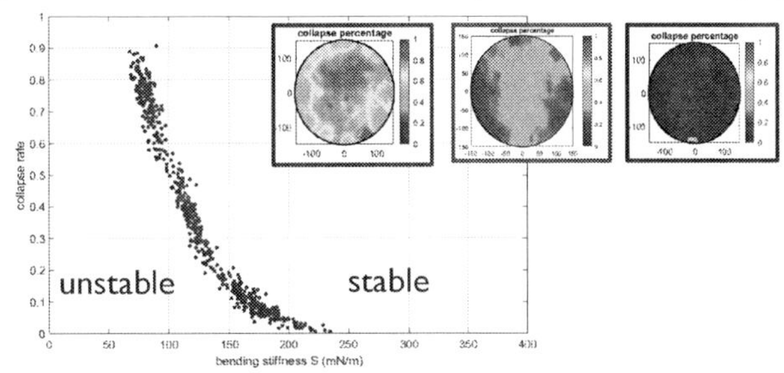

Xu, Solid State Phenom. (2018)

imec

BENCHMARKING DIFFERENT WET CLEAN AND DRYING PROCESS

COMPARE DAMAGE-FREE PROCESS WINDOW

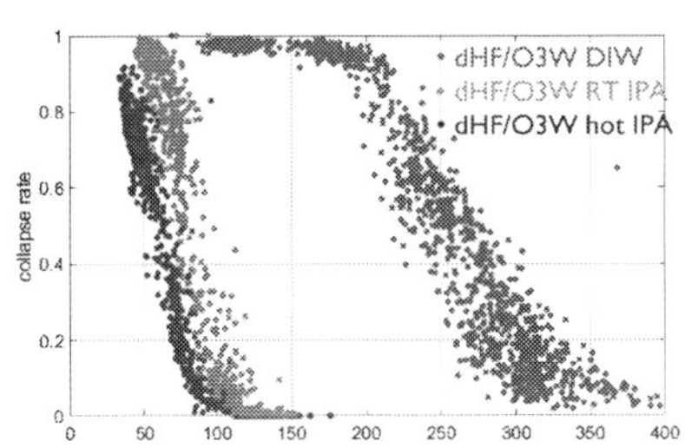

HF/O3W clean	DIW dry	RT IPA	Hot IPA
Capillary Force $\propto \sigma\cos\theta$	$\sigma_{H2O}=72$	$\sigma_{IPA}=22$	$\sigma_{HIPA}=17$
	$\theta \approx 0°$	$\theta \approx 0°$	$\theta \approx 0°$
Surface termination	Si-OH	Si-OH	Si-OH

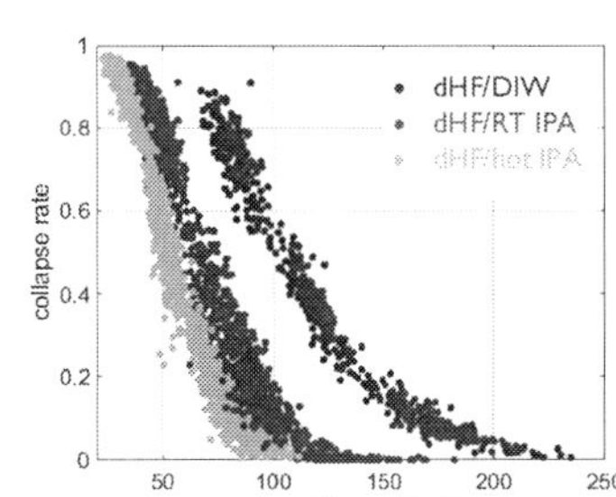

HF clean	DIW dry	RT IPA	Hot IPA
Capillary Force $\propto \sigma\cos\theta$	$\sigma_{H2O}=72$	$\sigma_{IPA}=22$	$\sigma_{HIPA}=17$
	$\theta \approx 55-75°$	$\theta \approx 0°$	$\theta \approx 0°$
Surface termination	Si-H	Si-H	Si-H

imec

PATTERN COLLAPSE REPAIR EFFICIENCY BY VAPOR HF

In situ TEM

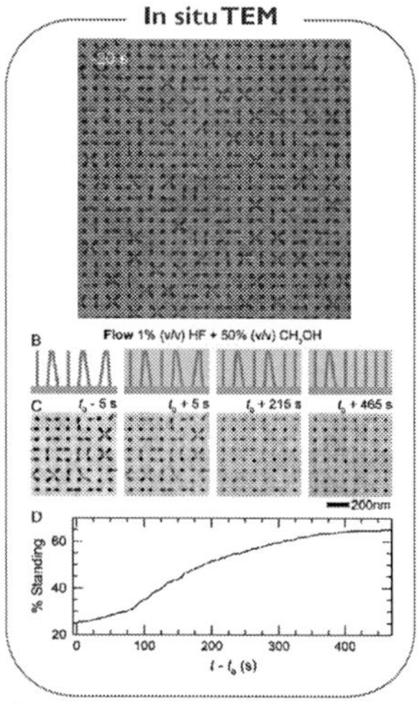

Single wafer HFv repair

- Wet clean/drying: O3W/HF/O3W/dAPM + RT IPA
- +120s HFv
- +300s HFv

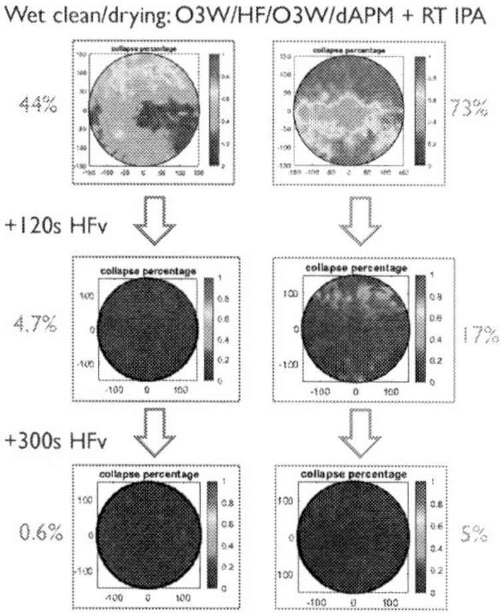

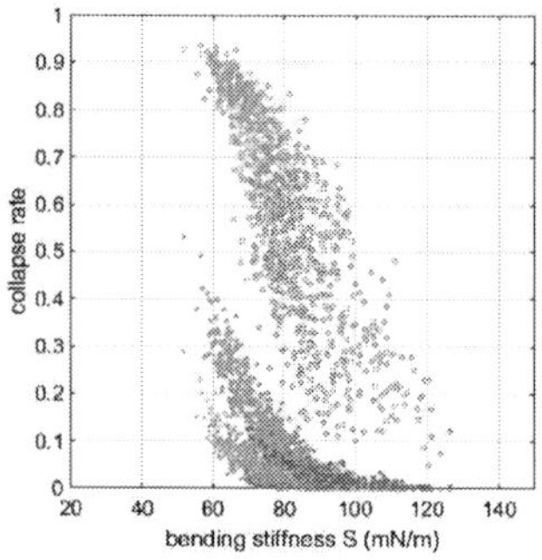

imec Xu, Solid State Phenom. (2016), Anand, ACS Appl. Nano Mater. (2021)

SINGLE WAFER DRYING PROCESS OPTIMIZATION
TO IMPROVE CENTER TO EDGE UNIFORMITY

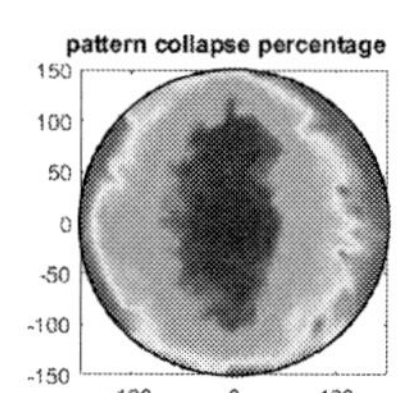

Non-optimized process with large center to edge variations

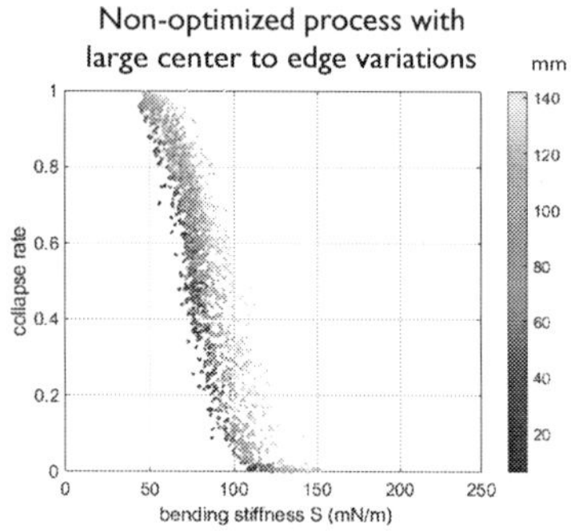

Optimized process with more uniform performance

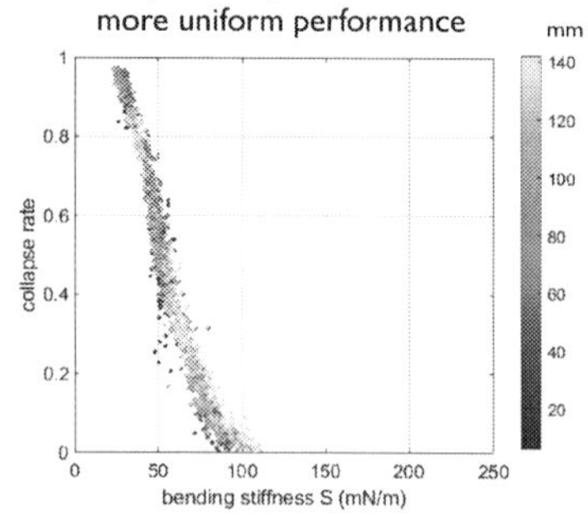

Uniform damage maps do not guarantee a uniform drying process, an optimized process should have less center-to-edge variations in the correlation curves

imec

COMPARING DIFFERENT PITCH

NEED TO INCLUDE CAPILLARY FORCE

Square packed pillars: P90x90 nm vs. P80x80 nm

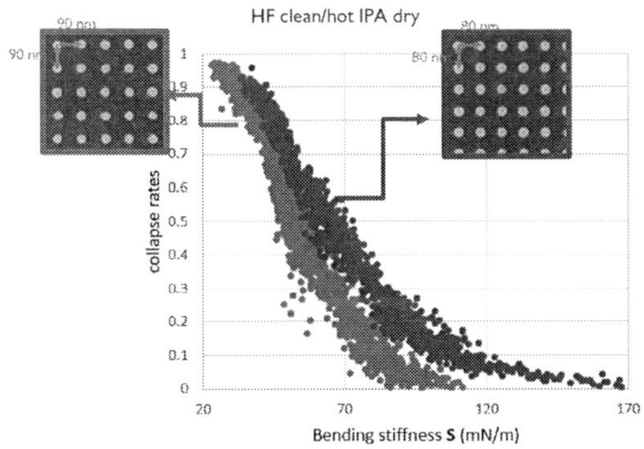

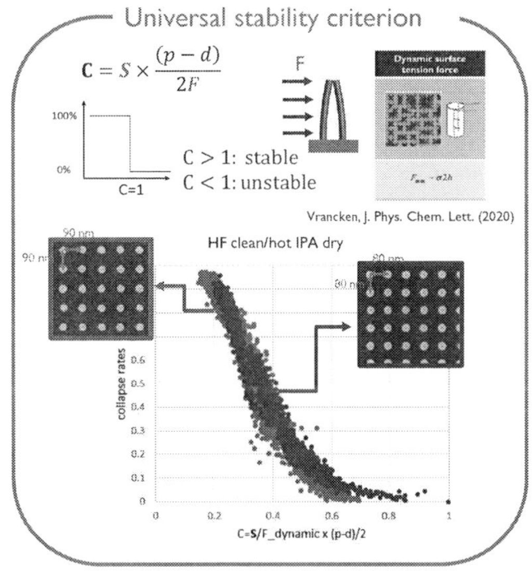

imec

COMPARING DIFFERENT DRYING SOLVENTS & PILLAR DIMENSIONS

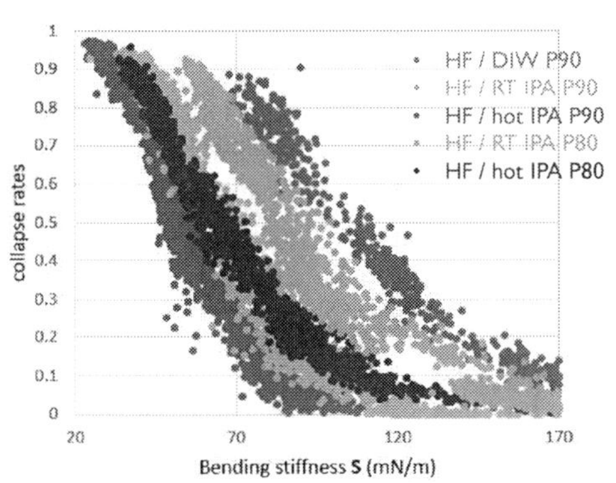

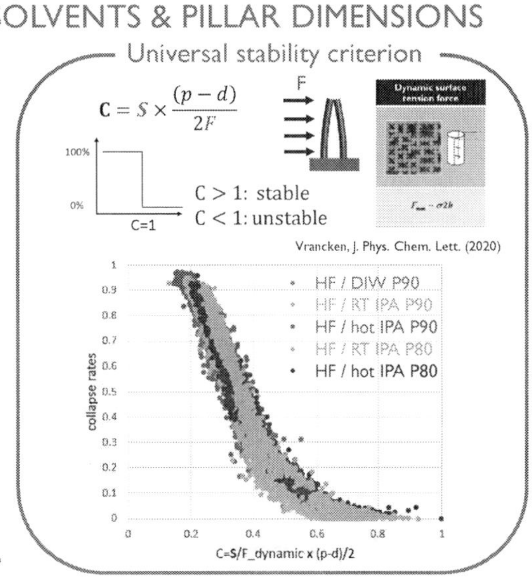

- Dimensionless plot shows self similar curves for different drying solvents and pillar dimensions
- Possible to extrapolate the process window for pillars with tighter pitch

imec

NEW TEST VEHICLE TO MIMICK FIN COLLAPSE
300 MM WAFER PATTERNED WITH SILICON FINS

- ❑ Cut-first single patterning (193i)
- ❑ Diverse designs patterned on the same wafer:
  - 3 fin pitch: FP76, 80, 84 nm
  - 4 fin length: FL84, 126, 168, 252 nm
  - Wide range of CDs: 30-50 nm (step 0.5 nm)
- ❑ Large array of uniform fins, suitable for scatterometry measurements

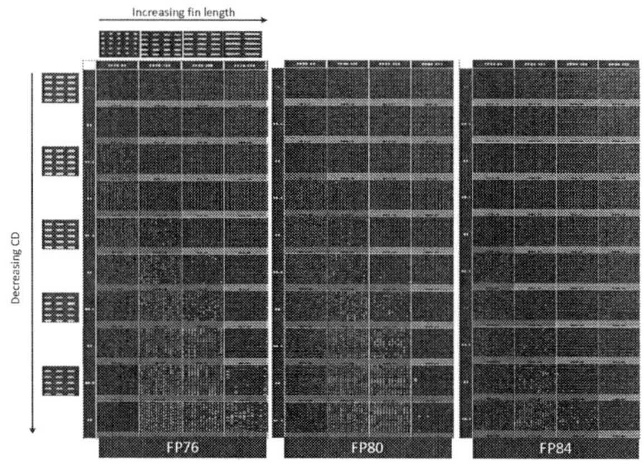

imec 15

SW PATTERN COLLAPSE EVALUATION PLATFORM @ IMEC

Test structure

Si nanopillars

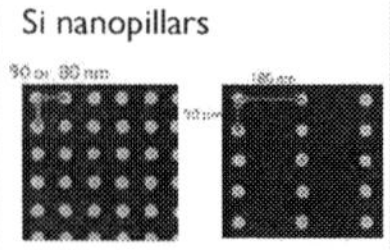

Si fins of various design

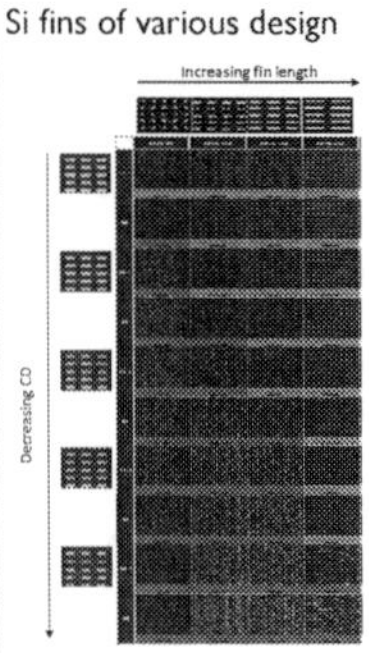

Metrology

Full wafer scatterometry characterization and mechanical modeling

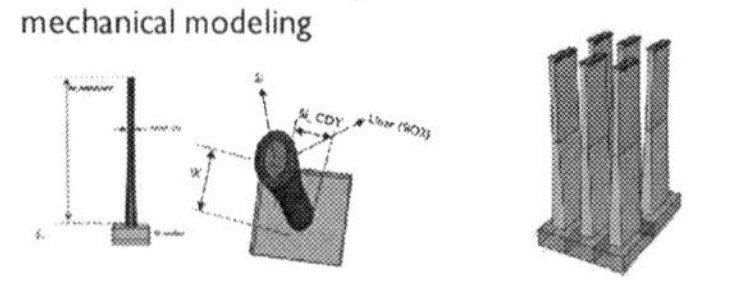

Build robust ways to compare different process and extrapolate process windows for structures with tighter pitch

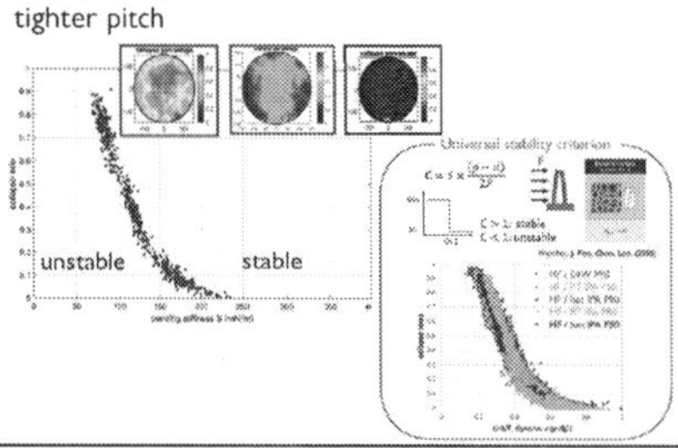

SW process evaluation

Damage-free process window comparison

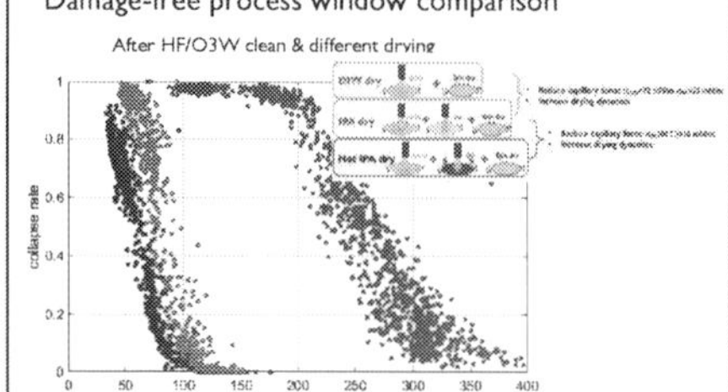

Center to edge uniformity in different drying process

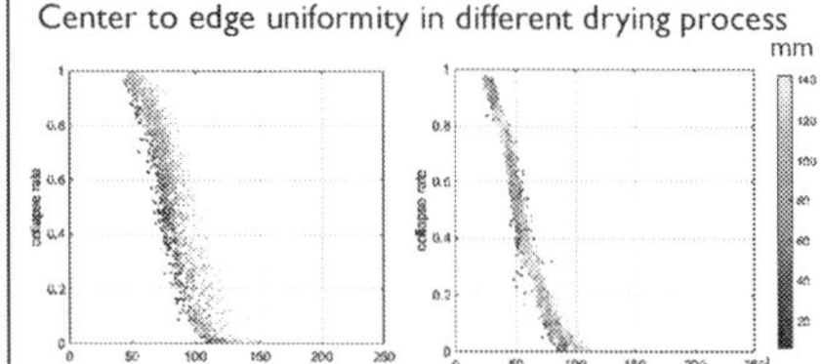

imec 16

Thank you for your attention!

Questions and remarks can be sent to

XiuMei Xu, Ph.D.
Surface and interface process
xiumei.xu@imec.be

imec

17

imec

embracing a better life

imec

PUBLIC

Extreme Silicon Thinning For Back Side Power Delivery Network Application: Need For a Highly Selective Alkaline Silicon Etch Stopping On SiGe Etch Stop Layer

Farid Sebaai [1], Roger Loo[1], Anne Jourdain[1], Kurt Wostyn[1], Eric Beyne[1]

[1] IMEC vzw, Kapeldreef 75, B-3001 Heverlee, Belgium

Overview

- Introduction
- Explanation of wafer back side thinning at IMEC
- Challenge for future back side silicon thinning
- Back side silicon thinning with $Si_{075}Ge_{0.25}$:B ESL
- Summary and on-going activities

imec

- **Introduction**
- Explanation of wafer back side thinning at IMEC
- Challenge for future back side silicon thinning
- Back side silicon thinning with $Si_{0.75}Ge_{0.25}$:B ESL
- Summary and on-going activities

imec

Introduction (1)

Back side power delivery network

Conventional approach: Connection through μTSV interconnect

A. Jourdain et al, ETCC, 2020

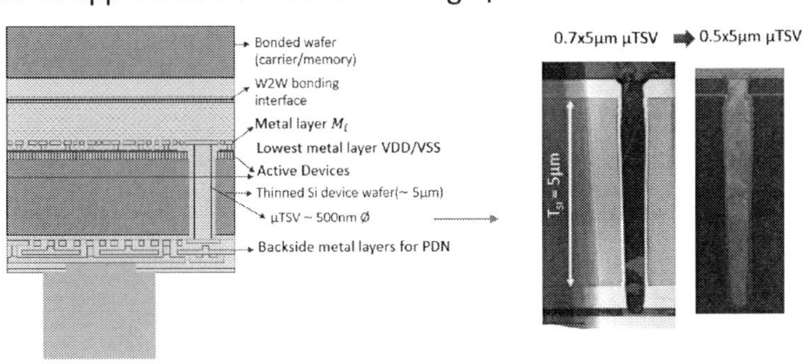

- Conventional approach where power delivery metal tracks are processed in the BEOL of the device wafer.
- Limited area overhead μTSVs : e.g. 500 nm Ø TSV at 5 μm pitch → 1% TSV area.

imec

Introduction (2)

Back side power delivery network

Connection through nTSV

A. Jourdain et al, ETCC, 2020

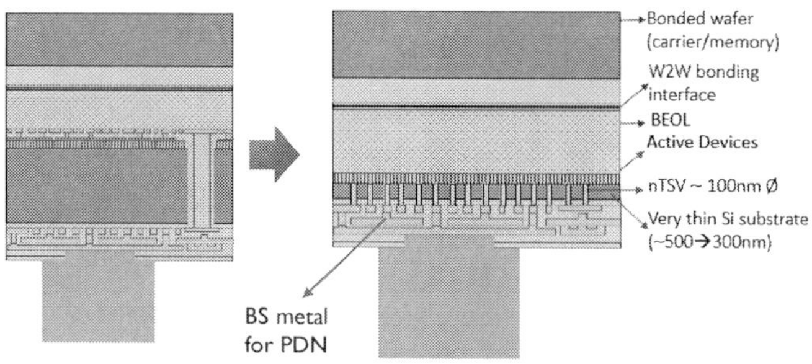

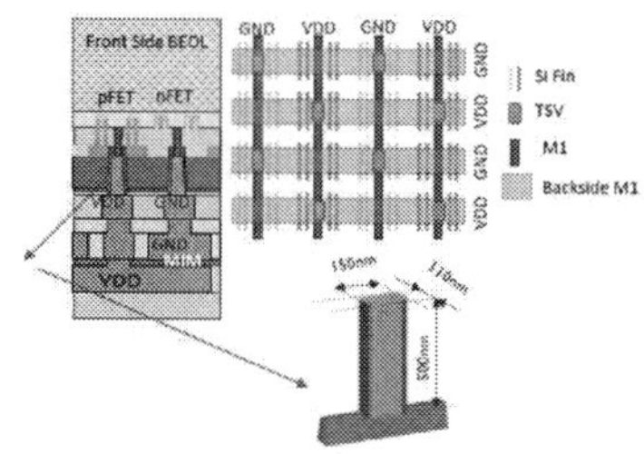

When pushing the limits a bit further and increasing the interconnect density:

- TSV becomes smaller.
- Power delivery lines are moved to the BS: Si becomes very thin
- BS becomes the new FS.

imec

Introduction (3)

Back side wafer thinning description

nTSV connected to buried power rail

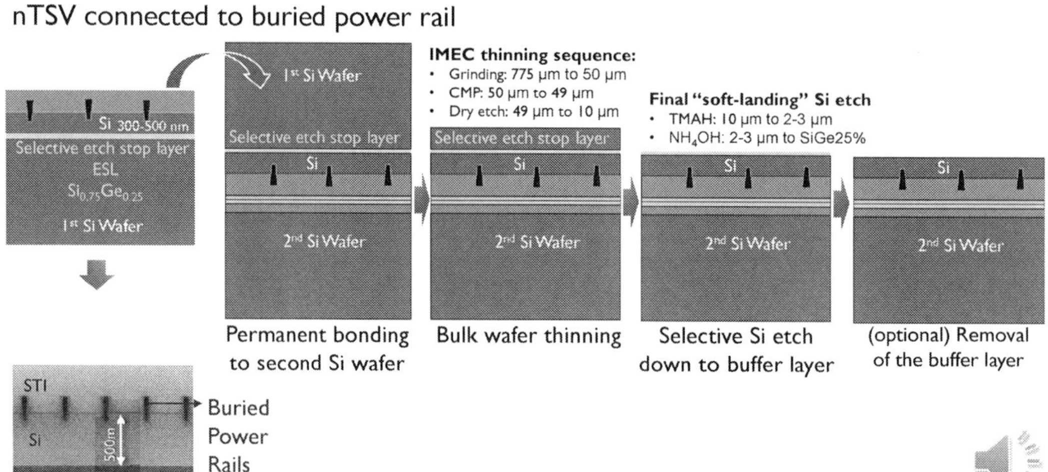

imec

- Introduction
- **Explanation of wafer back side thinning at IMEC**
- Challenge for future back side silicon thinning
- Back side silicon thinning with $Si_{0.75}Ge_{0.25}$:B ESL
- Summary and on-going activities

imec

Explanation of the wafer back side thinning at IMEC (1)

Grinding + CMP

F. Inoue et al, IEEE, 2016

- **Rough grinding + fine Grinding**
  - Rough grinding removes Si down to 120 μm.
  - Fine grinding removes Si down to 50 μm.
  - TTV at ~ 1.5 μm.
  - High damage induced.

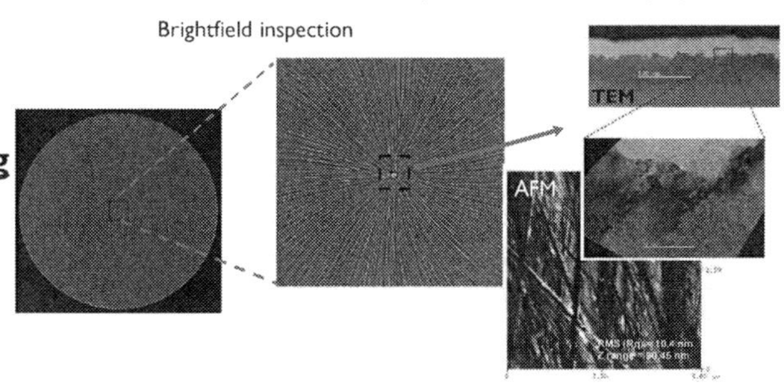

- **CMP**
  - Removes Si down to 49 μm → 1 μm removal.
  - Removes the damage induced by the grinding.
  - Keeps the same TTV after grinding but get increased if more Si is removed after CMP.

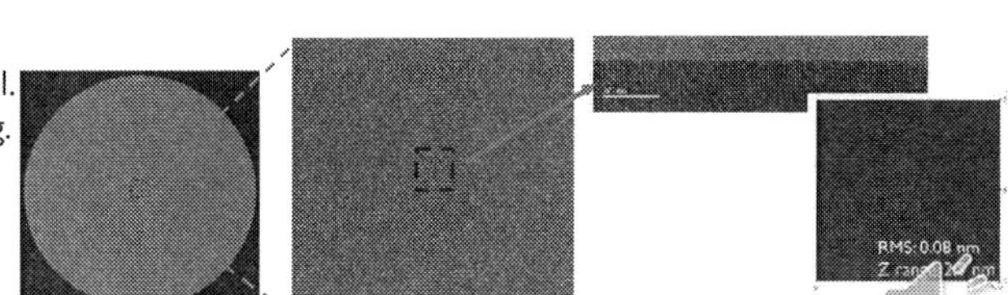

imec

Explanation of the wafer back side thinning at IMEC (2)

Dry etch

F. Inoue et al, IEEE, 2016

- Removes Si down the 10 µm.
- No induced surface damage.

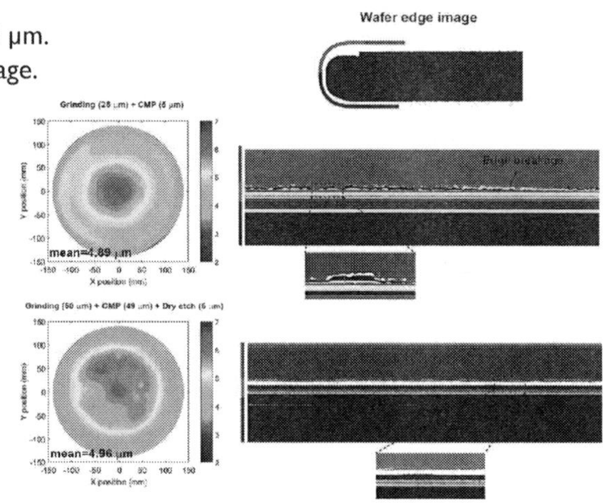

imec

Explanation of the wafer back side thinning at IMEC (3)

Alkaline etching

→ Soft landing Si etching with TMAH + dil NH_4OH stopping on $Si_{0.75}Ge_{0.25}$.

- **Si etching from 10 µm to 3 µm**
  - TMAH 5%, 80 °C → for a fast-etching rate.
  - TMAH not kept down to ESL because of lack of selectivity to $Si_{0.75}Ge_{0.25}$.

- **Si etching from 3 µm to the ESL**
  - Diluted NH_4OH 1_60 at 70 °C. Temperature chosen as a compromise between Si etching rate and selectivity to $Si_{0.75}Ge_{0.25}$ ESL.
  - Higher intrinsic selectivity to $Si_{0.75}Ge_{0.25}$ compared to TMAH at the same conditions.

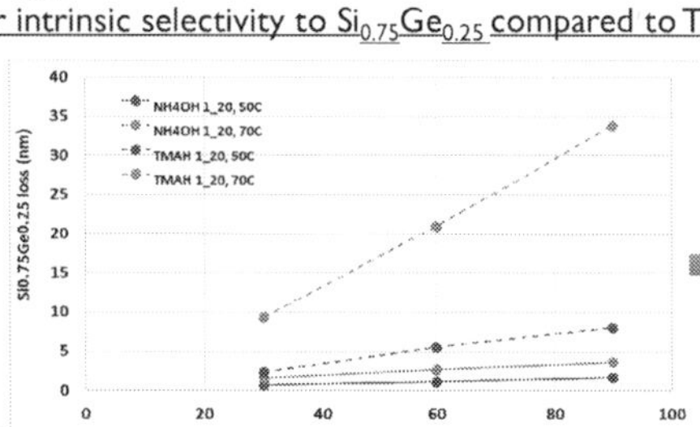

$$Si + 2OH^- + 2H_2O \rightarrow Si(OH)_2^{2+} + 2H_2.$$

- NH_4OH 1_20 → weak base, pH 9-10 → lower [OH$^-$]
  →less Si etching rate for the same initial concentration.
- TMAH 1_20 → strong base, pH 14 → higher [OH$^-$]
  → More Si etching for the same initial concentration.

imec

Explanation of the wafer back side thinning at IMEC (4)

Back side thinning performance

→ Thinning stopping on 100 nm $Si_{0.75}Ge_{0.25}$

A. Jourdain et al, ETCC, 2020

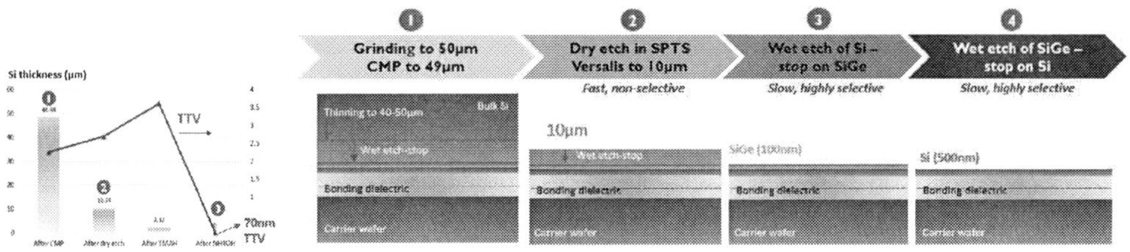

BS measurements

	SiGe after Si bulk removal	Si capping layer after SiGe removal	FS measurements
Mean thickness	98nm	542nm	SiGe: 98nm Si: 502nm
TTV	17nm	70nm	SiGe: 16nm Si: 75nm
Metrology	XRR, in-line FIB X-SEM	In-line FIB X-SEM	Mass measurements, SE

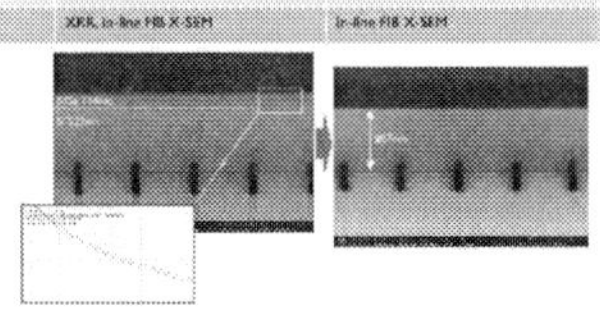

- Very good match between FS and BS measurements: no Si loss during wafer thinning.
- Metrology: IR interferometry, X-Ray Reflectivity (XRR), mass loss, in-line FIB and ellipsometry

imec

Explanation of the wafer back side thinning at IMEC (5)

Back side thinning performance

→ Thinning stopping on 50 nm $Si_{0.75}Ge_{0.25}$.

→ Full silicon back side thinning: Grinding + CMP + dry etch + TMAH + diluted NH_4OH + SiGe removal.

→ Thickness of the EPI Si after the full silicon back side thinning sequence (reflectometry).

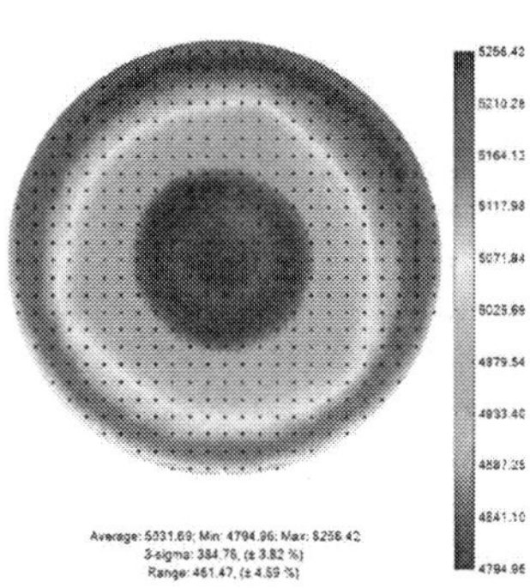

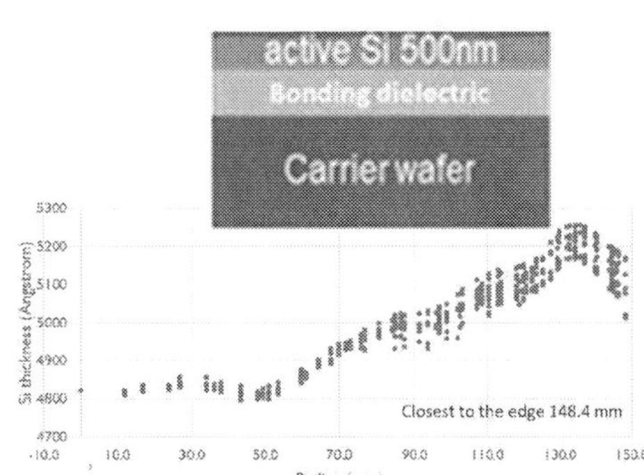

Thickness and TTV of the Si EPI retrieved after the full silicon back side thinning sequence.

imec

- Introduction
- Explanation of wafer back side thinning at IMEC
- **Challenge for future back side silicon thinning**
- Back side silicon thinning with $Si_{0.75}Ge_{0.25}$:B ESL
- Summary and on-going activities

imec

Challenge for future back side silicon thinning (1)

Need to reduce the SiGe ESL thickness

- For 50 nm $Si_{0.75}Ge_{0.25}$ etch stop layer (= $Si_{0.75}Ge_{0.25}$ thickness used in the current BSPDN integration) , the epitaxial growth occurs in the metastable region. → risk of SiGe relaxation is possible.

→ There is a need to growth the $Si_{0.75}Ge_{0.25}$ etch stop layer in the stable region
→ Chosen target at **10 nm $Si_{0.75}Ge_{0.25}$**

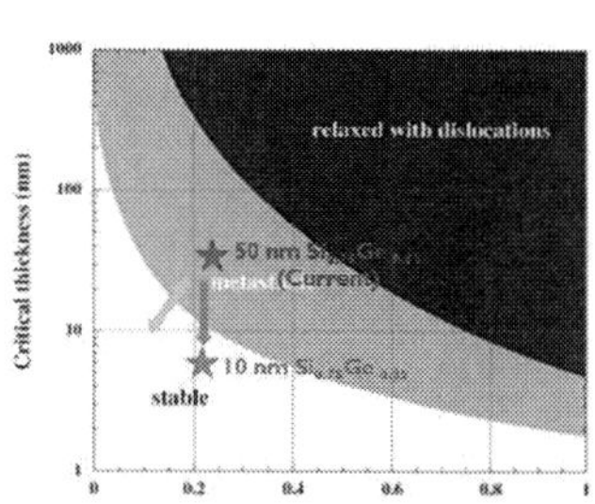

D. J. Paul, Semicond. Sci. Technol., 19, R75–R108 (2004)

imec

SiGe growth stable region

- **Reduced SiGe thickness**

→ Stricter control of the TTV before the Si etch soft landing step with dil NH_4OH.

- **Reduced Ge concentration**

→ Less process window for the Si etch soft landing step with dil NH_4OH (= more SiGe loss).

30' @ 500°C + 30' @ 700°C

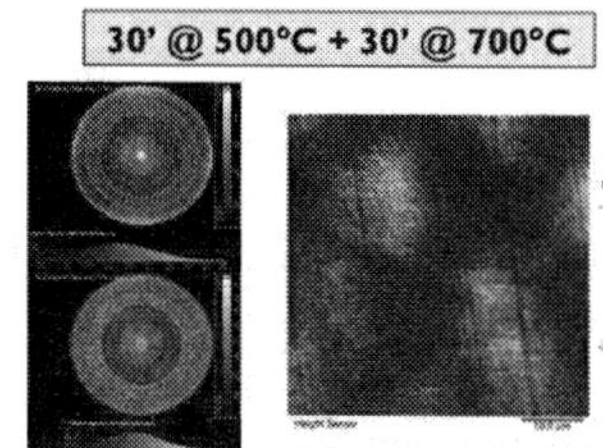

(~1 cm from wfr edge)

SPS
2.74 ppm
3.80 ppm

→ Still some misfits at the edge after EPI anneal

Challenge for future back side silicon thinning (2)

TTV control during Si thinning

- The TTV during the Si thinning decides the thickness of the SiGe ESL. We historically used a high $Si_{0.75}Ge_{0.25}$ thickness of 100 nm and later 50 nm to compensate the high TTV during the Si thinning.

→ For thinner SiGe ESL, lowering the TTV specifications after grinding + CMP + dry etch + wet etch is essential.

High TTV before dil NH_4OH | Thinning not well stopping on 10 nm $Si_{0.75}Ge_{0.25}$ ESL

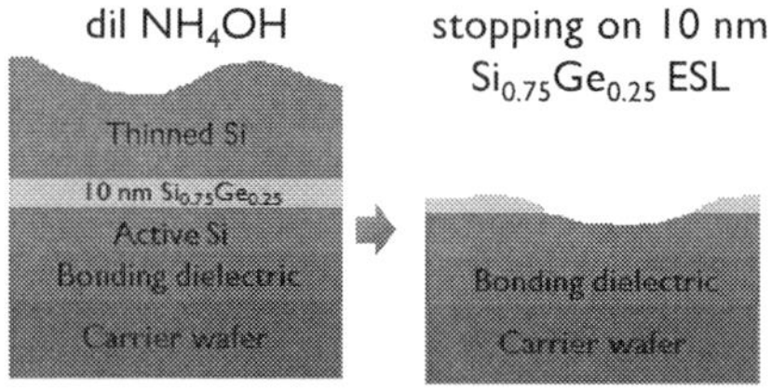

Low TTV before dil NH_4OH | Thinning well stopping inside the 10 nm $Si_{0.75}Ge_{0.25}$ ESL

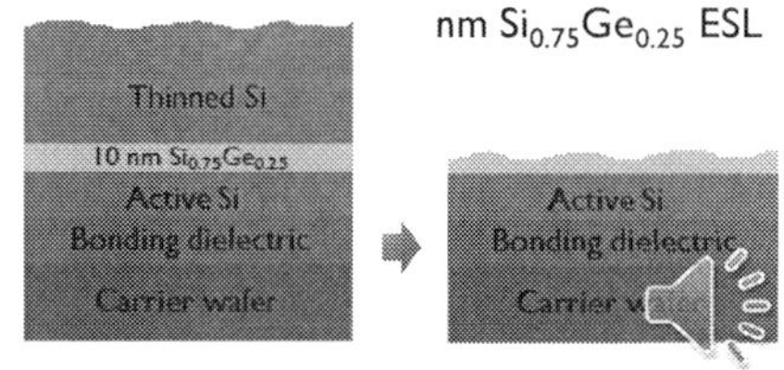

imec

- Introduction
- Explanation of wafer back side thinning at IMEC
- Challenge for future back side silicon thinning
- **Back side silicon thinning with $Si_{075}Ge_{0.25}$:B ESL**
- Summary and on-going activities

imec

Back side silicon thinning with $Si_{0.75}Ge_{0.25}$:B ESL (1)

Motivation

- B is an element that stops the Si etching in alkaline media when its concentration exceeds 1E19 at.cm^{-3}.
- Having B in the $Si_{0.75}Ge_{0.25}$ is then expected to enhance the selectivity towards the ESL during when finishing the Si thinning with diluted NH_4OH.

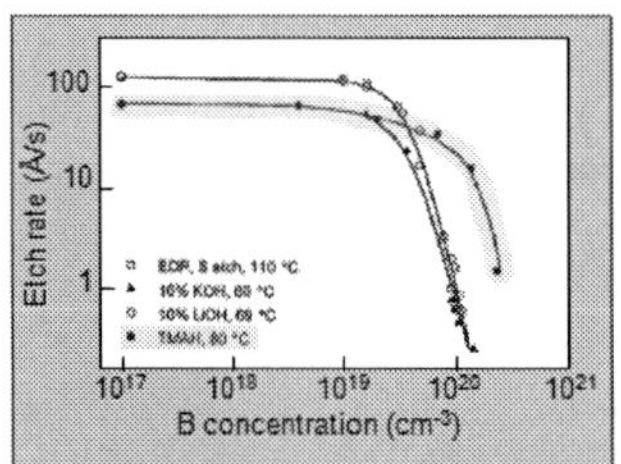

Ref: X. G. Zhang, 'Electrochemisty of Silicon and Its Oxide', Kluwer Academic/Plenum Publishers

imec

Back side silicon thinning with $Si_{0.75}Ge_{0.25}$:B ESL (2)

SiGe wet etch rate reduction with boron doping

→ Tracking the mass evolution on Si_$Si_{0.75}Ge_{0.25}$ stack wafers during the wet etching with dil NH4OH.

SiGe ESL conditions:
- 10nm
- $Si_{0.75}Ge_{0.25}$ vs $Si_{0.75}Ge_{0.25}$:B (10^{19}/cm^3)
- Anneal* vs no anneal

* 1000 °C_He_1.5s (activation anneal)
\+ 500 °C_steam_60min + 700C_N2_20 min
\+ 420C_N2/H2_20 min (STI)

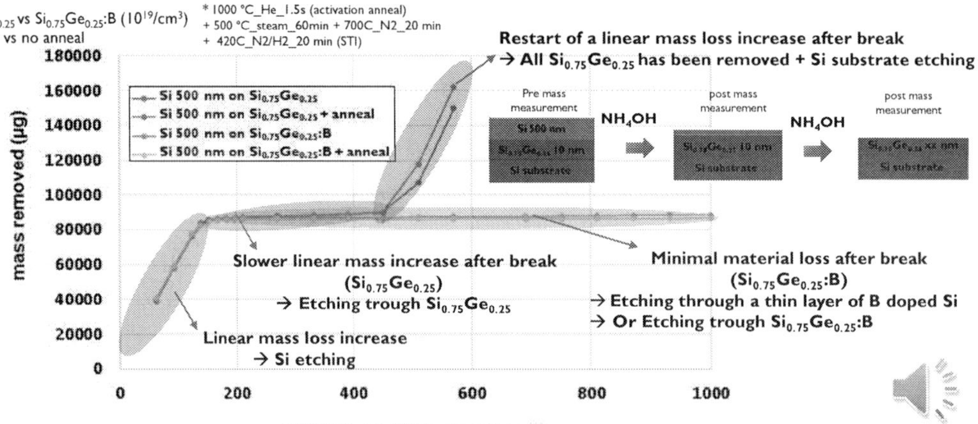

imec

Back side silicon thinning with $Si_{0.75}Ge_{0.25}$:B ESL (3)

SiGe wet etch rate reduction with boron doping

→ Tracking the mass evolution on Si_$Si_{0.75}Ge_{0.25}$ stack wafers during the wet etching with dil NH_4OH.

- 500 nm Si on 10 nm $Si_{0.75}Ge_{0.25}$:B + anneal + **1000s Dil NH_4OH 70C (High over etch)**
- 500 nm Si on 10 nm $Si_{0.75}Ge_{0.25}$:B + anneal + **210s Dil NH_4OH 70C (low over etch)**

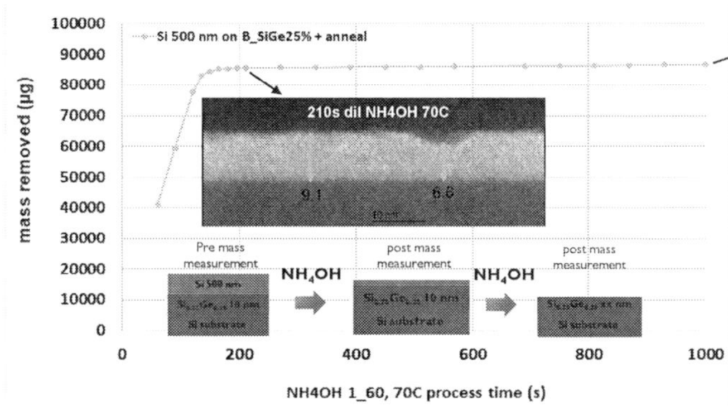

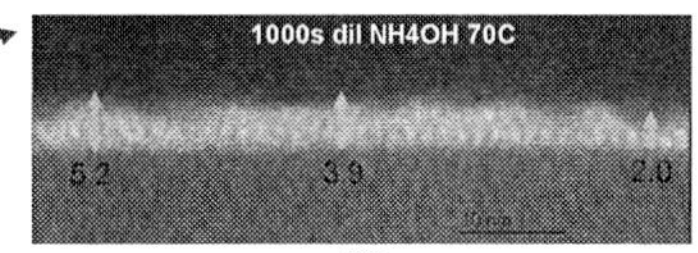

- **Dil NH_4OH at 70°C etches through the $Si_{0.75}Ge_{0.25}$:B with a very slow etching rate (defect etching).**

→ **Selectivity Si vs $Si_{0.75}Ge_{0.25}$:B at least > 500_1**

imec

Back side silicon thinning with $Si_{0.75}Ge_{0.25}$:B ESL (4)

B diffusion from $Si_{0.75}Ge_{0.25}$:B to Si after anneal

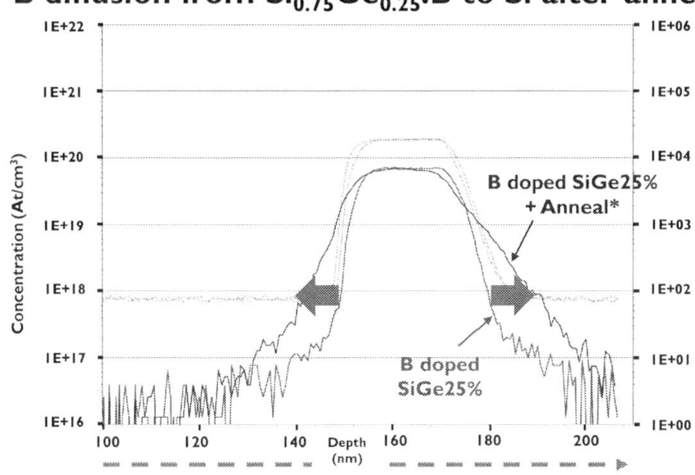

* 1000C_He_1.5s (activation anneal) + 500C_steam_60min + 700C_N2_20 min + 420C_N2/H2_20 min (STI)

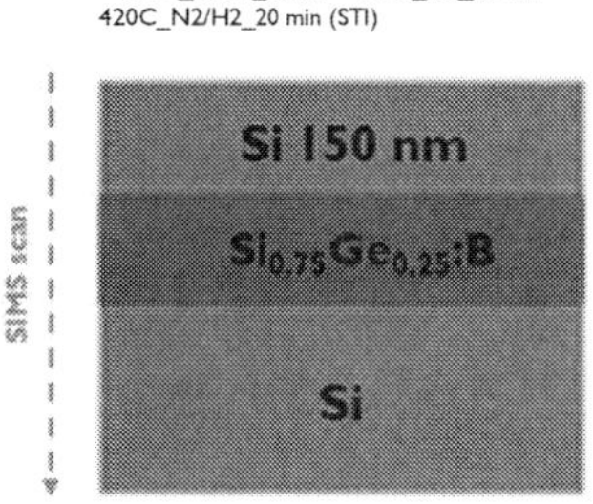

~ 30 nm of B diffused into the Si induced by the anneal steps.

imec

Back side silicon thinning with $Si_{0.75}Ge_{0.25}$:B ESL (5)

Discussion: impact of B diffusion into the EPI Si

30 nm of B diffusion on a 500 nm EPI Si channel

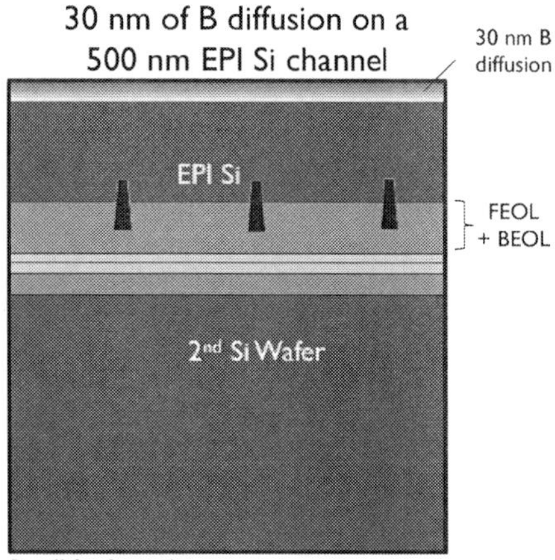

B still far from the transistors ➡ **$Si_{0.75}Ge_{0.25}$:B as an ESL seems safe enough**

30 nm of B diffusion on a 50 nm EPI Si channel (= possible integration involving thinner Si channel)

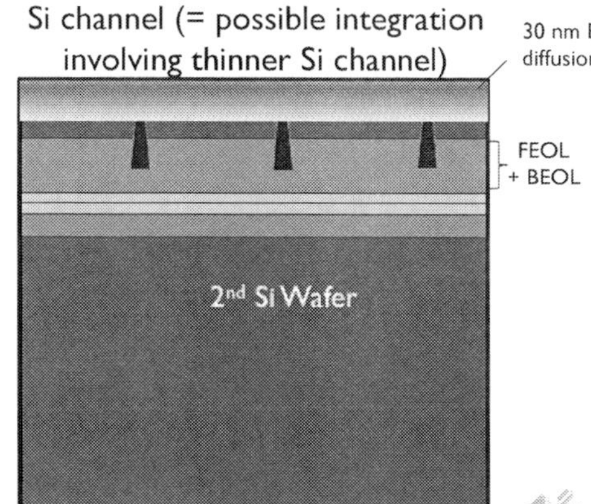

B much closer from the transistors ➡ **$Si_{0.75}Ge_{0.25}$:B as an ESL seems not safe enough**

imec

- Introduction
- Explanation of wafer back side thinning at IMEC
- Challenge for future back side silicon thinning
- Back side silicon thinning with $Si_{0.75}Ge_{0.25}$:B ESL
- **Summary and on-going activities**

imec

22

Summary and on-going activities

- **In this presentation we showed you:**

➢ A description of the wet etch steps (TMAH and diluted NH_4OH) used in our silicon back side thinning module targeting the BS PDN application in which a $Si_{0.75}Ge_{0.25}$ ESL is being used.
➢ The current performance of our silicon back side thinning stopping on 100 nm or 50 nm $Si_{0.75}Ge_{0.25}$ ESL.
➢ The need for using a thinner $Si_{0.75}Ge_{0.25}$ ESL.
➢ A proposal for using $Si_{0.75}Ge_{0.25:}$ B as an etch stop layer to enhance the selectivity of the Si etch during the last step of our thinning module with diluted NH_4OH.

- **Today, we are busy in enabling the thinning stopping on 10 nm $Si_{0.75}Ge_{0.25}$ ESL without B doping via:**

➢ Optimizing the grinding + CMP step.
➢ Proposing a full wet sequence after grinding + CMP: acidic etching (HF_HNO_3) + alkaline etching (optimized TMAH + diluted NH_4OH).

imec

SEARCHING FOR SUSTAINABILITY IN THE AI MICROELECTRONICS INDUSTRY

Dean W. Freeman, FTMA, 3DInCites

10/25/2022

1

3DInCites FTMA

WHAT DO.....

- Protect our Winters(POW)
- The 6th Extinction
- Tokyo Olympics
- The Microelectronics Industry

All Have in Common?

3DInCites FTMA

SUSTAINABILITY AND DECARBONIZATION EFFORTS

REDUCED SKI DAYS BY 2090*

Northstar	85%
Homewood	74%
Alpine Meadows	73%
Donner Ski Ranch	56%
Sugar Bowl	50%
Squaw Valley	45%

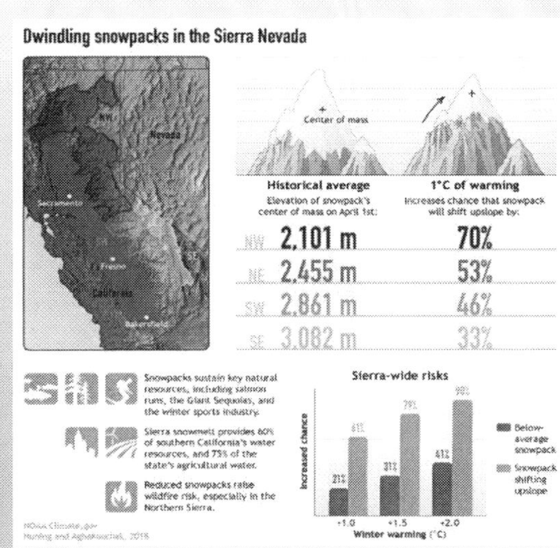

*published in the journal of Global Environmental Change- May 2017

CIRCULAR ECONOMY

- Japan Collected Enough Cell Phones to Produce all of the Olympic Medals from Recycling the Metals
- According to World Economic Forum 400,000 phones are buried or burned each day in the US

CO2'S RAPID INCREASE OVER PAST 250 YEARS

3DInCites FTMA

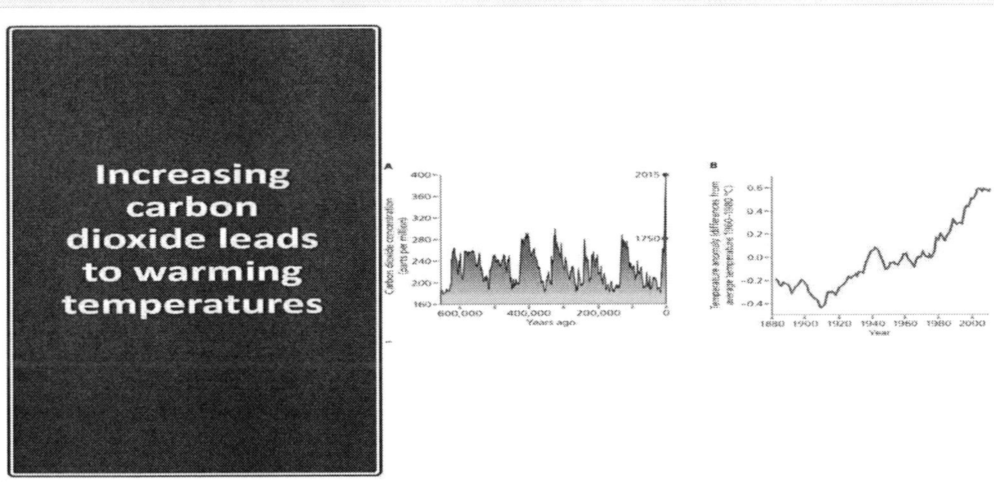

Source Dr. Montana Hodges TSM presentation

EXTINCTIONS INCREASING RAPIDLY

3DInCites FTMA

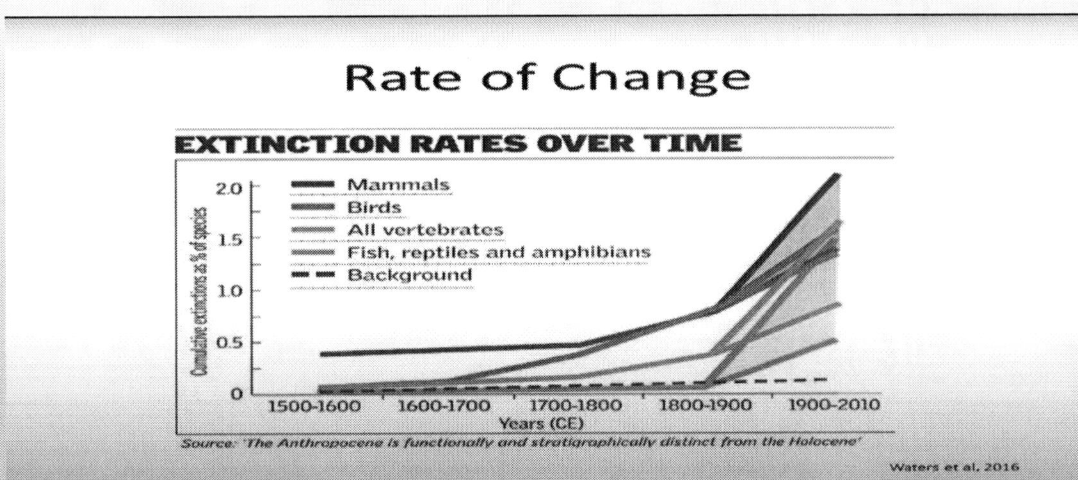

Source Dr. Montana Hodges TSM presentation

CLIMATE CHANGE CONFERENCES

- Stockholm 1972
- Montreal 1987 CFC, HFC
- Brazil 1992 Earth Summit
- Kyoto 1997 GHG
- Paris 2015 GHG
- SEC 2022 Rules

ARGUMENTS AGAINST

- Climate Change?
- Anti-Competitive
- Transfer of Wealth
- Rare Earths
- To Much Work
- Supply Chain
- Energy Supplies

3DInCites

HTTPS://WWW.CFR.ORG/BACKGROUNDER/PARIS-GLOBAL-CLIMATE-CHANGE-AGREEMENTS

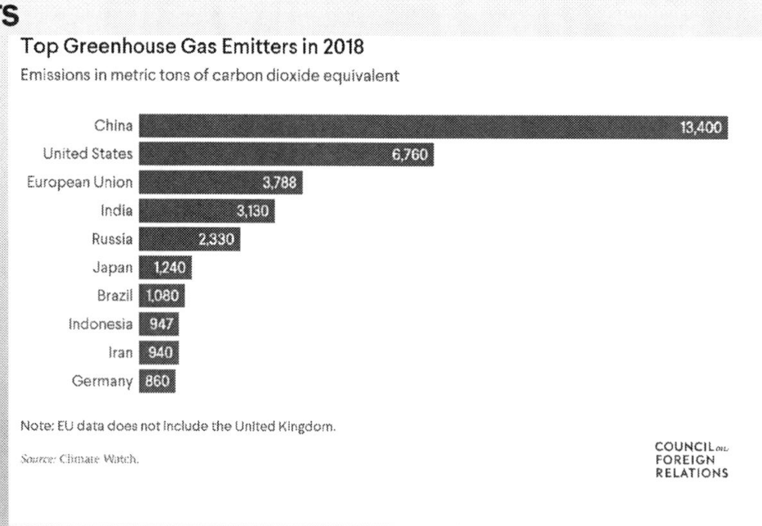

3DInCites FTMA

F T M A

SEARCHING FOR SUSTAINABILITY IN THE AI MICROELECTRONICS INDUSTRY

Dean W. Freeman, FTMA, 3DInCites

3DInCites FTMA

THE CRUX OF THE MICROELECTRONICS INDUSTRIES PROBLEM

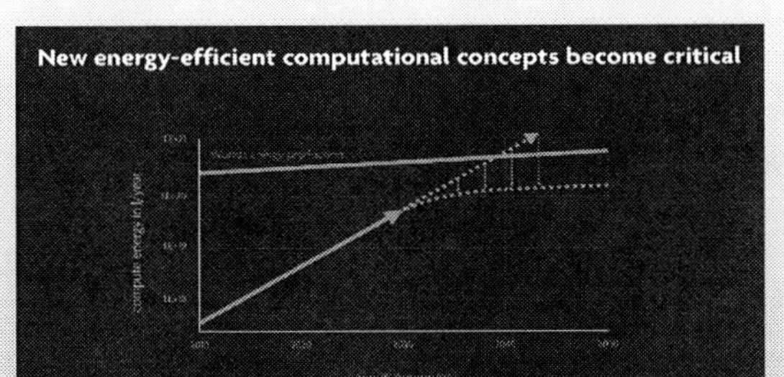

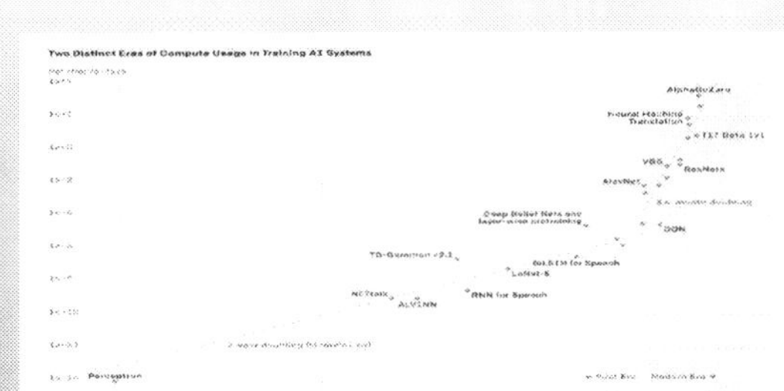

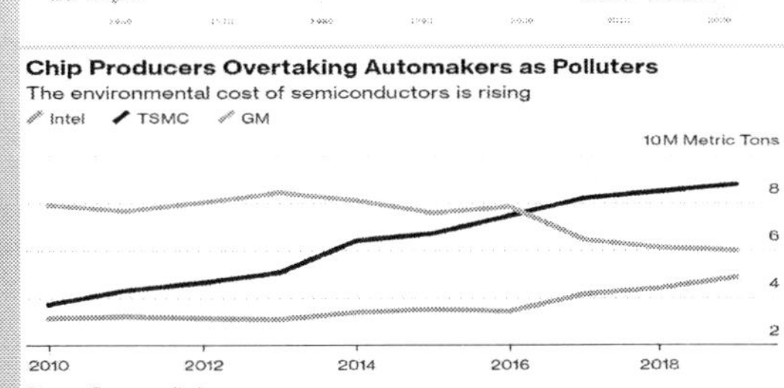

TECHNOLOGY ENERGY HOGS

- BitCoin Mining
  - Using old coal fired plants to support energy requirements.
    - Bitcoin mining has been the recent poster child of HPC energy consumption. The University of Cambridge study has estimated that the annual power consumption of bitcoin is approximately 130 terawatt hours, which is more than 3 times higher than at the beginning of 2019 (July 2021)
    - 130 terawatt hours is = 46 100kwspm memory fabs.

3DInCites

DATA CENTERS

- University of Massachusetts, Amherst found that the electricity consumed during the training of a transformer, a type of deep-learning algorithm, can emit more than 626,000 pounds of carbon dioxide. The energy amounts generated vary depending upon the requirements of the teach cycle
- https://www.pcmag.com/news/ai-could-save-the-world-if-it-doesnt-ruin-the-environment-first
- Data centers are estimated to use 52.8 MWh/day.
- Estimates 500,000 data centers WW (~80 new hyperscale DC built each year)
- Estimates 2.5 million wind turbines needed to meet energy demand (one turbine can produce 12-16 MWh/day 0.25 utilization)
- US and Germany have 100,000 wind turbines

Source Data Science Sept 2019 Marin Vlastelica

3DInCites FTMA

MANUFACTURING ENERGY KEEPS RISING

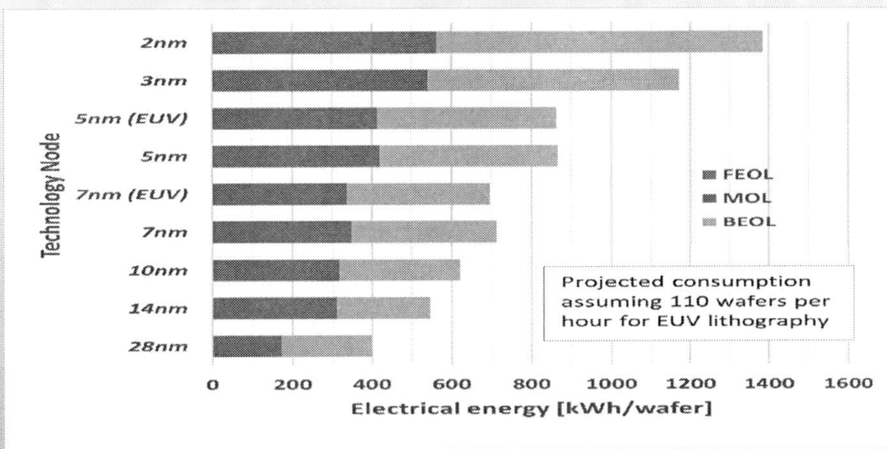

Source IMEC

3DInCites FTMA

THE GORILLAS ARE GOING GREEN

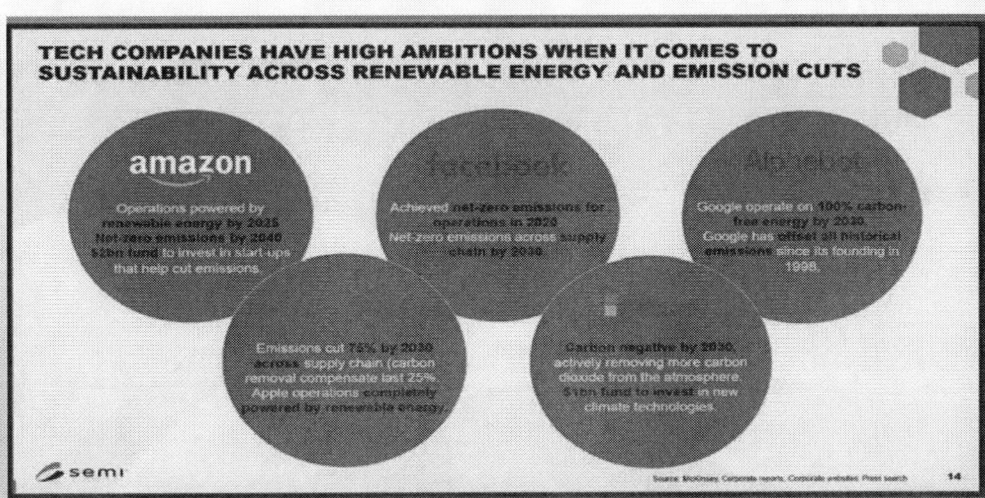

3DInCites FTMA

META 100% RENEWABLE IN 2020, BUT!!

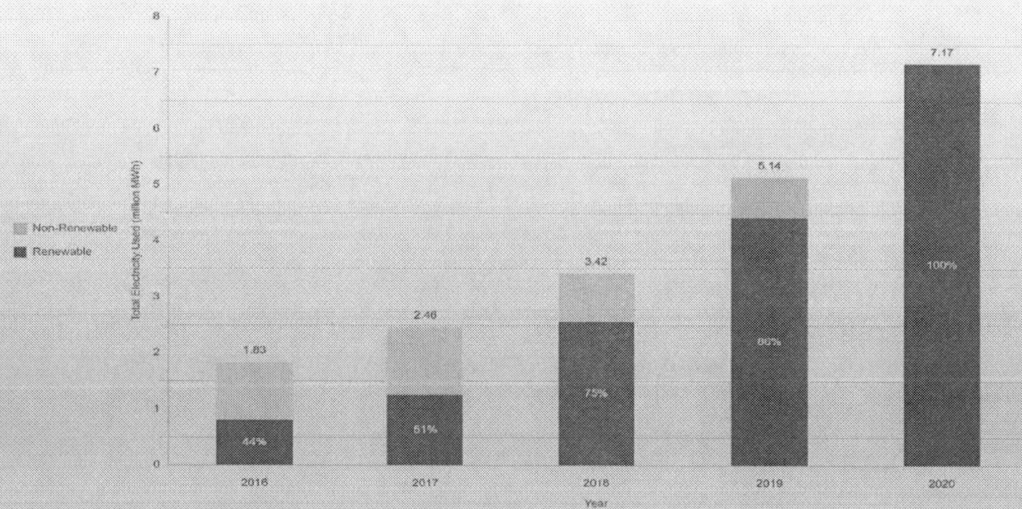

2021 ESG RESULTS (2020 DATA)

Company	CDP Climate Change	CDP Water Security	DJSI (environmental)	WSJ 100 Most Sustainable
Alphabet	A-	NA	47(73)	_
META	NA(previous years no response)	NA	NA	_
Microsoft	A	A	60(72)	_
Apple	A	F (NR)	32(52)	62(66)
Intel	A	A	67(75)	59(26)
TSMC	B	A	87(88)	38(16)
Nvidia	B	B	74(82)	94(35)

2021 ESG SCORES (2020 DATA)

3DInCites FTMA

Company	CDP Climate Change	CDP Water Security	DJSI (environmental)	WSJ 100 Most Sustainable
Applied Materials	B	C-		_
LAM	B	B	(49) NA	_
TEL	A	A	(83) Asia	_
ASML	C	C	(88) World	_
KLA	C	D		

RENEWABLE USE IN THE SEMICONDUCTOR INDUSTRY

3DInCites FTMA

Company	2021
TSMC	9.2%(2050)
Intel	80%, 100% USA,71% WW(2025)
Texas Instruments	18.81%
STMicroelectronics	51% (Carbon Neutral by 2027)
ASE Holding	24%
Lam Research	54% (2030)
Applied Materials	60% USA 20% Globally (2030)

Source Company Reports

RENEWABLES GROWING, CAN THEY KEEP UP?

3DInCites FTMA

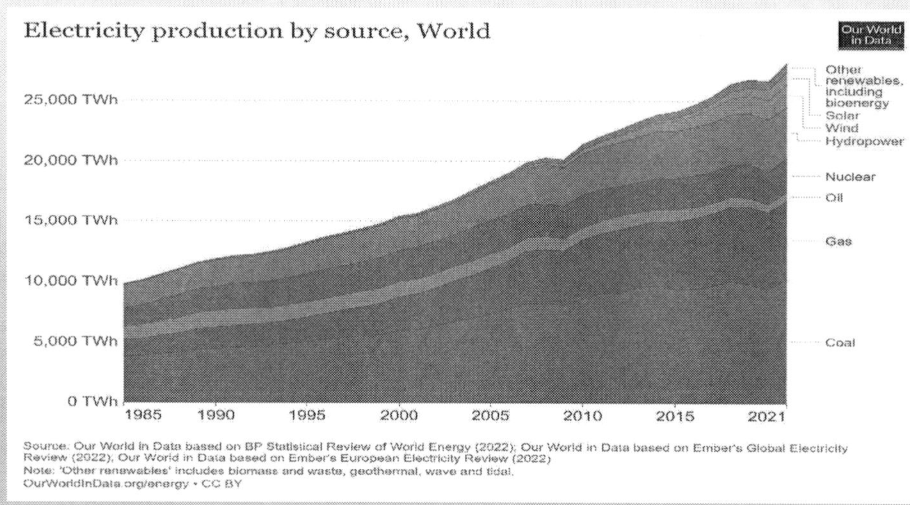

RENEWABLES GROWING, CAN THEY KEEP UP?

3DInCites FTMA

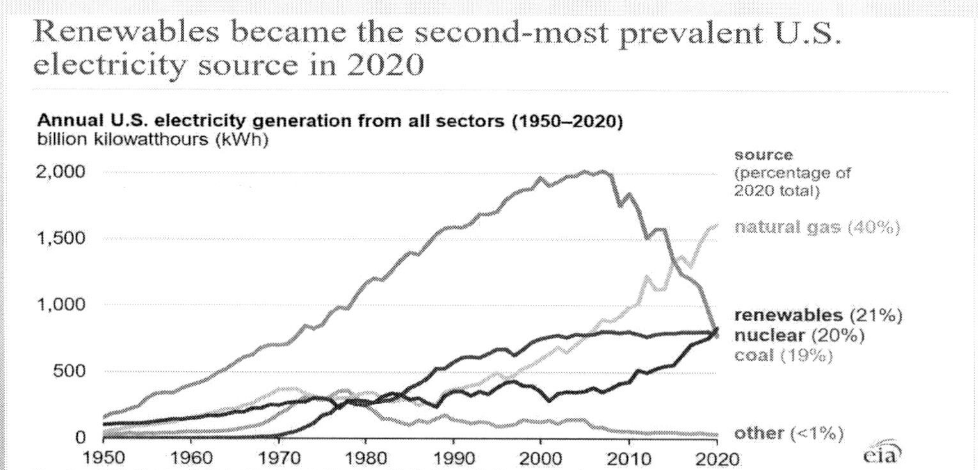

RENEWABLES

3DInCites FTMA

Are They Enough?

THE BATTERY CHALLENGE

3DInCites FTMA

Accelerating Demand

Metals demand from lithium-ion batteries is expected to top 17 million tons in 2030

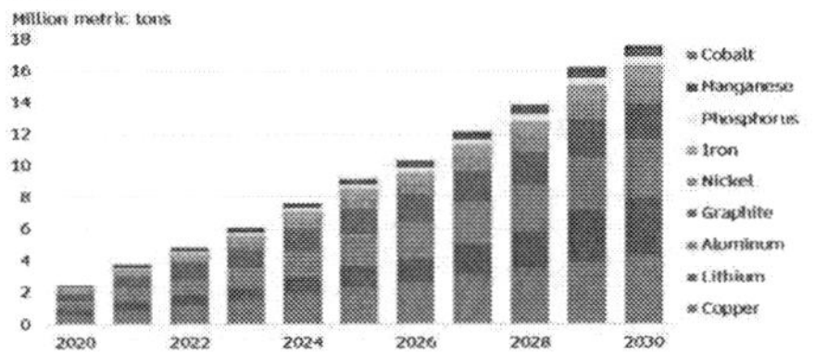

Source: BloombergNEF. Note: Metals demand occurs at the mine mouth, one year before battery demand.

Under Pressure

The lithium market could see a supply deficit this year

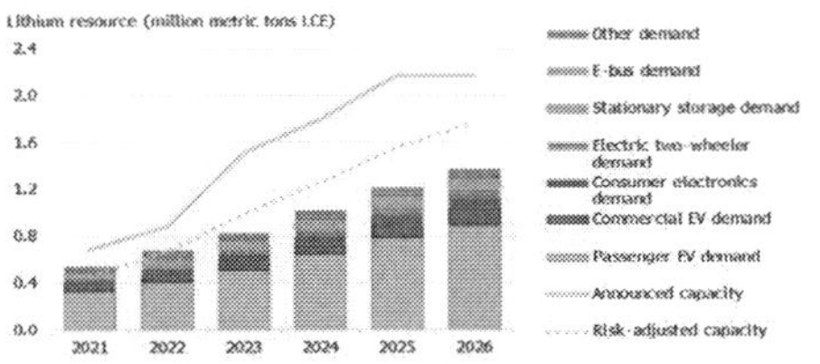

Source: BloombergNEF, Avicenne. Note: Demand occurs at the mine mouth, about one year before battery demand. LCE = lithium carbonate equivalent. Other demand includes pharmaceutical use.

Hit the Brakes

Battery prices could rise for the first time since at least 2010 this year

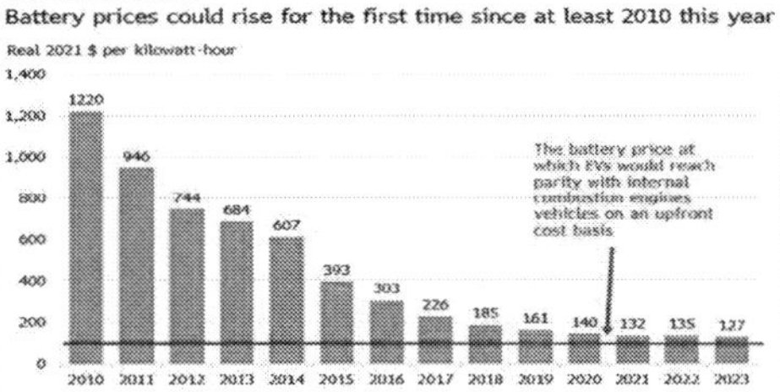

Source: BloombergNEF. Note: Forecast prices are in nominal terms, observed prices are in real 2021 $ per kilowatt-hour.

Changing Chemistries

Demand for cobalt is now less than previously expected as battery chemistries shift

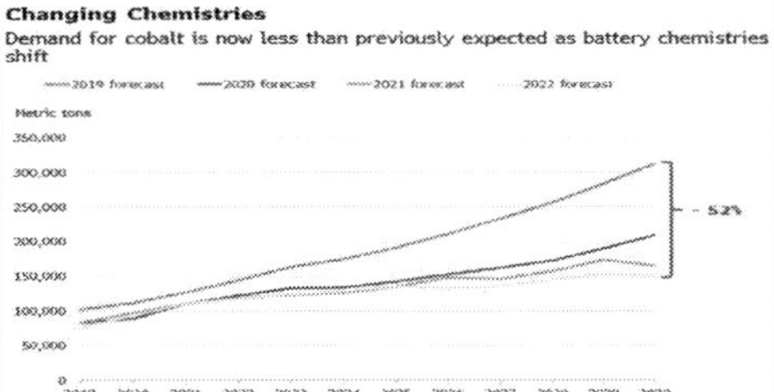

Source: BloombergNEF

RENEWABLE CIRCULARITY

3DInCites FTMA

10/25/2022 PRESENTATION TITLE 25

You Cannot Decarbonize the Grid Without:

- Nuclear
- Hydro

GETTING TO ZERO

8

Challenge: Minimize emissions from a small, resource intense geographic footprint.

- Solar PV needs ~8 acres per megawatt of power
- Fab 10's roof space is est. at 500,000 m^2, or 123 acres (from public info)
- 2.8 TWh/yr from Fab 10 would need appx. 15,000 acres of solar panels, or 23 square miles.

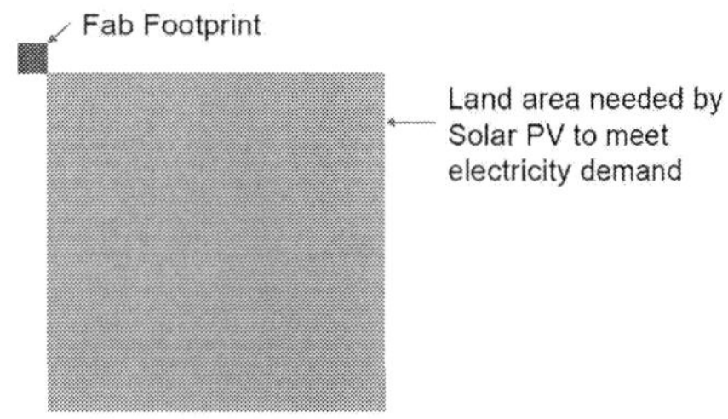

Micron

9

Big challenge: decarbonize on island grids

Current siting of semiconductor fabs present unique, intense sustainability challenges.

Startup barriers to entry:
- niche market
- rigid specifications

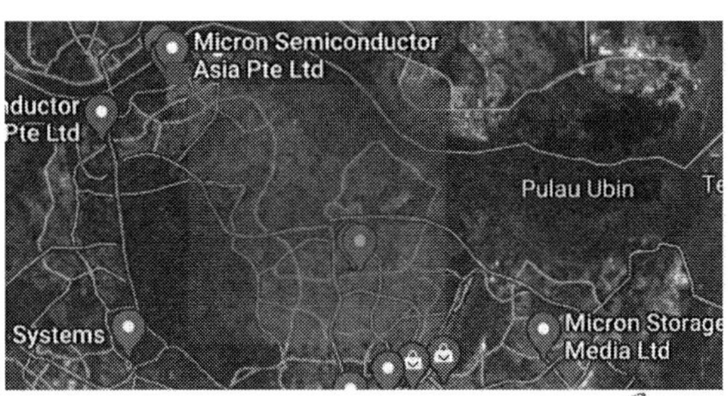

Micron

THE CHALLENGES OF GETTING TO ZERO

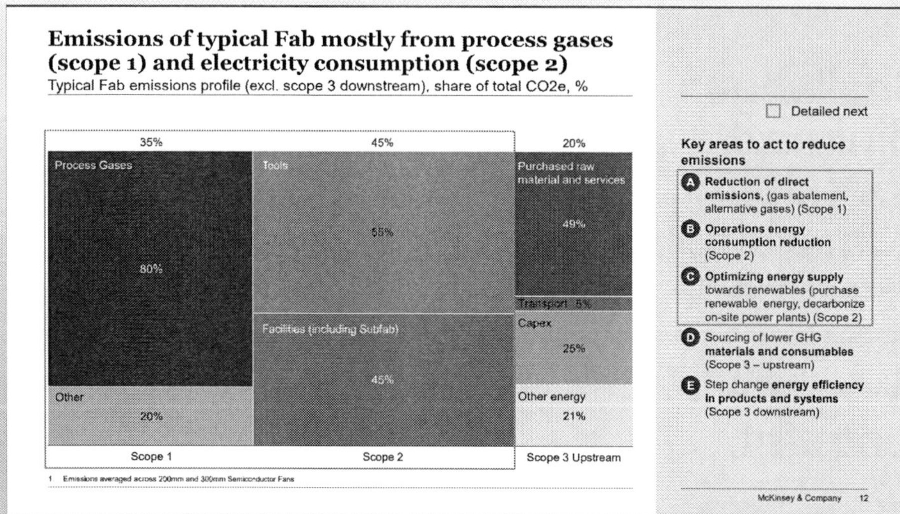

3DInCites FTMA

NEED TO MEASURE ALL EMISSIONS

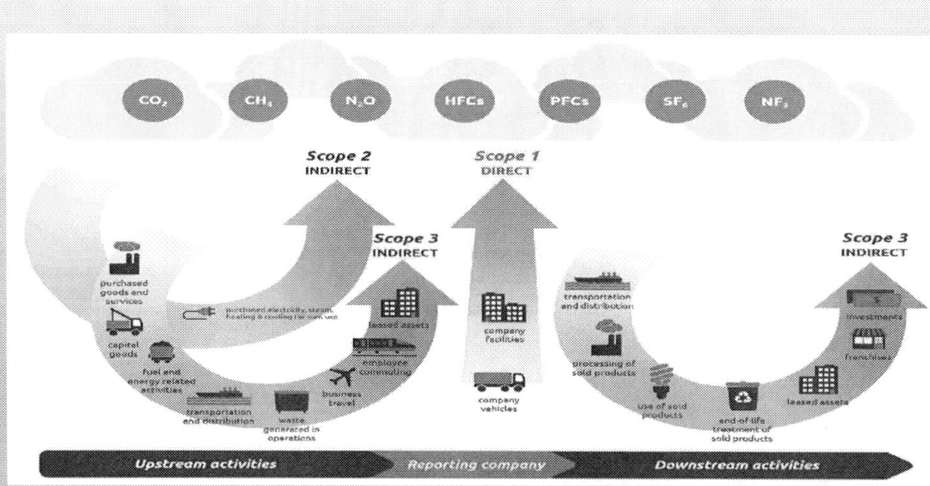

3DInCites FTMA

GETTING YOUR COMPANY TO ZERO

3DInCites FTMA

Renewables
Automation/Conservation
Innovation
20% reduction

REC/PPA
Carbon Credits

IS THERE HOPE?

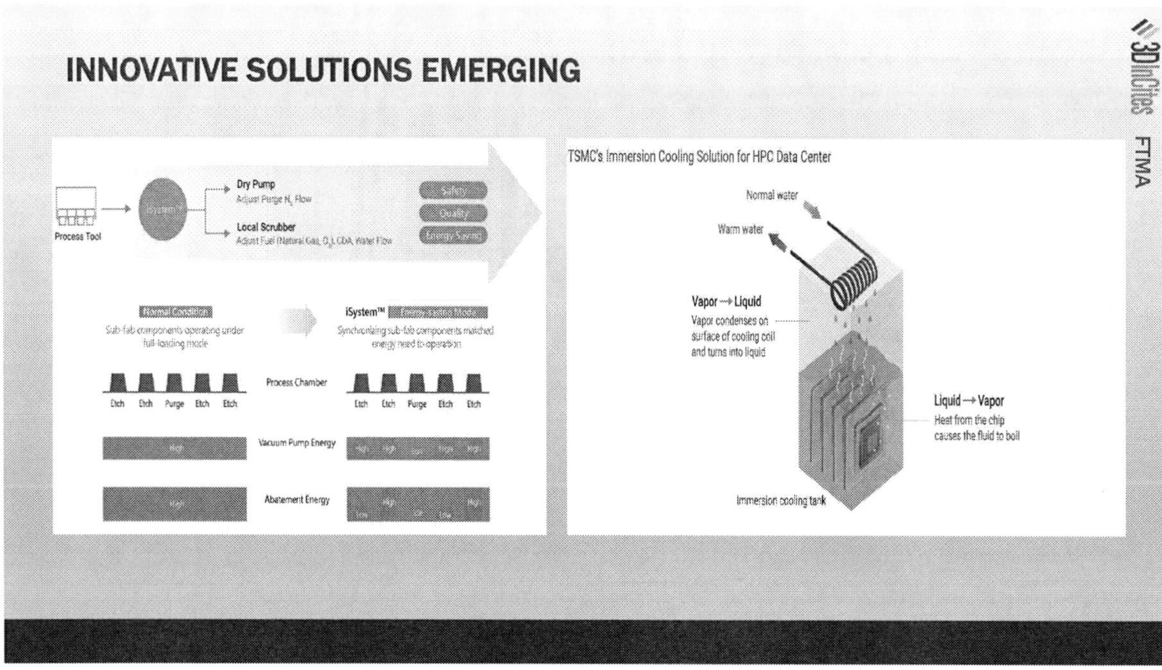
INNOVATIVE SOLUTIONS EMERGING
3DInCites FTMA
Process Tool
Dry Pump
Local Scrubber
iSystem™
Process Chamber
Etch Etch Purge Etch Etch
Vacuum Pump Energy
Abatement Energy
TSMC's Immersion Cooling Solution for HPC Data Center
Normal water
Warm water
Vapor → Liquid
Vapor condenses on surface of cooling coil and turns into liquid
Liquid → Vapor
Heat from the chip causes the fluid to boil
Immersion cooling tank

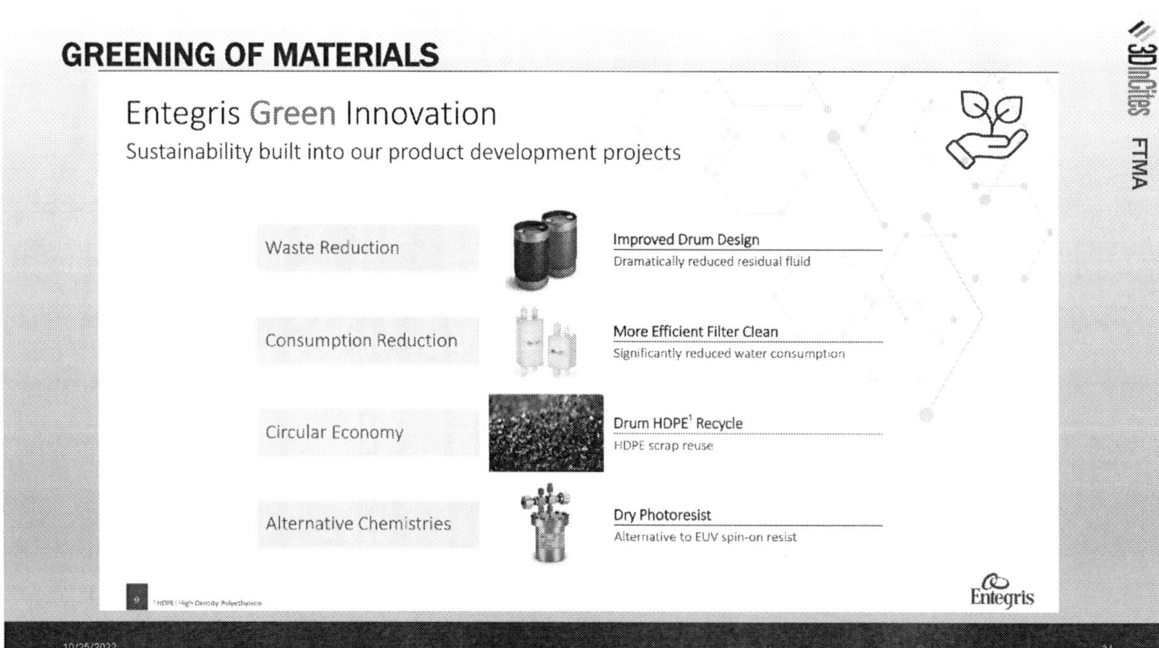
GREENING OF MATERIALS
3DInCites FTMA
Entegris Green Innovation
Sustainability built into our product development projects
Waste Reduction
Improved Drum Design
Dramatically reduced residual fluid
Consumption Reduction
More Efficient Filter Clean
Significantly reduced water consumption
Circular Economy
Drum HDPE[1] Recycle
HDPE scrap reuse
Alternative Chemistries
Dry Photoresist
Alternative to EUV spin-on resist
Entegris
10/25/2022
34

ARE WE MAKING PROGRESS?

3DInCites FTMA

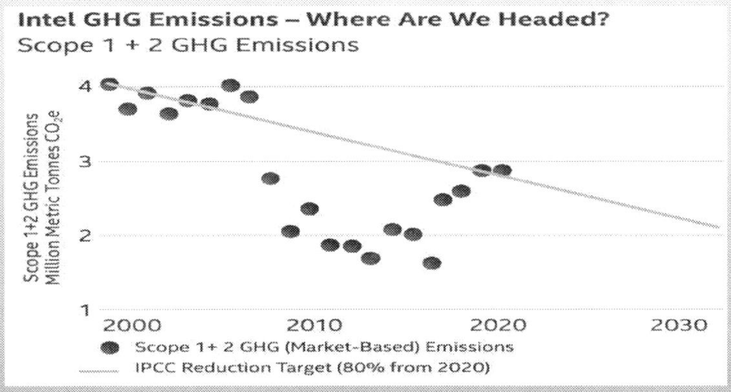

WHERE ARE WE AT?

3DInCites FTMA

- Sustainability Programs Being Executed
  - Need more Scope 3 data
- Adding Renewables
  - Not the entire solution
  - Supply chain issues on motors and batteries
  - Circular economy for renewables.
- New Chip Designs Emerging, Along with Improved Algorithms
  - Will it be enough soon enough?
- Innovative Programs Being Implemented Industry Wide

WHAT NEEDS TO CHANGE?

3DInCites FTMA

- More Conservation
  - More Programs like TSMC
- Different Business Models
  - Circular Economy
- Get More of the Industry on Board
  - CDP Environmental Scores Across Industry are Poor
- Start Understanding and Reporting Scope 3 Emissions
- Tie Sustainability into Executive Compensation!
- More Voices! More Action!

10/25/2022 37

3DInCites EST. 2009 TM

FTMA

Particle Precursors – a Nonobvious Source of Defectivity Issues

Based on Yield Enhancement IRDS and SEMI Standards Studies

Gary Van Schooneveld, CT Associates

Slava Libman Ph.D., FTD Solutions

Surface Preparation and Cleaning Conference 2022

IRDS and SEMI Collaborative R&D Supporters

IRDS UPW Task Force
- Slava Libman – Co-Chair
- Gary Van Schooneveld – Co-Chair

IRDS Critical Components Task Force
- Bob McIntosh – Co-Chair
- Archita Sengupta – Co-Chair

Integrated Device Manufacturers – Global Foundries, Intel, Micron, Samsung

Equipment Suppliers - ASML, Screen

Component Suppliers – Asahi, Daiken, Entegris, Georg Fischer, Pall, Saint Gobain

Material and System Providers – Evoqua, Ovivo, Kurita, Lanxess, Solvay, 3M

Technical and Experimental Services – Balazs, CT Associates, Environmental Energy Services, FTD Solutions, Page/imes, Unisers

Why is Collaborative R&D Necessary?

The Team 2

Defectivity and Reliability

- Chips getting more complex
  - Yield Risks
    - More process steps
    - New materials
    - Higher aspect ratio
    - Increasing die size due to memory and machine learning
      - >100mm2 for high-end AI
  - Reliability Risks
    - High temperature (energy) of HP devices
- Stringent operating range
  - 24/7 continuous operation of HP chips
  - >5-10 years for server/AV chips at >115-125C
- Reliability specs getting hard to meet
  - Critical defect sizes are at the single-nm scale
  - Molecular contamination is in priority
- Time-to-market implications
  - Faster ramp
  - Heterogeneous integration

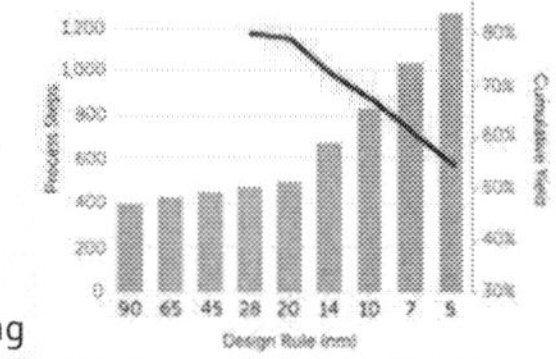

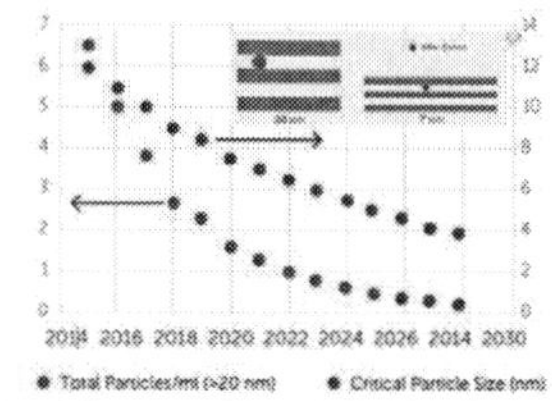

Source: Semiconductor Digest 2019

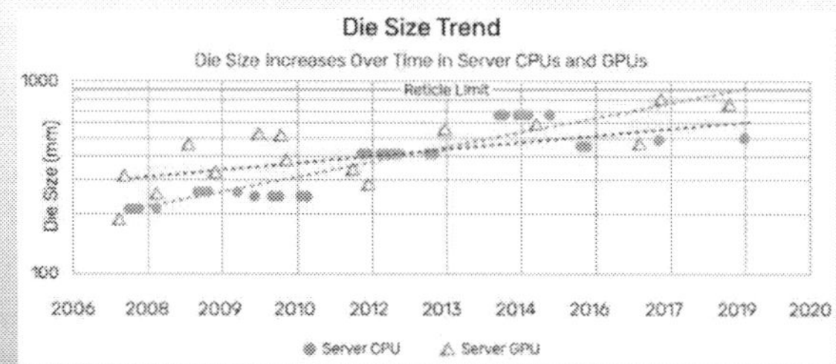

Source: CadenceLIVE Americas 2020

3

What is a Particle Precursor?

- UPW IRDS, in communication with the National Institute of Standards and Technology (NIST), defined particle precursor as "*a dissolved molecular compound, which may form particles when dried on the wafer surface*".

- Examples – Medium to high molecular weight organics and silicates.

4

Ion Exchange Resin Effluent

- Sample collection by Focused Aerosol Deposition (FAD)
- Sample analysis by FESEM (Hitachi SU8230 – U of MN CharFac)

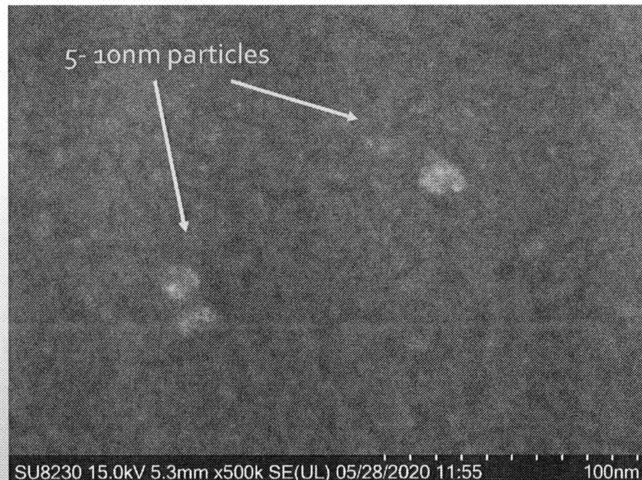

Source: Van Schooneveld, et al, Ultrapure Micro 2020

5

Hot UPW Fluoropolymer Piping Extract

- Sample collection by Focused Aerosol Deposition (FAD)
- Sample analysis by FESEM (Hitachi SU8230 – U of MN CharFac)

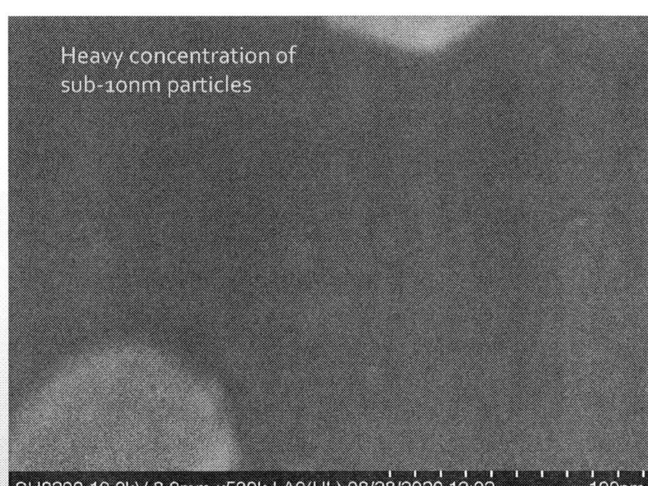

Source: Van Schooneveld, et al, Ultrapure Micro 2020

6

Gigabit Isopropyl Alcohol

- Sample collection by Focused Aerosol Deposition (FAD)
- Sample analysis by FESEM (Hitachi SU8230 – U of MN CharFac)

7

Source: Van Schooneveld, et al, Ultrapure Micro 2020

Why are particle precursors becoming a significant risk?

- Evolving chip design and yield constraints.
- Limited effectiveness of filtration and alternate mitigation options.
- Particle precursor are invisible to traditional particle measuring technologies based on light-scattering such as optical particle counting (OPC) and dynamic light scattering (DLS).
- Online metrology is limited, and interpretation of results can be challenging.

8

Chip design and yield constraints

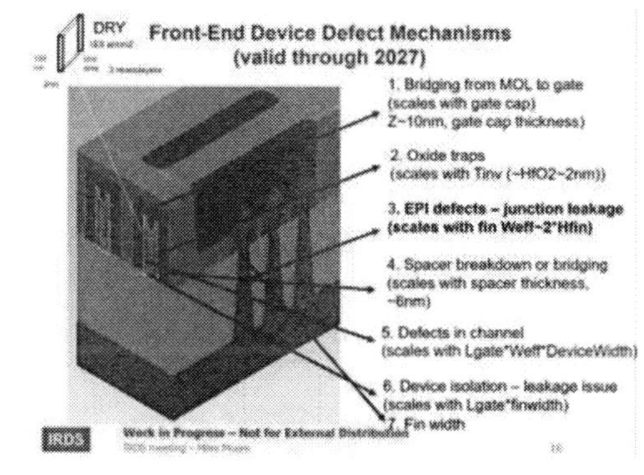

Particle Killer Size Effect Based on the Device Structure

Yield distribution

- D0 = Integral of D(x)=k/x^q.dx from x=Xc to Inf. = k/2/Xc^2 where Xc : minimum critical size, for x<Xc, D(x)=0
- K,q=Fab constants, q~3.

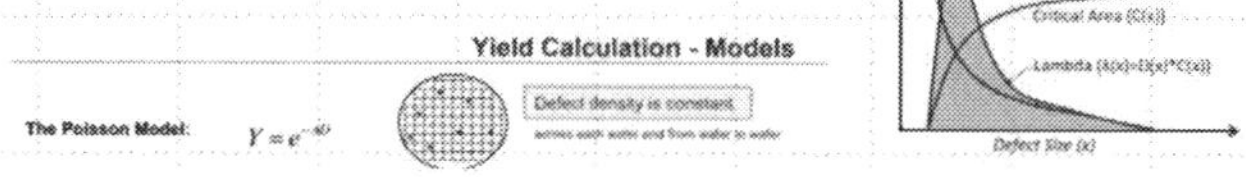

Allowable defect density distribution of each layer established by minimum yield requirements.

Source: 2022 IRDS Yield Roadmap

9

Chip design and yield constraints

2020	Width (nm)	2020 Defect Size (nm)	2022 Defect Size (nm)	2025 Defect Size (nm)	2020 Dx/wafer	2022 Dx/wafer	2025 Dx/wafer	Defect Mechanism	Process Type for predominant defect mechanism
Gate	20	10.0	9.0	7.0	5.7	5.0	6.6	Patterning, Gate stack	Dry etch, Wet Etch (GAA), Wet Clean
Fin	7	3.5	3.0	3.5	133.5	136.1	52.8	Gate stack, EPI	Dry etch, Dry Clean (SiCoNi) or Wet Cleans
VC	16	8.0	9.0	9.0	11.2	5.0	3.1	Clean	Dry etch, Wet Clean, Wet Fill (Electroplating), Wet Clean
MetalC	16	8.0	9.0	9.0	11.2	5.0	3.1	Patterning, Metal	Dry etch, Wet Clean, Wet Fill (Electroplating), Wet Clean
Via0	15	7.5	6.0	5.0	13.6	17.0	18.1	Clean	Dry etch, Wet Clean, Wet Fill (Electroplating), Wet Clean
Metal0	15	7.5	6.0	5.0	13.6	17.0	18.1	Patterning, Metal	Dry etch, Wet Clean, Wet Fill (Electroplating), Wet Clean
Viax	18	9.0	8.0	6.0	7.9	7.2	10.5	Clean	Dry etch, Wet Clean, Wet Fill (Electroplating), Wet Clean
Metalx	18	9.0	8.0	6.0	7.9	7.2	10.5	Patterning, Metal	Dry etch, Wet Clean, Wet Fill (Electroplating), Wet Clean
Viay	40	20.0	20.0	20.0	0.7	0.5	0.3	Clean	Dry etch, Wet Clean, Wet Fill (Electroplating), Wet Clean
Metaly	40	20.0	20.0	20.0	0.7	0.5	0.3	Patterning, Metal	Dry etch, Wet Clean, Wet Fill (Electroplating), Wet Clean

Link required...correlation between particles in the liquid and deposition rate on the wafer

Significant collaborative work is being done by IRDS UPW and Critical Components Teams

Source: 2022 IRDS Yield Roadmap

10

Limitation of filtration and OPC metrology

Retention testing of poly(sodium 4-styrensulfonate) in UPW (HMWO compound)

30 nm OPC

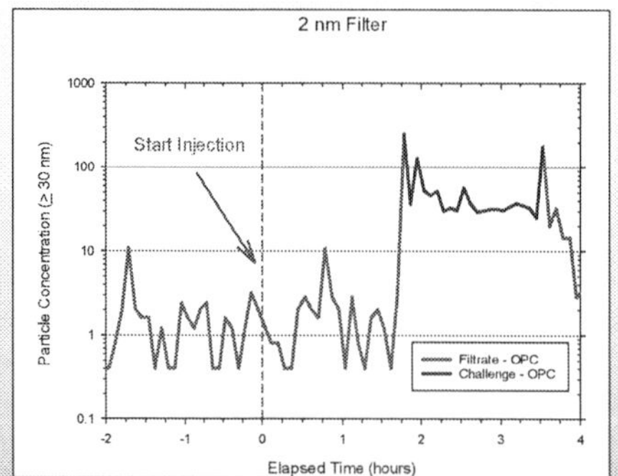

4 nm Nebulization - CPC

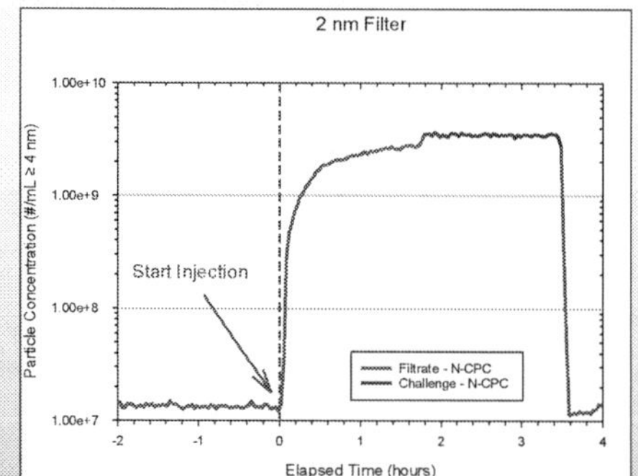

- OPC able to detect large particles > 30 nm but HMWO contaminates are invisible.
- While retention of OPC detectable particle is > 99.9%, PP retention is less than 10%

Source: Van Schooneveld, et al, Ultrapure Micro 2020

11

Particle Precursor Detection Enabling Technology: Nebulization – Aerosol Particle Counting

Liquid Nanoparticle Sizing (LNS)

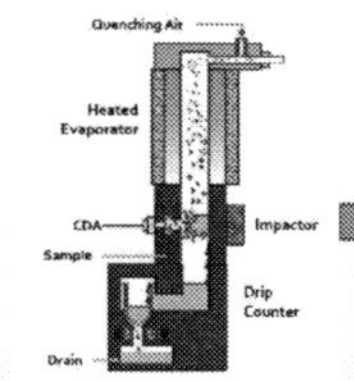

Nebulization

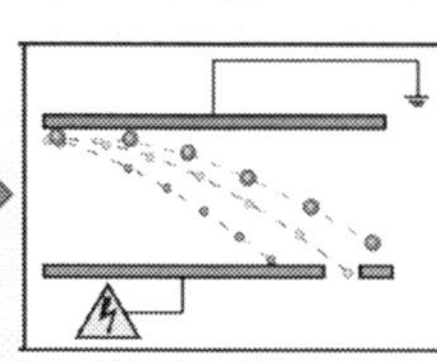

Size Classification by Charge Mobility

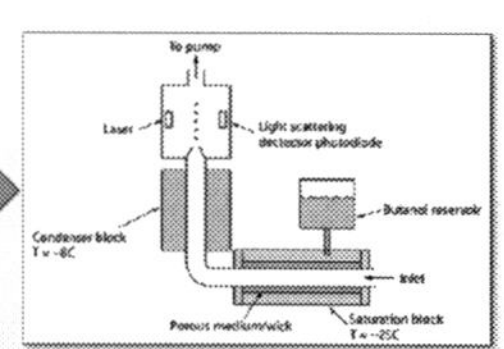

Condensation Particle Counting (CPC)

IX Resin Particle Size Distribution

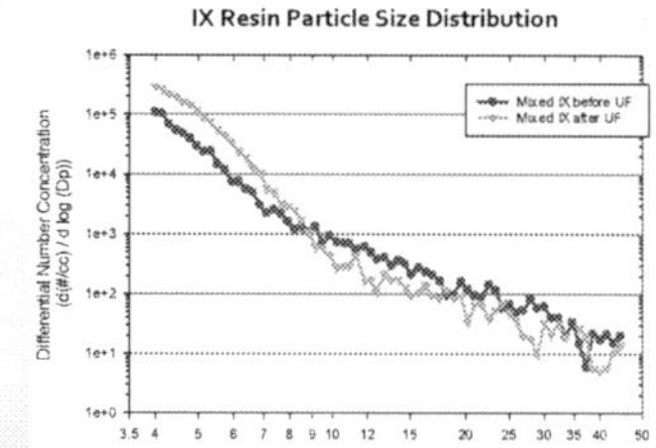

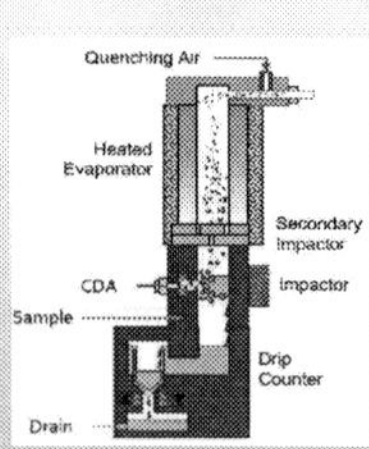

Nebulizer

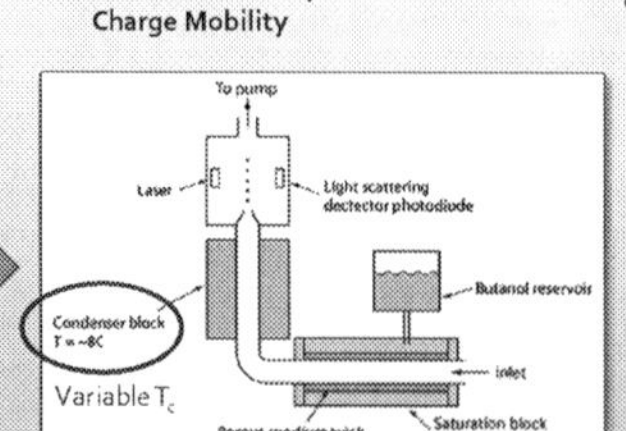

Condensation Particle Counting (CPC)

Scanning Threshold Particle Counting (STPC)

Illustrations courtesy of Kanomax FMT

IX Resin Flush

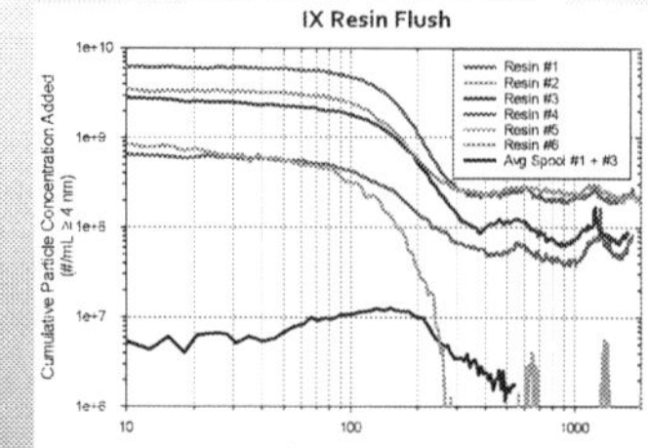

IRDS Particle Precursor Risk Assessment

Sponsor – IRDS UPW Task Force

@ CTA (USA)

- Liquid sample preparation

IX Resin PP Extraction

- LNS characterization of liquid particle count (4nm -65nm)

@ Screen (Japan)

- Spin-drying of samples to 12-inch silicon wafer
- Full-wafer scan (SP7)

@ Unisers (Switzerland)

- Defect inspection (8nm – 160nm)

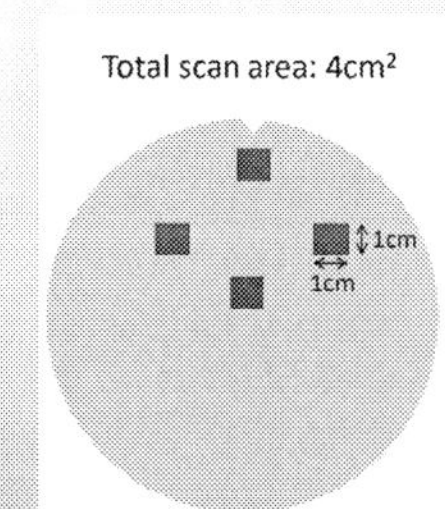

- Surface Enhanced Particle Sizing (SEPS)

Particle Precursor Test Approach

Mixed IX Polish Resin → (Hydrodynamic Separation) → Anion IX Polish Resin / Cation IX Polish Resin

Prepare Extract: SEMI C79 Grab Sample Prep

Reduce Native Particles: Filter with 6K MWC Ultrafilter

Measure Extract PSD: Liquid Nanoparticle Sizing Analysis

Dilute to Final Deposition Concentrations

500:1 (mixed)
100:1 (mixed, anion, cation)
20:1 (mixed)

Spin-coated Deposition by Screen Japan

On-wafer PSD by TLA-Tencor SP7 and UNISERS Surface-Enhanced Particle Sizing

Particle Precursor Deposition Results

LNS, SP7, UNISERS CORRELATION – Mixed Resin

500:1 dilution, Mixed resin

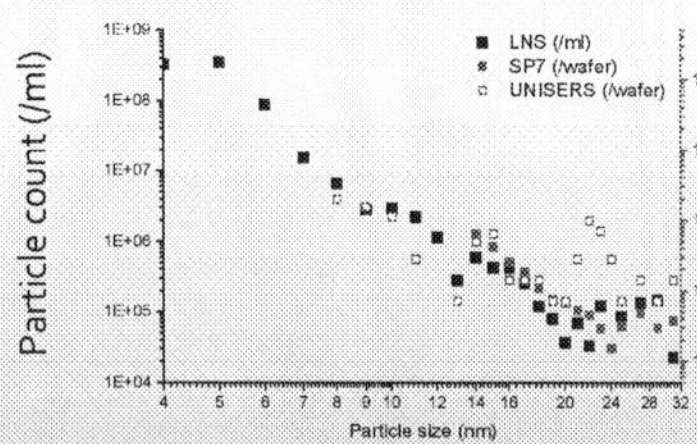

~ 2E3 particles/ml

1 particle/wafer

100:1 dilution, Mixed resin

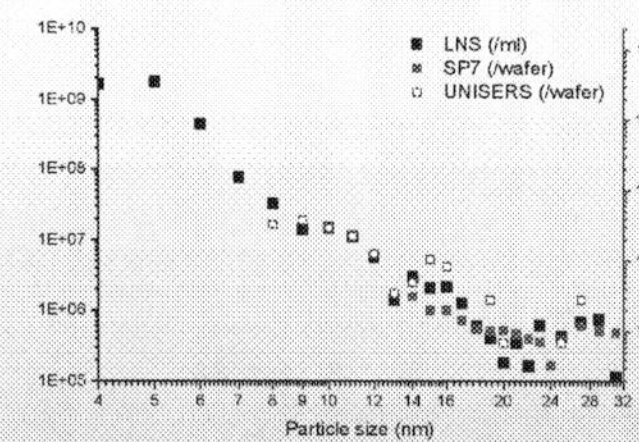

~5E3 particles/ml

1 particle/wafer

20:1 dilution, Mixed resin

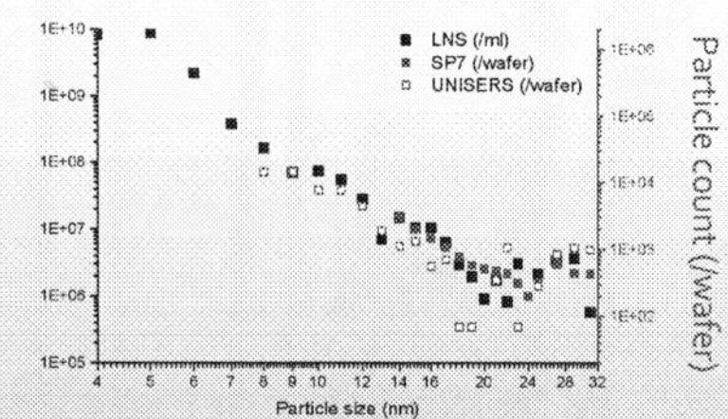

~ 5E3 particles/ml

1 particle/wafer

Source: UNISERS

Particle Precursor Deposition Results

LNS, SP7, UNISERS CORRELATION – Mixed Resin

500:1 dilution, Mixed resin

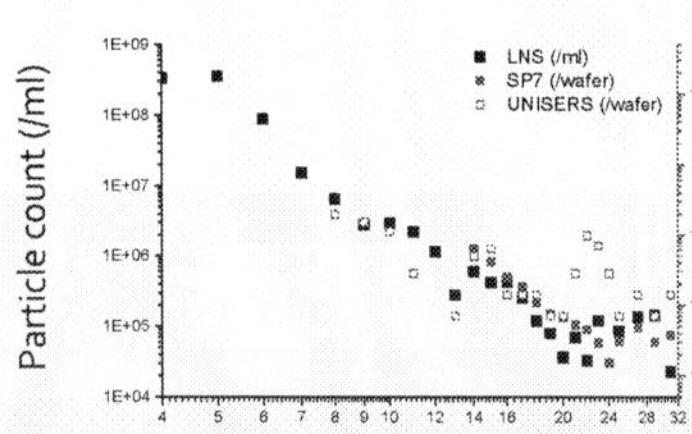

~ 2E3 particles/ml

1 particle/wafer

100:1 dilution, Mixed resin

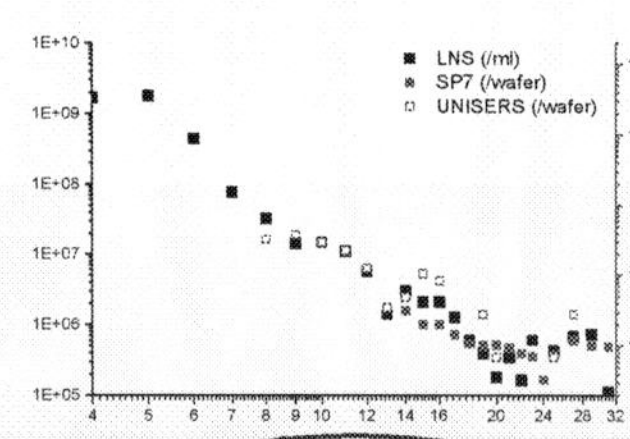

~5E3 particles/ml

1 particle/wafer

20:1 dilution, Mixed resin

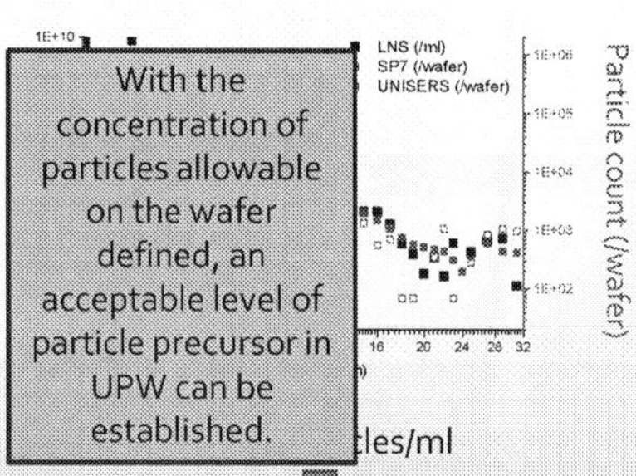

With the concentration of particles allowable on the wafer defined, an acceptable level of particle precursor in UPW can be established.

les/ml

1 particle/wafer

Source: UNISERS

International Roadmap for Devices and Systems (IRDS™) 2022 Edition

Table YE3 Technology Requirements for Surface Environmental Contamination Control

Year of Production	2021	**2022**	2023	2024	**2025**
Add Pitch designation					
Add Pitch designation					
Logic industry "Node Range" Labeling (nm)	"5"	**"3"**	"3"	"3"	**"2.1"**
IDM-Foundry node labeling	i7-f5	**i3-f2.1**	i3-f2.1	i3-f2.1	**i2.1-f1.5**
Logic device structure options	FinFet	**finFET LGAA**	finFET LGAA	finFET LGAA	**LGAA**
Logic device mainstream device	FinFet	**finFET**	finFET	finFET	**LGAA**
MPU/SoC Metalx ½ Pitch (nm)[1,2]	12.0	**12.0**	12.0	12.0	**12.0**
Critical particle size non-electrically active (non-EAP) (nm) based on 50% of Logic 1/2 Pitch (nm (contacted) [1]	10	**9**	9	9	**7**
Critical particle size (nm) of Electrically Active particles based on 50% width of fin Logic SiGe Front End or other device critical dimensions for LGAA **(>2 monolayers)**	3.5	**3**	3	3	3.5
Particle Precursors, *#/ml [56]* — this level is expected to produce 5 particles per 300 mm wafer of 10nm particles and greater.	**20,000 (see note)**	20,000 (see note)	20,000 (see note)	20,000 (see note)	20,000 (see note)

[56] The critical particle size for the manufacture of semiconductors is now below 5 nm. The semiconductor industry is entering a region where particles, particle precursors and molecules in liquids, begin to overlap. A particle precursor is defined as a dissolved molecular compound, which may form particles on the wafer. The ability to distinguish particle precursors from solid particles in UPW is becoming critical. While advanced filtration can remove nanometer sized solid particles, the same filter may have little or no ability to remove particle precursors. The use of combination of Nebulization and Condensation Particle Counting (N+CPC) measurement techniques have shown promise in detecting these particle precursors. This measurement techniques use aerosol particle detection, reconfigured to measure particles in liquids. NIST has extensively used the Nebulization and Particle Counting after Electrical Mobility Size Classification method of measuring particle size. The precursors are measured in the units of the number of particles produced in N+CPC instrument per milliliter of UPW. **It is important to note that the particle precursor parameter cannot be detected with use of currently available metrology at that level defined in the roadmap and therefore should not be used as specification for any purpose other than a target for future technology development around metrology, material purity, and treatment technology.** The available metrology does not have a standard to verify the quality of the data produced. The quality of the results relies on the source specific calibration/verification methods.

17

IRDS Particle and Precursor of High-Purity Pipe Risk Assessment

Sponsor – IRDS Critical Components Task Force

Technical Objectives:

1. To quantify critical organic extracted from high-purity piping using hot UPW; specifically, PFA and PVDF.
2. Assess the affinity of the organic contaminants to the wafer surface during spin processing.
3. Determine the relative concentrations of organic contamination remaining on the wafer surface as a function of temperature.

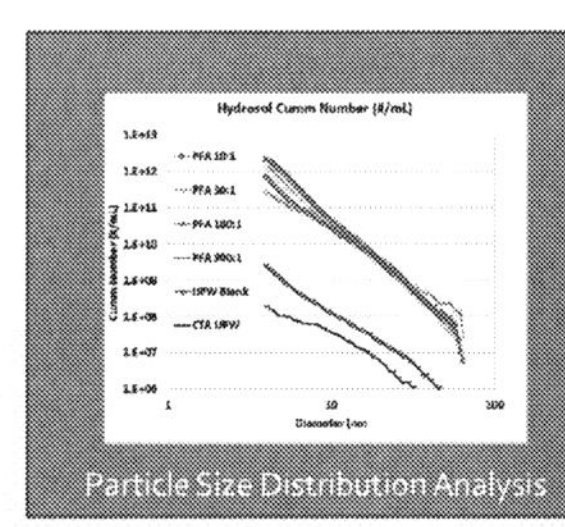

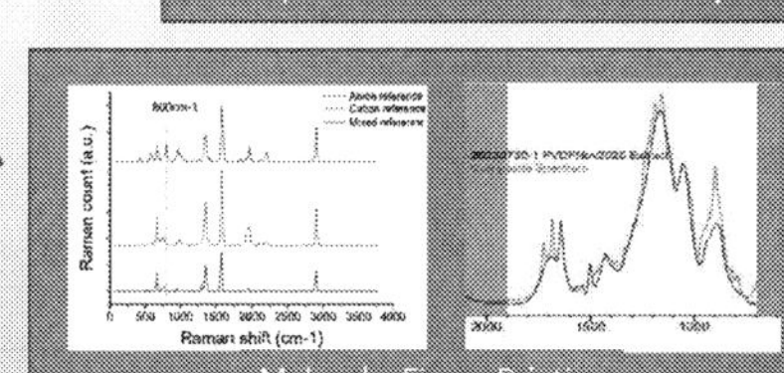

18

LNS Extract from UPW, 14 Day 85°C

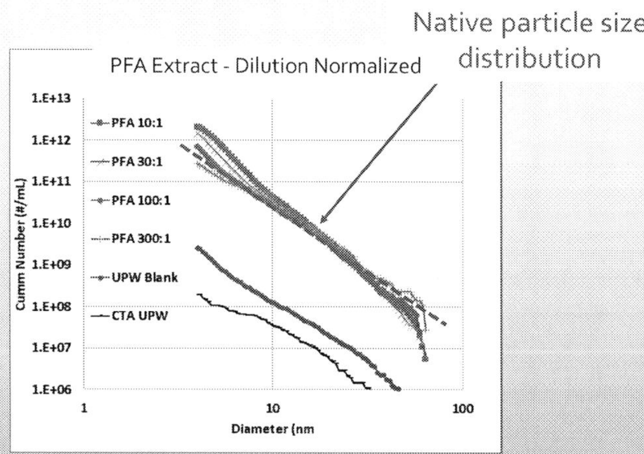

Source: Van Schooneveld, et al, Ultrapure Micro 2022

19

LNS Extract from UPW, 14 Day 85°C

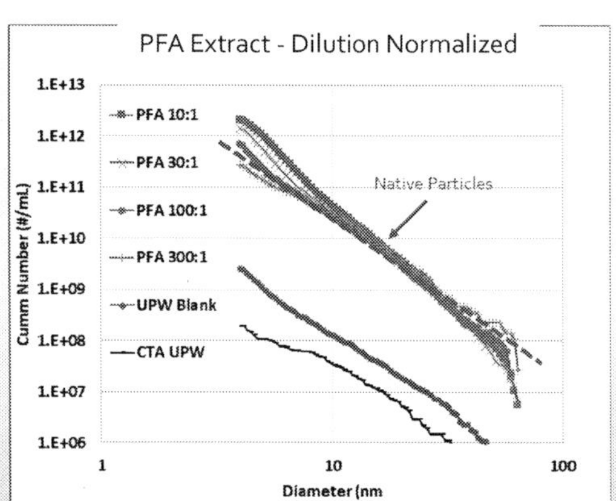

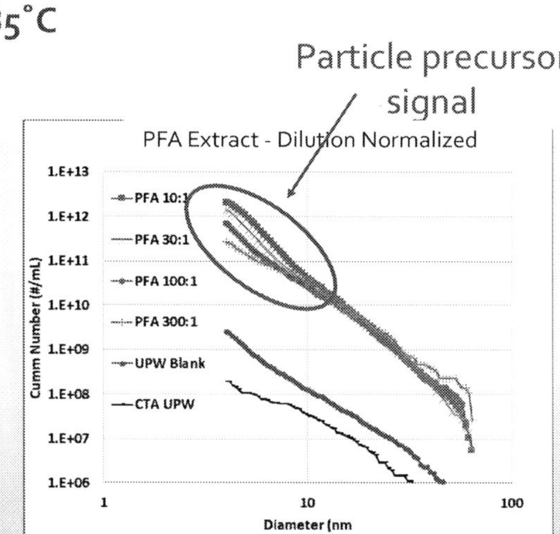

Native particles and particle precursors evident in both hot UPW PFA and PVDF extract

Source: Van Schooneveld, et al, Ultrapure Micro 2022

20

SEMI UPW TF –Addressing Precursor Issues

- New document in work addressing Particle Precursor Metrology
- Revision of SEMI C79 (Filter Cleanliness/Performance)
  - Developing IX resin extract as a filter/membrane challenge
- SEMI C93 (IX Resin Quality) – updated with smaller particle size
- SEMI F61 (UPW System), F63 (UPW Quality), F75 (UPW Metrology)
  - Will incorporate proactive precursor management in next revisions

SEMI Draft Document 6715 -Guide for Measuring Particle Precursors in Ultrapure Water

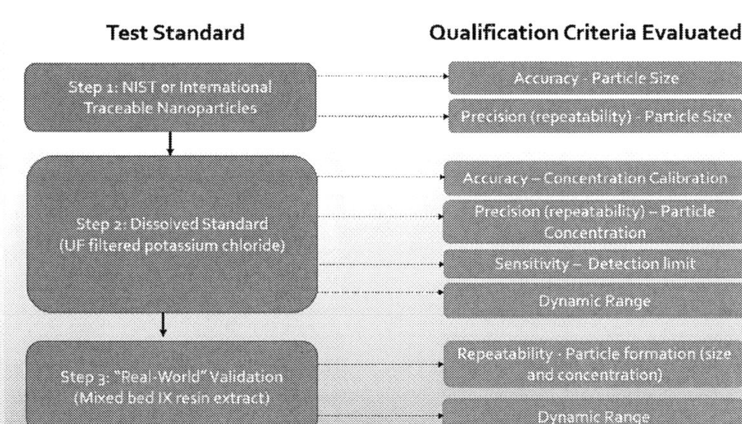

Diafiltration preparation of gold nanoparticles

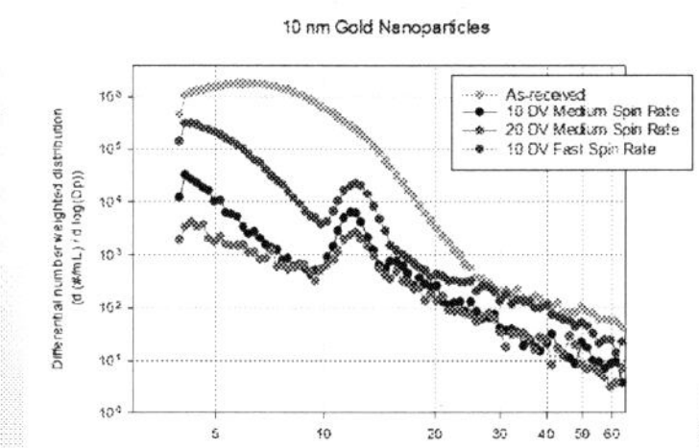

22

Guide for Measuring Particle Precursors in Ultrapure Water - KCl Calibration Curve Example

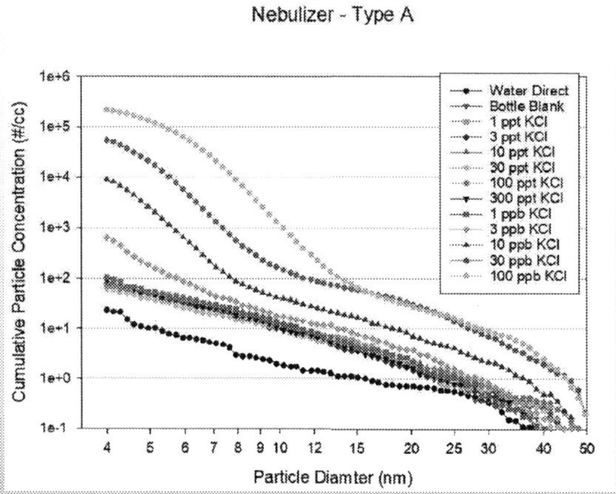

23

Source: SEMI UPW Task Force Internal Communication

Guide for Measuring Particle Precursors in Ultrapure Water - KCl Calibration Curve Example

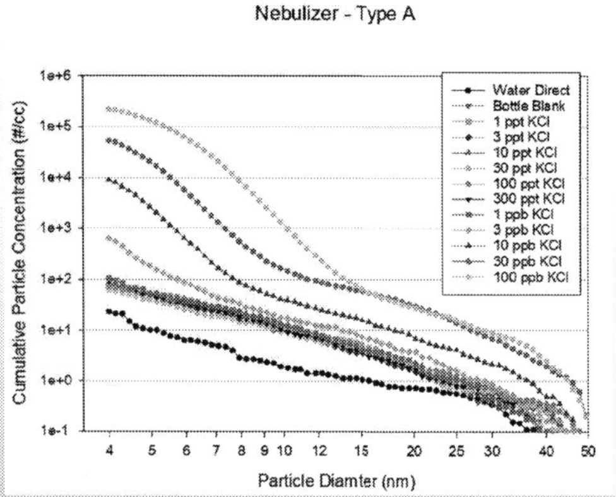

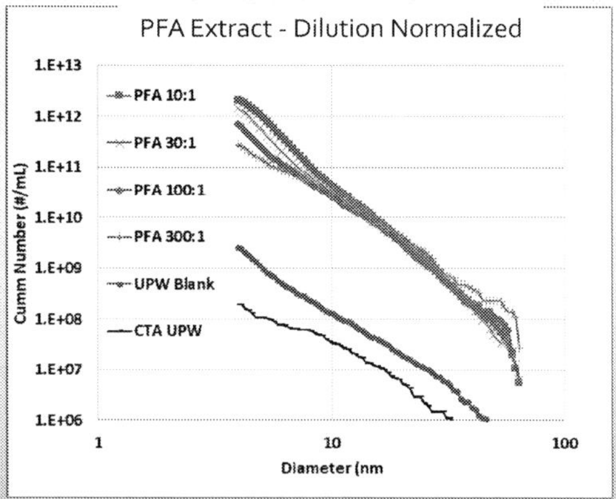

24

Source: SEMI UPW Task Force Internal Communication

Closing Comments

- Particle precursors pose an increasing risk to manufacturing yield.
- Current filtration and purification techniques have limited ability to remove particle precursors necessitating proactive contamination management to minimize these risks.
  - Improvements needed in IX resins
  - Reduced release from high surface area components such as filtration devices, membrane contactors and polymer components is needed.
- Particle precursor contamination is not limited to UPW. Particle precursors have been detected in IPA, sulfuric acid and CMP slurries.
- Online metrology is available that can identify the presence of particle precursor; SEMI UPW TF working on method for validation and quantification.

25

Questions?

Gary Van Schooneveld
CT Associates, Inc
Eden Prairie, MN
952-470-0166 x24

Email – Gary@CTAssociatesinc.com

Creative Technology CT Associates, Inc.

FTD solutions

IRDS UPW Team

Slava Libman, co-chair	**FTD Solutions**
Gary Van Schooneveld, co-chair	CT Associates
Bernie Zerfas	Independent
Derek Oberreit	KanomaxFMT
Rick Godec	Independent
Alan Knapp	Evoqua
Marcel Teunissen	ASML
Tim Miller	Purdue
Deena Starkel	Micron
Jim Snow	Screen SPE USA
Andreas Neuber	AMAT
Yoichi Tanaka	Kurita

Abbas Rastegar	AMAT
Jochen Ruth	Pall Corporation
Philippe Rychen	Ovivo
Steven Smith	Texas Instruments
Sung In Moon	Entegris
Dan Wilcox	Page
Varinder Malik	Samsung
Brett Clark	Suez
Glen Slater	Intel
Jason Tewksbury	Intel

IRDS Critical Components Team

Member Name	Organization	Region
Robert McIntosh, Co-chair	Enviro E	US
Archita Sengupta, Co-chair	Intel	US
Albert Lueghamer	Agru	Europe
David Tarantino	3M	US
Matt Orr	Daikin	US
Gary Van Schooneveld	CT Associates	US
James Henry	Arkema	US
Jenell Mccall	Chemours	US
John Leys	Entegris	US
Katrin Wallheinke	Georg Fischer	Europe
Kimberly Farnsworth	Chemours	US

Member Name	Organization	Region
Quynh Le	Air Liquide	US
Stephane Domy	St Gobain	Europe
Steve Powell	Parker	US
Thomas Labour	Arkama	Europe
Tommaso Crisenza	Solvay	Europe
Per Nelson	3M	US
Jim Tu	Entegris	US
Paolo Toniolo	Solvay	Europe
Wim Devos	Solvay	Europe
Nick Dotzenrod	3M	US

28

Correlation Between Aerosolization Based Metrology and Enhanced Surface Scanning

Derek Oberreit PhD, Kanomax FMT
Derek.Oberreit@kanomaxfmt.com
Gary Van Schooneveld, CT Associates
Ali Ö. Altun PhD, Unisers
Siqin He PhD, Kanomax FMT

The Surface Preparation and Cleaning Conference 2022
Phoenix, AZ

UNISERS UNIVERSAL CONTAMINATION ANALYZER
KANOMAX FMT A Kanomax Company NANOPARTICLE MEASUREMENT SOLUTIONS
Creative Technology
CT Associates, Inc.

Objective

- Display the effectiveness of Aerosolization-Based and Surfaced Enhanced Particle Sizing technologies for quantifying the concentration of particles and particle precursors in Isopropyl Alcohol (IPA)
- Display the ability of these technologies to show variability in Semiconductor Grade IPAs supplied by different manufacturers
- Characterize the relationship of Aerosolization Based Metrology and UNISERS measured concentrations using controlled levels of added particles and particle precursors in IPA

Aerosolization + Ion Mobility Spectrometry
Operating Principle

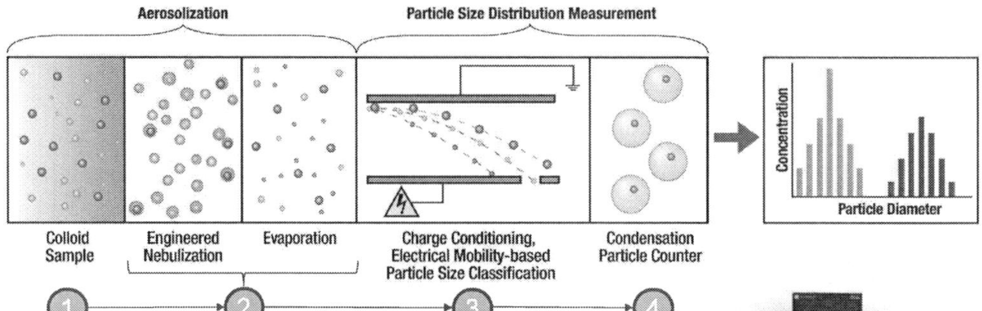

Injection ->Aerosolization -> Classification -> Counting

- **6 nm to 360 nm particles are individually measured regardless of shape or composition.**
- **64 size bins per decade are sequentially characterized.**
- **Complete concentration vs. particle size distribution in about 5 minutes.**
- **No *a priori* assumptions about the particles.**

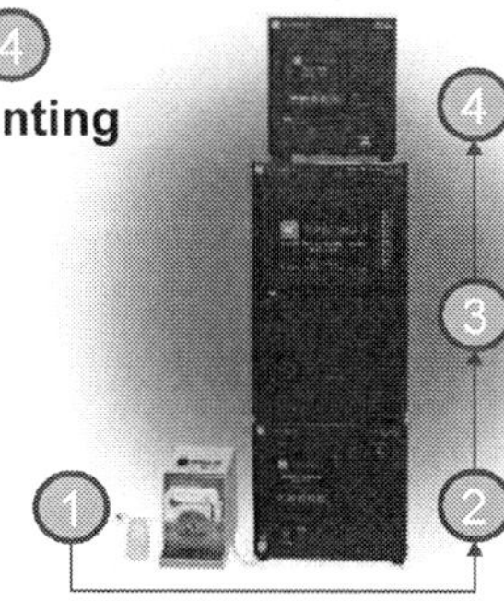

Surface Enhanced Particle Sizing (SEPS)
Operating Principle

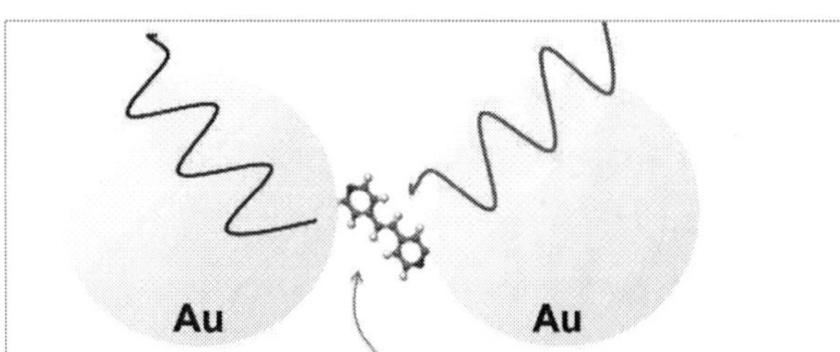

Theory: Molecule resides in an electromagnetic hotspot (narrow gap btw noble metal nanoparticles). Excitation of localized surface plasmons of metal nanoparticles by incident light enhances the near field intensity. Raman signal amplification is proportional with the 4th power of the near field enhancement.

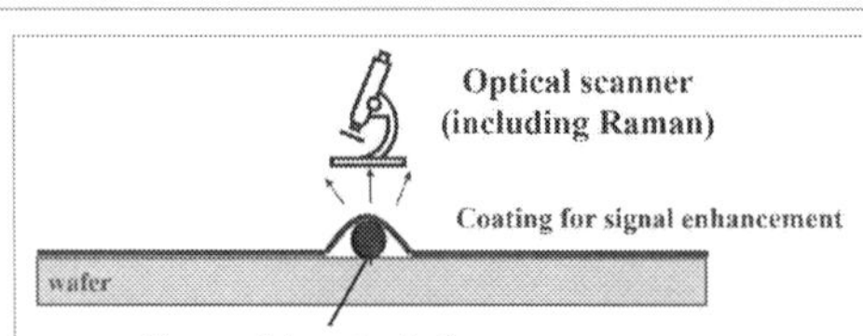

The coating creates optical resonance around the particles on the wafer, enhancing both total scattering and inelastic (Raman scattering).

Scan areas

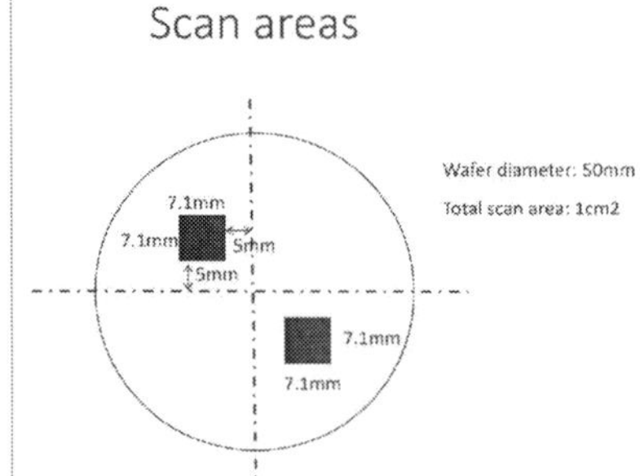

Methodology cont. – Silicon wafer prep for SEPS/SERS

- Sequential Spin Coating used to deposit IPA onto wafers
- For each sample
  - IPA sample placed in pressurized vessel
  - Wafer transferred to spin coater
  - Wafer spun @ 500 RPM with drying at 2,500 RPM and 8,000 RPM.
  - 10-300 drops of the sample liquid applied to the center of the wafer every 18 seconds using an automated pinch valve
  - After wafer is visibly dry, remove and transfer to carrier

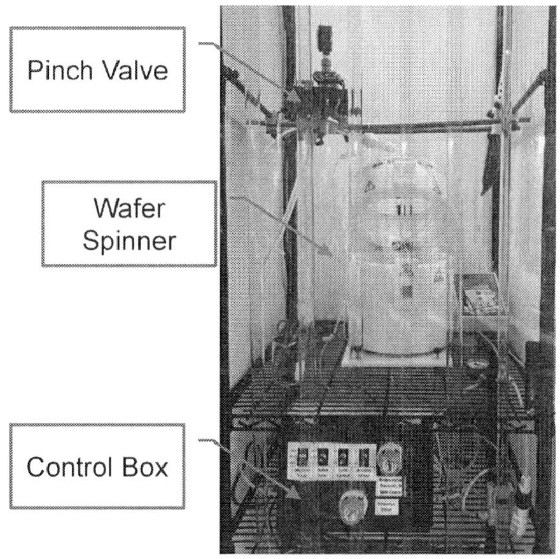

Experimental plan

- Prepare all samples in high purity 125ml Nalgene FEP bottles
- Determine optimal number of drops to apply to wafer
- Measure the particle size distributions from three different IPA suppliers using Aerosolization + IMS (Kanomax FMT nano-AFIMS)
  - Pressurized sample chamber
  - KFMT nanoparticle nebulizer (direct injection)
  - Membrane dryer
  - KFMT nano-Annular Flow Ion Mobility Classifier (AFIMC)
  - KFMT FastCPC (boosted for lower detection limit)
- Identify the highest quality IPA to use for spiked samples
- Prepare the following samples:
  - Pure IPA from three vendors
  - IPA spiked with an organic acid at 0.1 and 1.0 mM
  - IPA spiked with colloidal silica at 1E8 and 1E9 #/ml
- Coat 2" diameter wafers using sequential spin coating and analyze using Surface Enhanced Particle Sizing (SEPS)
- Measure particle size distributions of IPA samples using Aerosolization + Ion Mobility Spectrometry

Results – Successive Spin Drying Optimization

- Wafers prepared at four different number of applied coats of the same IPA grade
- Total deposited particles showed little change above 100 coats

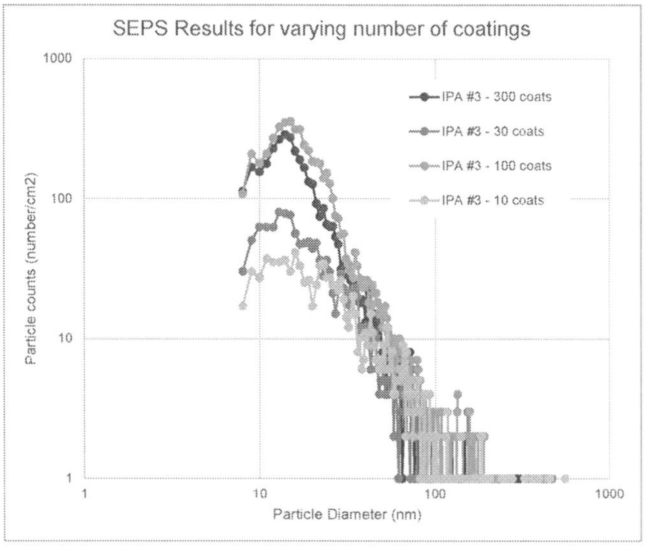

Page 7

Results – Comparison of three IPA Grades

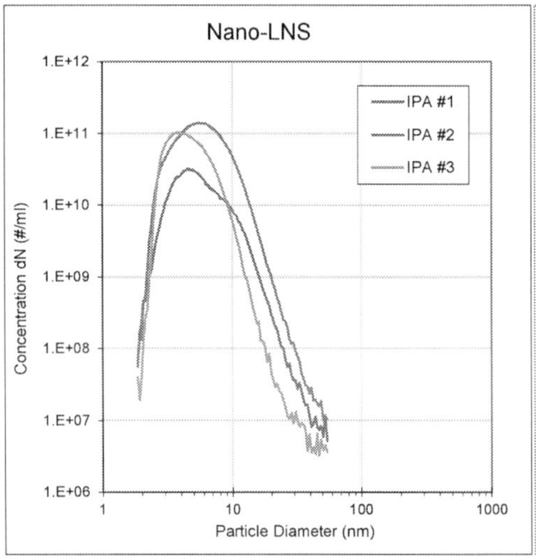

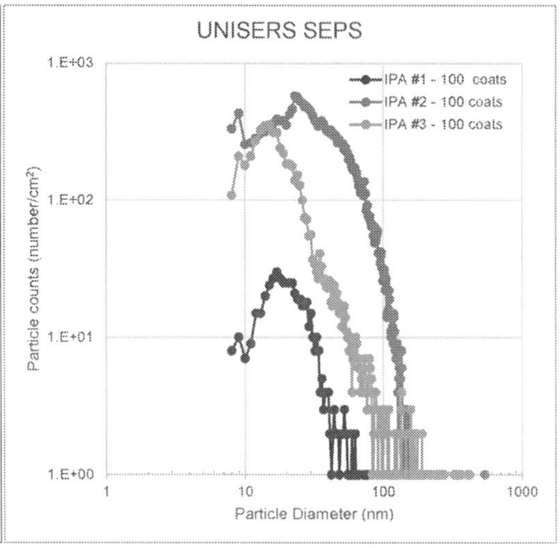

Page 8

Results – Comparison of three IPA Grades

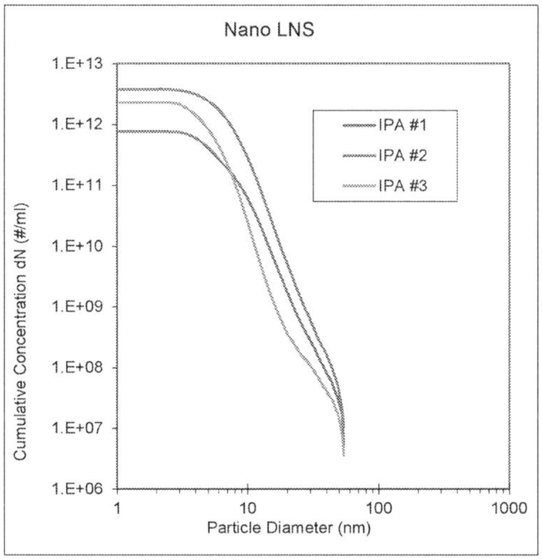

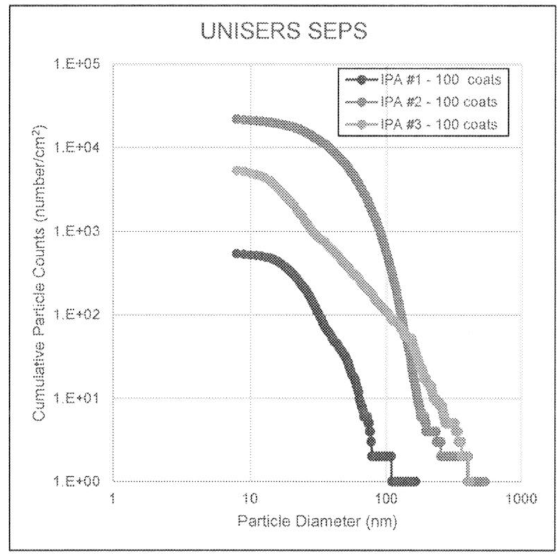

Page 9

Results – comparison of three IPA grades (Images)

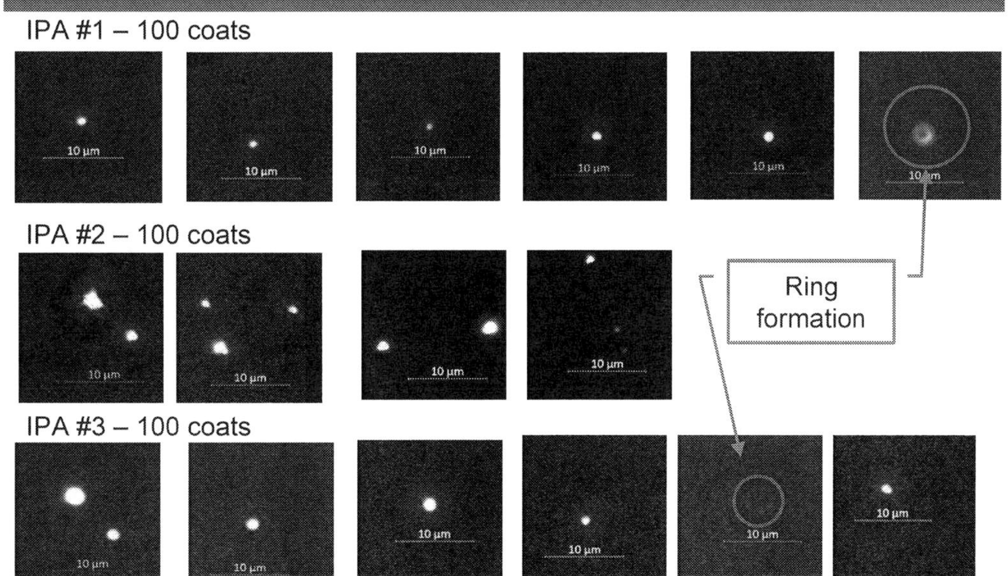

Note: Scale bars do not represent particle size. Particle diameters are 8-100 nm

Page 10

Results – comparison of three IPA grades (Images)

IPA #2 – 100 coats

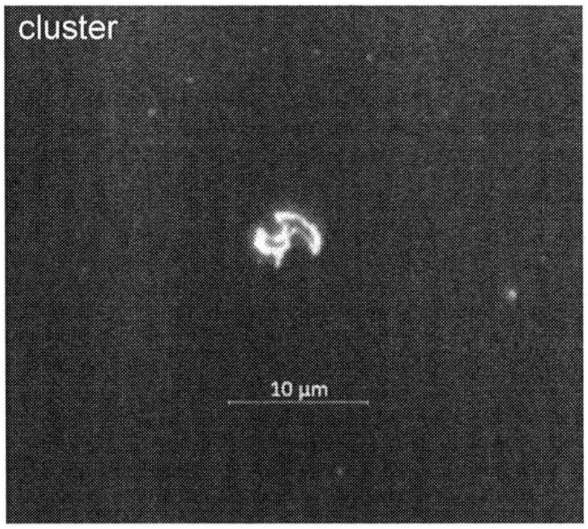

IPA #3 – 100 coats

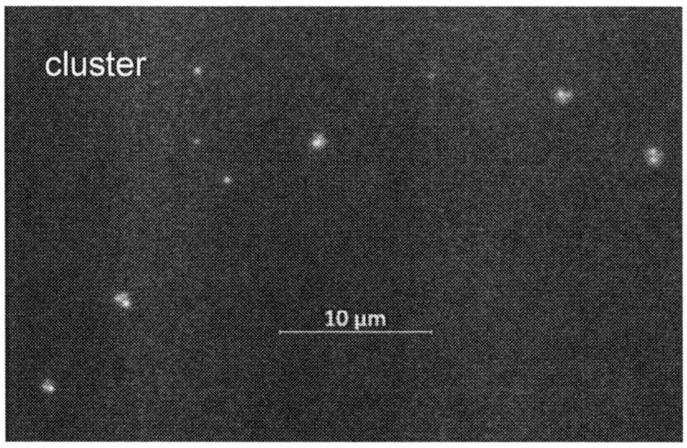

Note: Scale bars do not represent particle size. Particle diameters are 8-100 nm

Discussion – comparison of three IPA grades

Sample	Nano-LNS > 8nm (#/ml)	Net Conc from SEPS > 8nm (#/cm^2)	Deposition Factor (#/cm^2)/(#/ml)
IPA #1	1.30E+11	411.5	3.2E-09
IPA #2	7.20E+11	21680.5	3.0E-08
IPA #3	1.00E+11	5148.5	5.1E-08

- Deposition factor for IPA #1 significantly lower than other IPA samples
- Nano LNS showed higher concentration for IPA #1 versus IPA #3 above 8nm; however, IPA #1 showed a significantly lower concentration across the entire Nano LNS scan range.

Results – IPA spiked with 30nm Colloidal Silica

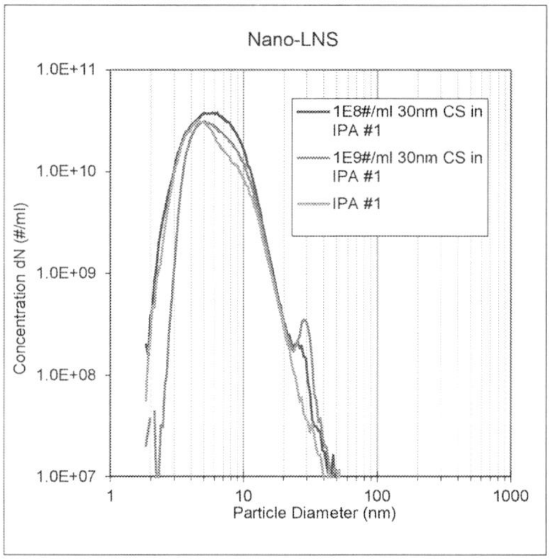

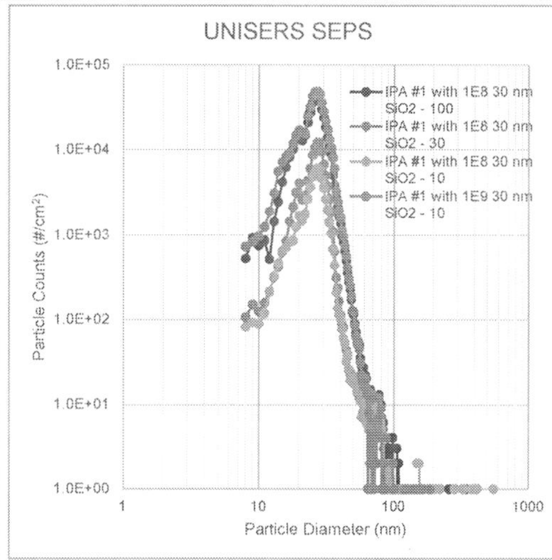

Results – IPA spiked with Colloidal Silica (images)

1E9 30nm SiO2, 10x coats	1E9 30nm SiO2, 30x coats	1E9 30nm SiO2, 100x coats
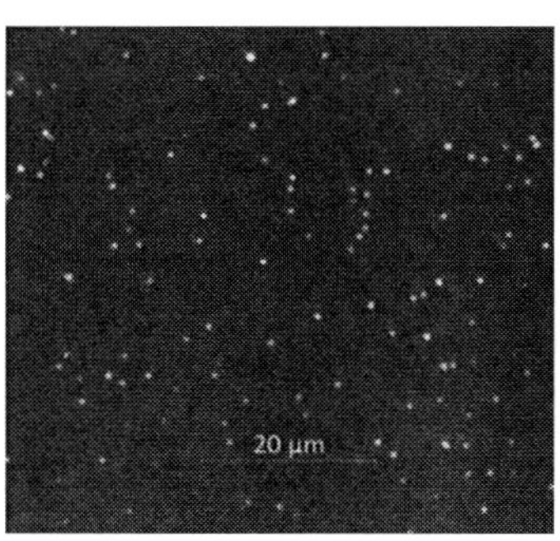		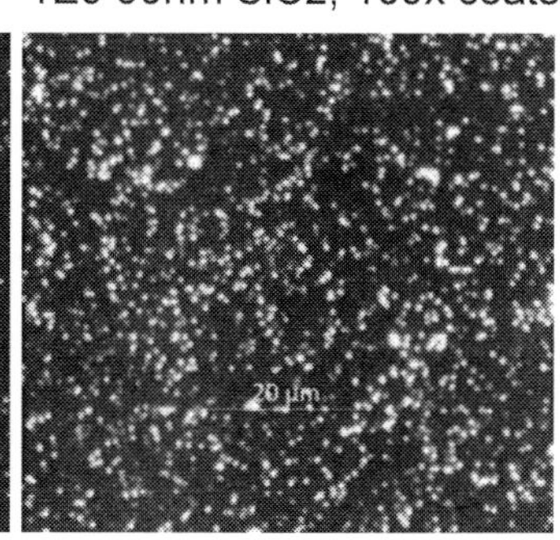
5E6 particles/cm^2	Overloaded	Overloaded

Note: Scale bars do not represent particle size. Particle diameters are 8-100 nm

Discussion – IPA Spiked with 30nm Colloidal Silica

Sample	Nano-LNS > 8nm (#/ml)	Net Conc from SEPS >8nm (#/cm^2)	Deposition Factor (#/cm^2)/(#/ml)
1E8 CS	2.40E+11	420502.5	1.8E-06
1E9 CS	1.78E+11	508471.5	2.9E-06

Used value from 10 coats for 1E9 CS due to overloading

- Deposition factor significantly higher for CS compared to clean IPA
- Nano LNS had significant interference from precursor material in the stock colloidal silica
- Deposition observed by SEPS appears to correlate with the product of the number of coats and the concentration.

Page 15

Results – IPA spiked with Organic Acid

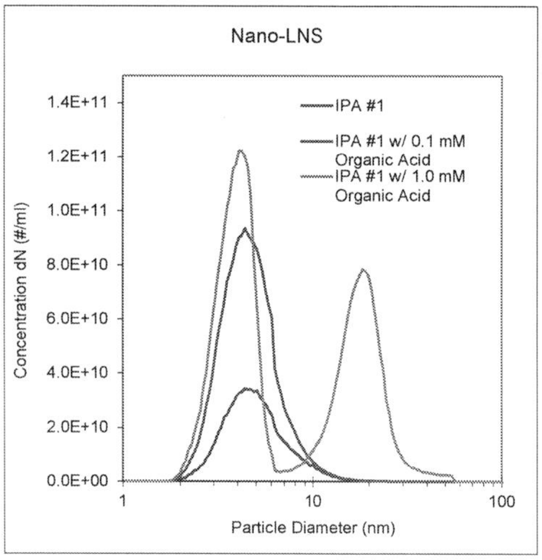

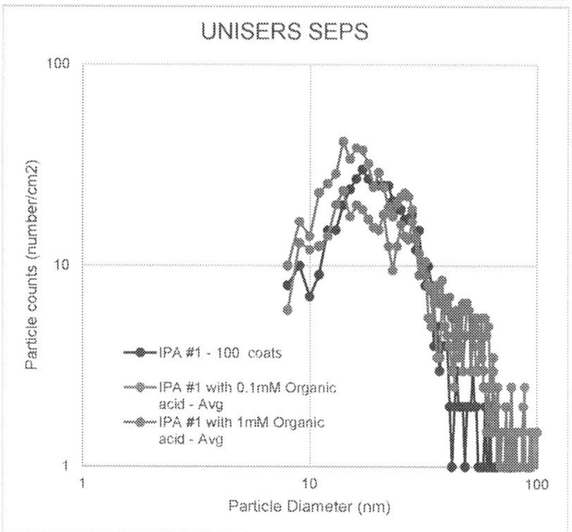

Page 16

Results – IPA spiked with Organic Acid

1mM Organic acid

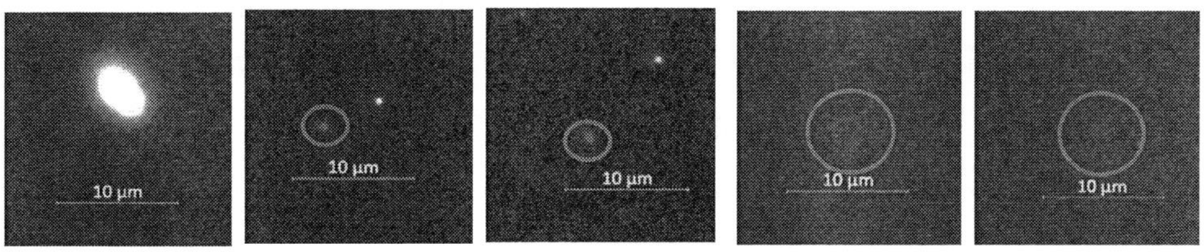

0.1mM Organic acid

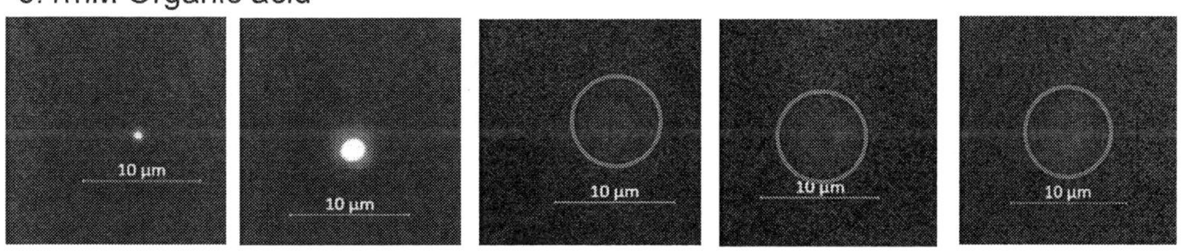

Organic acid showed additional “drying rings”

Note: Scale bars do not represent particle size. Particle diameters are 8-100 nm

Discussion – IPA Spiked with Organic Acid

Sample	Nano-LNS > 8nm (#/ml)	Net Conc from SEPS > 8nm (#/cm^2)	Deposition Factor (#/cm^2)/(#/ml)
0.1 mM Organic Acid	1.21E+11	443	3.7E-09
1 mM Organic Acid	1.41E+12	651.5	4.6E-10

- Nano-LNS showed formation of a second mode at higher OA concentration. Possibly due to the formation of micelles.
- SEPS did not show a significant difference between the two concentrations.
- Possible causes of the difference with the SEPS measurement
  - Change in the OA concentration during deposition leading to the breakup of micelles or other types of meta-stable agglomerates
  - Collapse of micelle leading to a large, faint ring that isn’t counted as a particle

Takeaway

- Impurities in IPA samples may have different deposition factors onto wafers
- Particle and Particle Precursor concentrations may not correlate for some IPA samples
- Organic acid appears to form an additional mode above a threshold concentration.
- Organic acid leads to a high number of "drying rings"

Page 19

Follow on work

- Repeat study using additional metrologies
  - –Optical particle detectors
  - –Aerosolization + Threshold Condensation Particle Counting
- Capture Surface Enhanced Raman Spectroscopy (SERS) data
  - –Was not possible for this presentation due to a laser failure
- Correct data for detection efficiency of SEPS and transmission efficiency for nano-LNS

Page 20

Thank you!

The Surface Preparation and Cleaning Conference 2022
Phoenix, AZ

UNISERS UNIVERSAL CONTAMINATION ANALYZER | KANOMAX FMT A Kanomax Company NANOPARTICLE MEASUREMENT SOLUTIONS | Creative Technology | CT Associates, Inc.

Supplemental Materials

Nano-LNS detailed schematic

The Surface Preparation and Cleaning Conference 2022
Phoenix, AZ

UNISERS UNIVERSAL CONTAMINATION ANALYZER | KANOMAX FMT A Kanomax Company NANOPARTICLE MEASUREMENT SOLUTIONS | Creative Technology | CT Associates, Inc.

Liquid Nanoparticle Sizer (LNS) System

System Schematic: Nebulizer -> AFIMC -> Fast CPC

- **6 nm to 360 nm particles are individually measured regardless of shape or composition.**
- **64 size bins per decade are sequentially characterized.**
- **Complete concentration vs. particle size distribution in about 5 minutes.**
- **No *a priori* assumptions about the particles.**

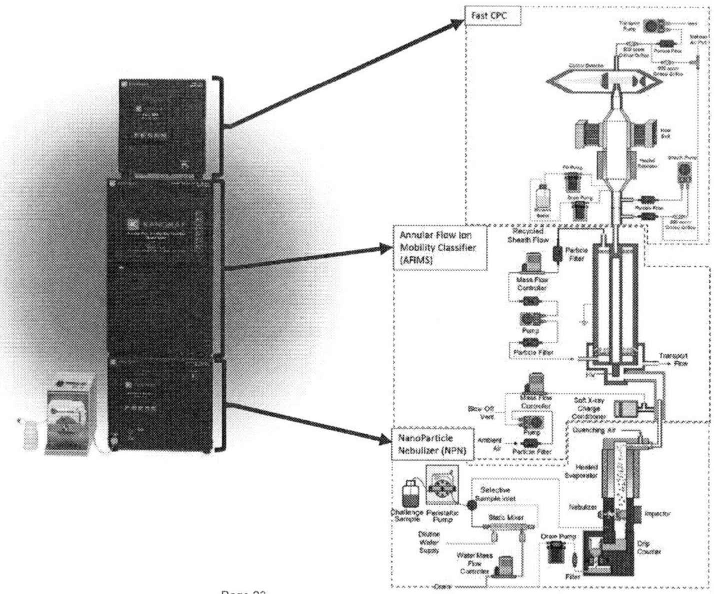

Page 23

Akrion Technologies

Silicon Etching utilizing Near-Infrared and H_2 Mitigation in MEMS Applications

Ismail Kashkoush, Tyler W., Darian W., Dennis N., Steven M.

Email: ikashkoush@akriontech.com Phone:+1(610)530-3379

2022 SPCC Conference – Chandler, AZ

Outline

- Introduction
- NIR Chemical Concentration Control
  - Background information
  - Experimental findings
- Hydrogen Gas Production Management
  - Background information
  - Experimental findings
- Si Etching throughput
  - Background information
  - Experimental findings
- Conclusions

Introduction

- Bulk micromachining is performed using a wet chemical etching technique involving KOH or TMAH. TMAH is typically used in CMOS applications when it is compatible and no cross contamination.
- This technique results in anisotropic etching of the substrate where etch rates vary depending on the crystalline structure.
- Resulting figures from micromachining etching can include grooves, cantilevers and through holes.

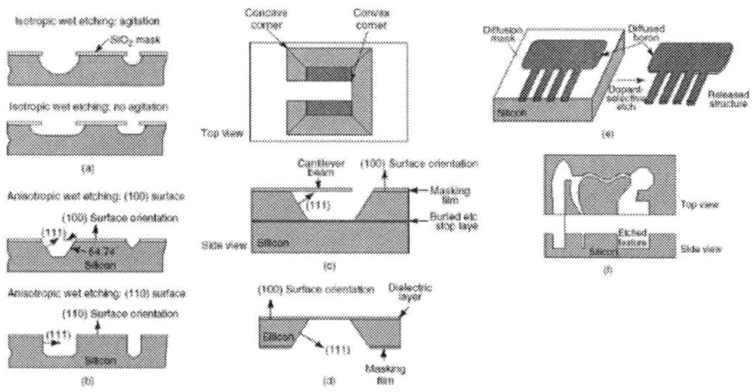

Introduction

- Wet Si etching has a few process challenges involved with it:
  - Through Si etching the byproduct of silicate accumulates within the chemical bath which can cause short bath lives and decrease in etch rates.

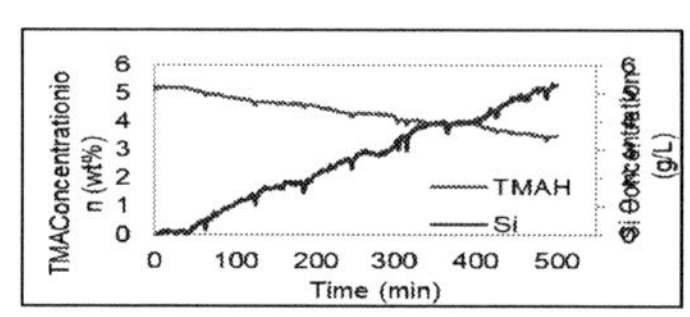

  - A byproduct of Si etching is H_2 bubble production which can impact uniformity and Si etch rates via masking of Si.

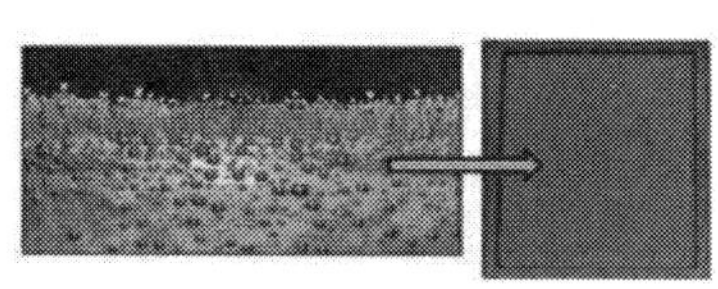

  - Addressing the silicate and H_2 gas production increases the throughput of silicon wafer etching.

Introduction

- Wet Si etching has a few process challenges involved with it:
  - Through Si etching the byproduct of silicate accumulates within the chemical bath which can cause short bath lives and decrease in etch rates.
  - A byproduct of Si etching is H_2 bubble production which can impact uniformity etch rates.
  - Addressing the silicate and H_2 gas production increases the through put of silicon wafer etching.

Background

- Originally the silicate build up was determined to be controlled for consistency and cost of ownership. However, it was later found that the etch rate was impacted based on the concentration of the silicate in the solution.

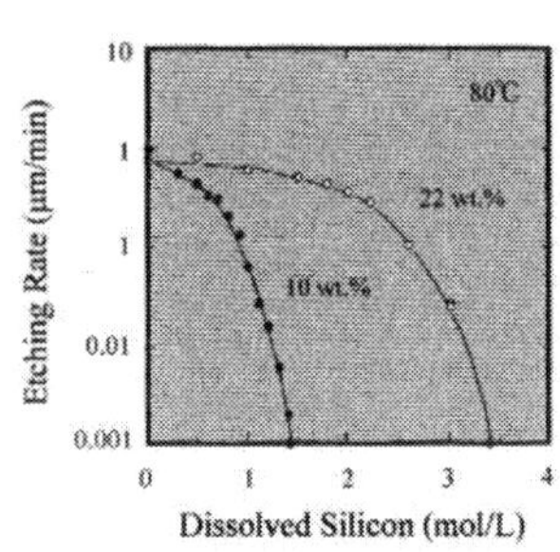

- Near-Infrared (NIR) control is used in Si etching to monitor the concentration of Si and the silicate build up separately. This allows for total control over the bath and etch rates.

Background

- NIR Sensor is placed within a bypass from the recirculation loop. The solution goes through a desgassifier to eliminate bubbles that could cause inaccurate readings.
- Utilizing algorithms previously developed for the relationship of TMAH and silicate concentrations.
- Controlled spiking of chemicals/DIW maintains chemical concentration at desired level.
- Feed and Bleed system extends bath life and maintains desired etch rate with minimal/short bubble breaks.

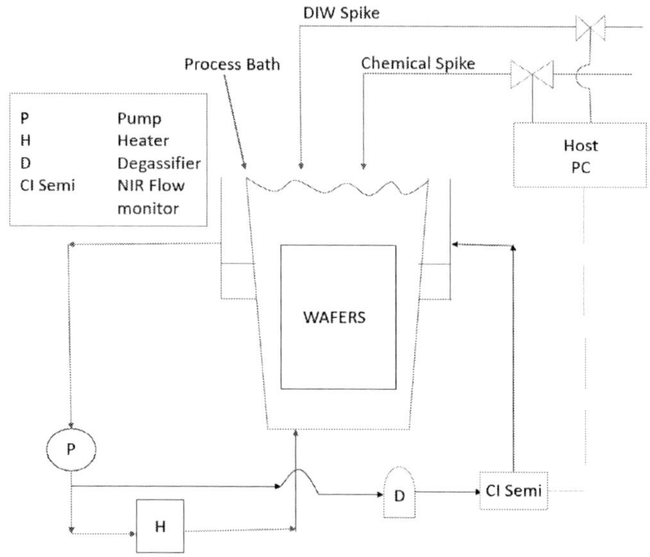

Background

- Previously it was proven, through experimental data, that the stoichiometry of TMAH to Si fits a 1:1 ratio rather than a 2:1 ratio for modeling the concentration of TMAH. It was originally theorized at 2:1 ratio due to the Si and OH^- stoichiometry in the balanced chemical reaction at the wafer surface.
- This ratio of TMAH was determined to be 1:1 due to the reduction of water at the wafer surface, which creates an additional OH^- compound.
- TMAH can now be monitored and controlled accurately using NIR with models developed using the TMAH:Si ratio of 1:1

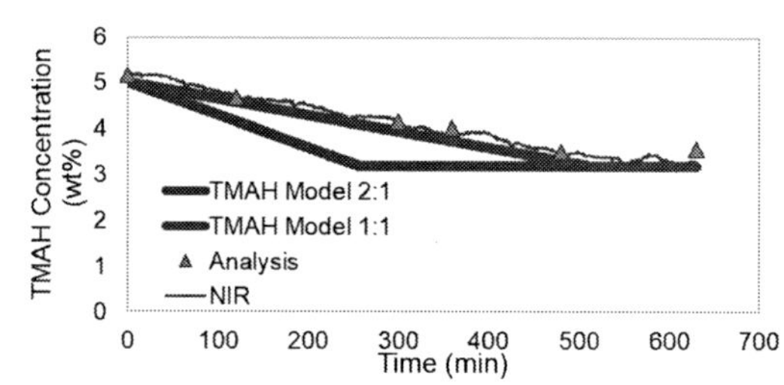

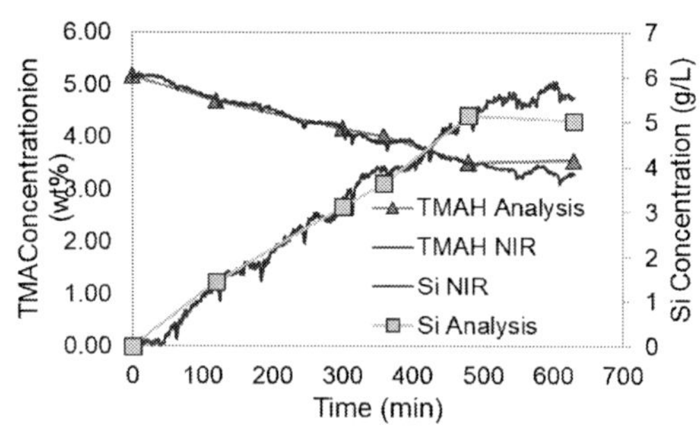

Experiment

- We have developed a system to keep the concentration in the bath fresh and the silicate levels to a desired percentage. This helps prevent silicates blocking the wafer surface and impeding the etch rates.
- Using NIR the chemical concentrations for TMAH and Si can be monitored and controlled within a 0.1% tolerance. Using this control in the field it allows longer bath lives and consistent etch rates with TMAH.

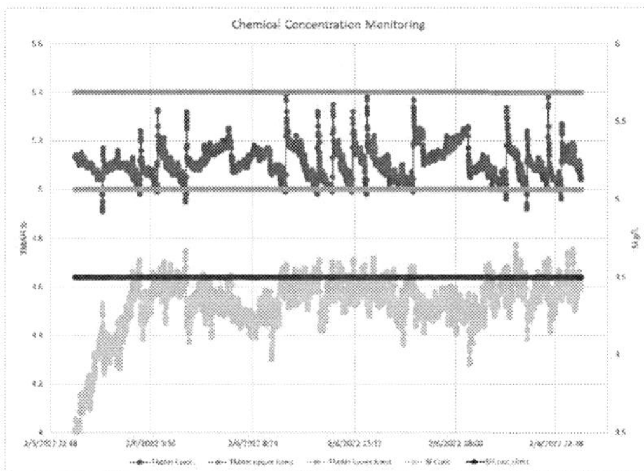

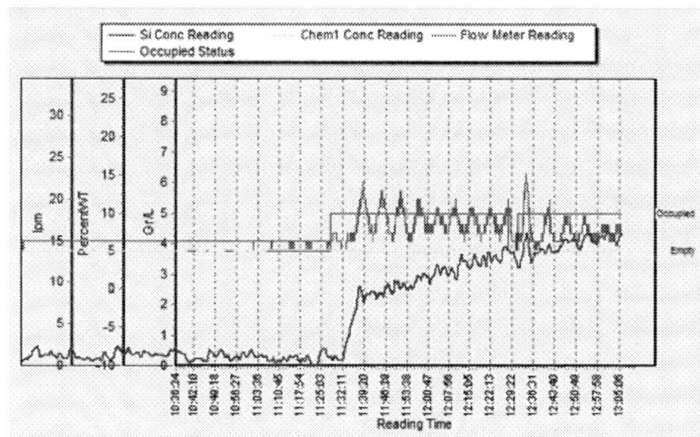

Introduction

- Wet Si etching has a few process challenges involved with it:
    - Through Si etching the byproduct of silicate accumulates within the chemical bath which can cause short bath lives and decrease in etch rates.
    - A byproduct of Si etching is H_2 bubble production which can impact uniformity etch rates.
    - Addressing the silicate and H_2 gas production increases the through put of silicon wafer etching.

H_2 production background

- H_2 production is a byproduct of the chemical reaction on the surface of the wafer. The production of gas is directly proportional to the number of wafers in the lot.
- This production inhibits the etch rate and uniformity by sticking inside the features and blocking Si sites from TMAH not allowing it to etch which is shown in the top picture.
- Through 1 theoretical point and 2 field data points the limit of hydrogen is calculated that can be withstand in the bath. Hydrogen at 24 wafers is severely over saturated.

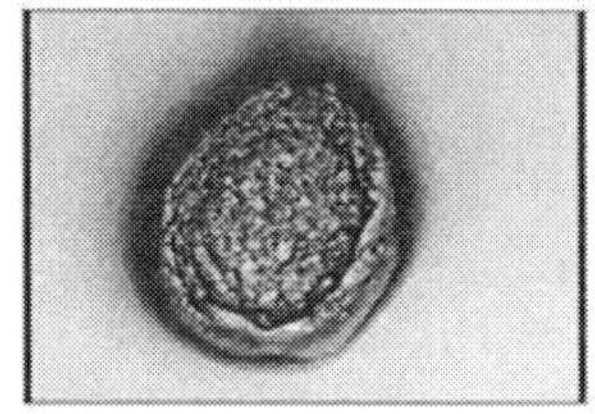

Amount of H2 produced per minute

Min/Max is coming from 3 points, 1 theoretical and 2 experimental.

H2 L/min			
12 wafers		24 wafers	
Min	Max	Min	Max
0.76	0.83	1.53	1.66

Allowable limit for saturation in TMAH tank. This shows the tank is super saturated with Hydrogen.

L H2 allowed in bath	L H2 produced per wafer	#wafers	H2 Produce	Percent excedeed
0.575328	0.063658839	12	0.763906	132.78%
		24	1.527812	265.55%

	per wafer								wafers per batch		
								6	12	25	50
Device	Si loss in 10 hours (g)	Si loss in 10 hours (moles)	H2 in 10 hours (moles)	H2 in 10 hours (g)	H2 vol in 10 hours (m3)	H2 vol in 10 hours (ft3)	H2 vol in 10 hours (L)		H2 L/min	H2 L/min	H2 L/min
0.55	22.37	0.80	1.59	3.19	0.038	1.35	38.20	0.38	0.76	1.59	3.18

H_2 Experiment

- Previously developed system increases the uniformity by breaking up the hydrogen in the tank that would stick on the wafer surface.
- Akrion has developed another proprietary process-related system that mitigates the hydrogen within the system. This allows the hydrogen to be redistributed through the tank and not affect the etch rate during process. This can be shown in the bottom right graph where Akrion proprietary system was installed after January, giving an increased Pass/Fail rate.
- With data from the field utilizing a bubble break after 1 hour of etching (bubble break time of 5 minutes minimum) it allows our etch rates to average 51 μm/hr which is just under the setpoint of 51.5 μm/hr. This is approximately a 10% increase in etch rates prior to the proprietary process-related system.

Slot spacing	Si etch-rate um/hr	Wafers/tank	Agitation	Oxide etch-rate TMAH	Bubble Break
With H_2 mitgation system					
1	51.0	24	Yes	514.7 A/hr	5mins
Without H_2 mitgation system					
1	50.4	24	Yes	500.7 A/hr	0.5hr
1	46.4	24	Yes	538.4 A/hr	1hr
1	40	24	Yes	516.3 A/hr	5hr

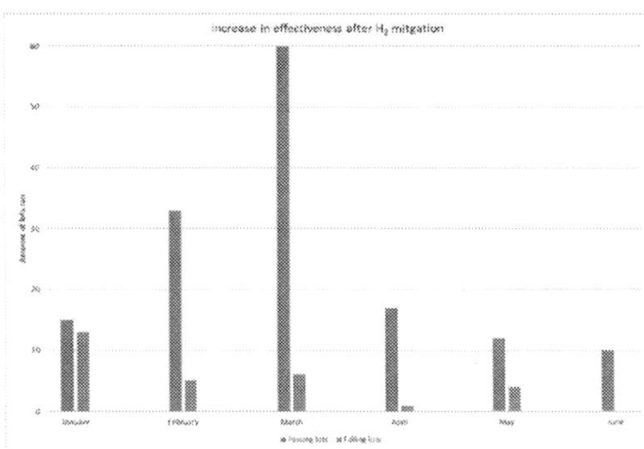

H_2 Experiment

- Using both proprietary systems show an increase in Si etching while maintaining the SiO_2 etch rates.
- With a higher Si etching increases the average selectivity to about 1000x Si to SiO_2 etching.

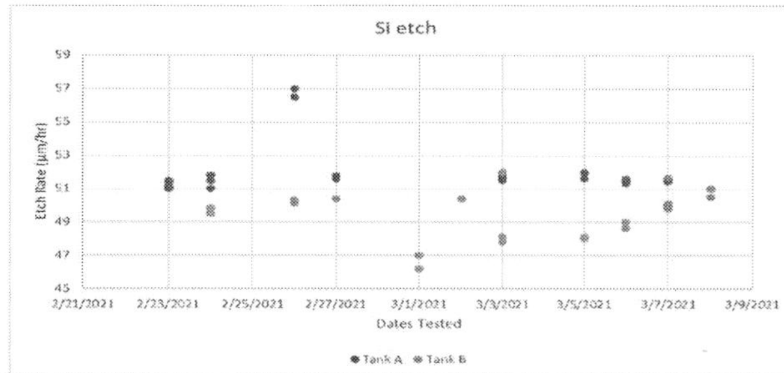

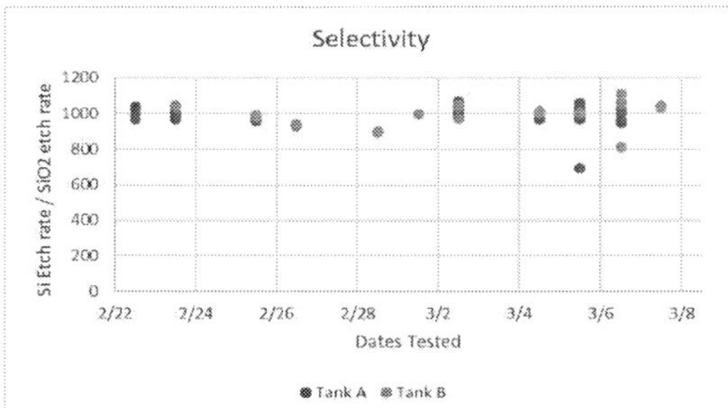

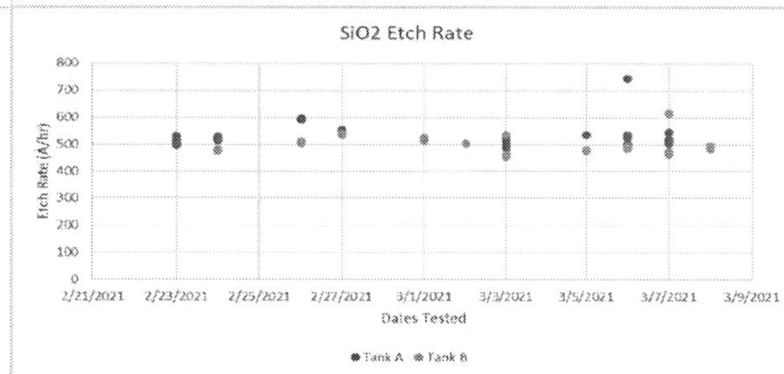

Introduction

- Wet Si etching has a few process challenges involved with it:
  - Through Si etching the byproduct of silicate accumulates within the chemical bath which can cause short bath lives and decrease in etch rates.
  - A byproduct of Si etching is H_2 bubble production which can impact uniformity etch rates.
  - Addressing the silicate and H_2 gas production increases the through put of silicon wafer etching.

Background

- As previously mentioned, the Silicate and H_2 production have been issues for uniformity and etch rates.
- This is directly proportional to the number of wafers in each lot being processed. As the numbers of wafers increase per lot the silicate and hydrogen production increases in at least a linear relationship.

- The table shows that as the wafers increase the etch rates decrease and the oxide etch rates increase. This also decreases the selectivity of the etching.
- Due to these issues Si etching in wet chemistry was not feasible because the low throughput of minimal wafer lots.

Wafers/tank	Si etch-rate µm/hr	Oxide etch-rate TMAH1	Oxide etch-rate TMAH2	Bubble Break [hr]
6	52.4	511.6 ± 17 Å/hr	545 ± 16 Å/hr	1
12	50	537.8 Å/hr	570.5 Å/hr	1
24	46.4	538.4 Å/hr	571.8 Å/hr	1

AKrion

Throughput Experiment

- Through Akrion's chemical control systems and proprietary process-related systems the wafer lot has been increased. When first studying Si etching the numbers of wafers originally were 6 per lot and have been increased to 24 wafers per lot.
- With chemical control systems when increasing from 6 wafers to 12 wafers per lot, the tool has a 95.8% passing efficiency on a total of 518 lots.
- Adding the second proprietary process-related system, the tool can process 24 wafers at a time with an initial 87.9% passing efficiency on a total of 176 lots.
- While controlling the Si selectivity and Si etch rate, the wafer count per lot has increased 400% from initial runs
- 48 wafer has had only 3 runs and is preliminary data to show future goals for throughput.

Wafers /tank	Si etch-rate µm/hr	Oxide etch-rate TMAH1 (Å/hr)	Oxide etch-rate TMAH2 (Å/hr)	Bubble Break [hr]
6	52.5	495	531.35	1
12	51.5	496.5	525.9	1
24	50.4	500.7	548.9	0.5
24	46.4	538.4	571.8	1
24	40	516.3	552.4	5
24	51.3	506.4	551.3	1
48	51	502	543	1

AKrion

Conclusion

- Wet Si etching provides several challenges due to silicate and hydrogen levels, which directly affects throughput and cost of ownership.
- Utilizing NIR for concentration control allows for extended bath lives while maintaining a consistent Si etch rate and selectivity.
- Utilizing NIR and a Feed and Bleed system developed by Akrion technologies, silicate levels can be maintained to not interfere with the process and minimize amount of bubble breaks.
- Two proprietary process-related solutions were developed to eliminate hydrogen bubbles from sticking to the silicone surface creating more uniform etching.
- These advancements in Si etching allowed the wafers per lot to increase ultimately increasing the throughput of each process bath.

- With continuous research and potential implementations, the wafer lot size is planned to be increased to 48 wafers per lot. This will help minimize the disadvantages of wet etching with through put and cost of ownership.

Hydroxylamine Free Formulation Development for Post Etch Residue Cleaning
Laisheng Sun*, Yi Chia Lee, Aaron Pejlovas, Aiping Wu and Seowhwa Soh
Contact:
Laisheng Sun, PhD
8555 South River Parkway, Tempe AZ, 85284
Laisheng.sun@emdgroup.com
Phone 602-282-0995
EMD Electronics

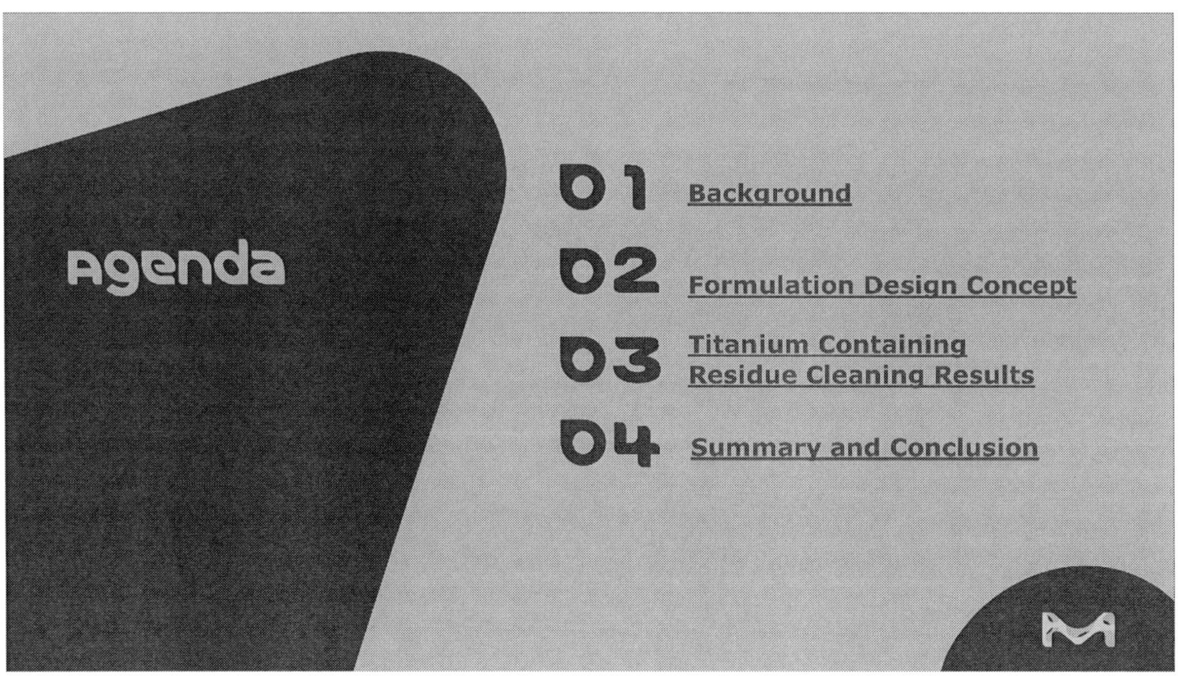
Agenda
01 Background
02 Formulation Design Concept
03 Titanium Containing Residue Cleaning Results
04 Summary and Conclusion

Background

01

Different Kinds of Al post etch Residues

Post Etch Residues from Pattern Wafer Processing

↓

Polymer residues
CFx
SixCyFz
CxClx
Others

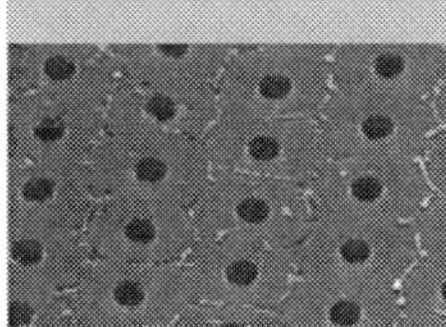

Metal containing residues
TiOFx
AlOx
AlClx
Others

↘ ↙

Cleaned by Hydroxylamine (HA) based formulations

Hydroxylamine in Alkanolamine Formulations

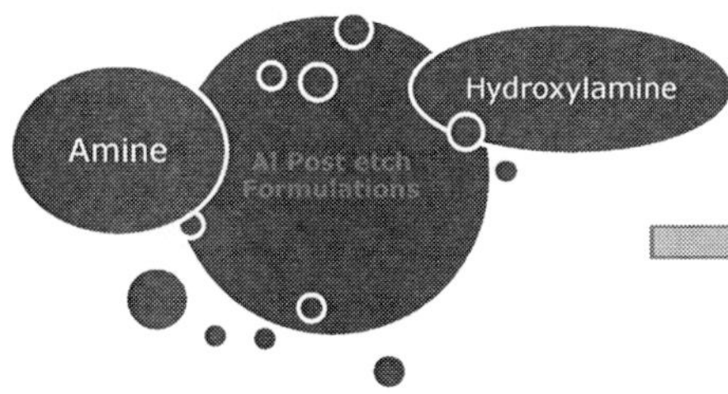

Hydroxylamine based formulations

- Photoresist removal or polymer residues after dry etch and ash process.
- Clean metal containing (i.e. Ti) residues.
- HA functions: reducing and complexing agent.

5

02 Formulation Design Concept

Replacement of Hydroxylamine in Amine Based Formulations

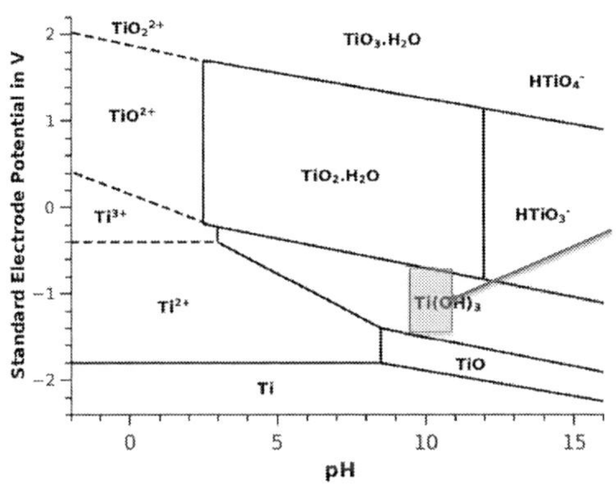

Commercial HA formulations
- Good cleaning for Ti-containing residues.

Ti(IV)Ox + HA → Ti(III)(OH)x --> Ti-HA complex

Hydroxylamine replacement for cleaning Ti residues:

Ti(IV)Ox + L → TiLx Complex

7

Design Concept for Hydroxylamine Free Formulations

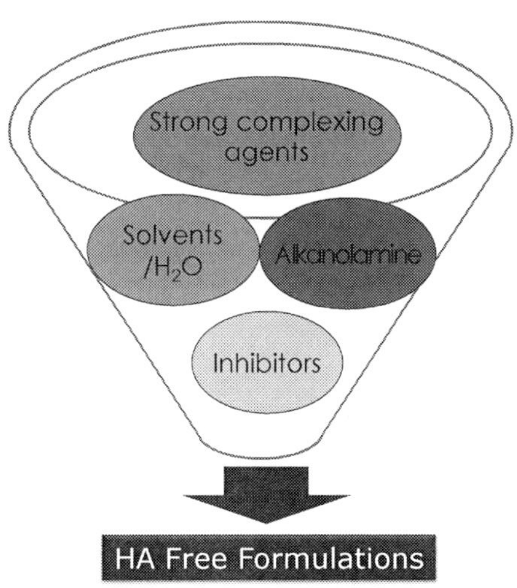

Strong complexing agent

Provide cleaning capability to remove Ti and other metal containing residue;

Solvents/ H_2O

Removes organic/inorganic residues;

Adjusts viscosity;

Improves the compatibilities w/ MoCs (materials of construction)

Alkanolamine

Stabilize pH

Inhibitors

Protects AlCu and other dielectrics

8

Ti containing residue cleaning results

03

Cleaning Performance of HA formulation and Alkanolamine Formulation

Pre	HA Formulation	Alkanolamine Formulation

- Without hydroxylamine, alkanolamine formulation could only partially remove Ti containing residues.
- Process conditions: 75 °C for 20min.

10

Electrochemical method for TiOx Dissolution Tests

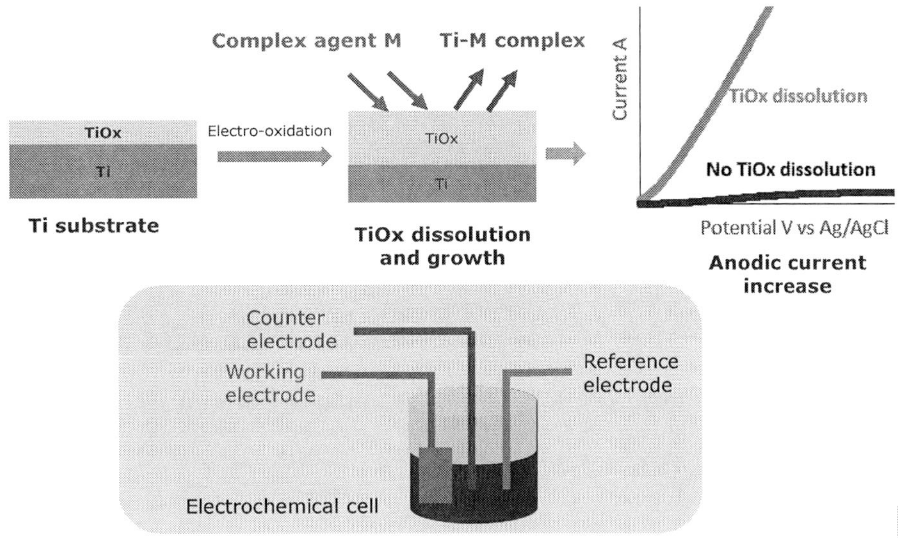

11

Effect of Ti Complex Agents on TiOx Dissolution Rates

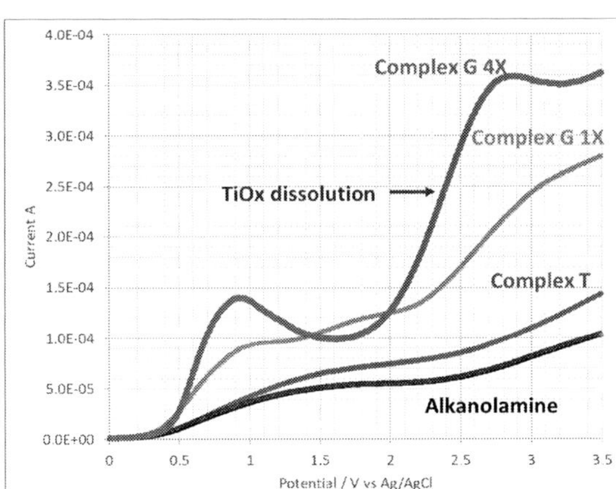

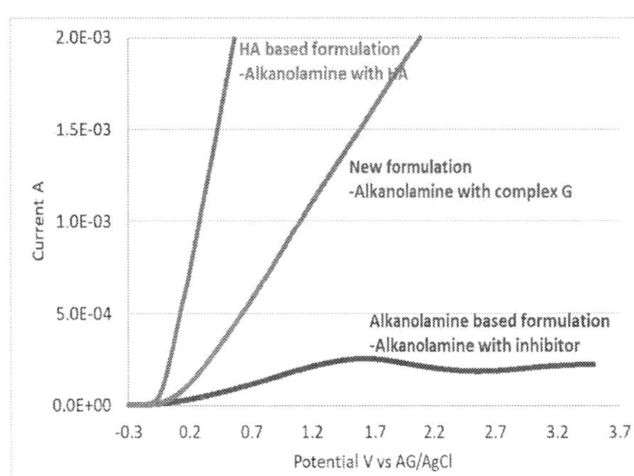

Complex agent G showed significant TiOx dissolution compared to alkanolamine alone.

The new formulation with complex G showed significant TiOx dissolution rate.

12

Ti containing Residues Cleaned by New Formulation

Alkanolamine Formulation	HA formulation	New Formulation

- The new formulation showed comparable cleaning performance to HA formulation on Ti containing residues.
- Process conditions: 75 °C for 20min.

13

Metal line residues Cleaned by the New Formulation at 75 °C 10 min

Pre	HA Formulation	New Formulation

AlCu Etch Rates at 75 °C

	HA formulation	New Formulation
AlCu ER Å/min	3	3

14

Via residues Cleaned by the New Formulation

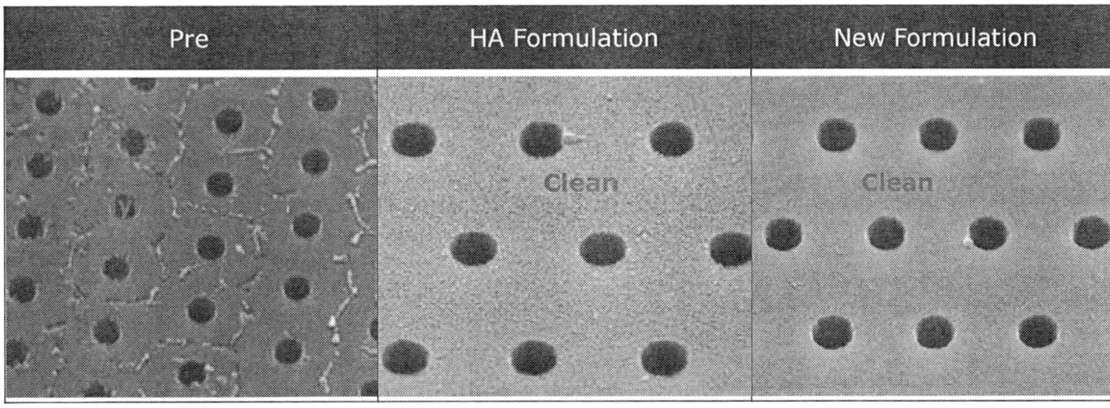

- The new formulation showed comparable cleaning performance to HA formulation on Via residues.
- Process conditions: 75 °C for 30min.

15

summary and conclusions

04

Summary

1. New formulations were developed by using a new strong complexing agent to replace hydroxylamine for cleaning Ti metal containing residues.

2. Electrochemical methods were used to evaluate the capability of the complexing agent to dissolve titanium oxide which is related to clean Ti containing residues.

3. The new formulation showed comparable cleaning performance on Ti containing residues to a HA based formulation

4. The new formulation also showed compatible cleaning performance on metal line etch residues and Via residues to a HA based formulation.

17

Thank you

SUSTAINABLE, HIGHLY-EFFICIENT WATER-BASED AND NMP-FREE THROUGH SILICON VIAS CLEANING FOR QUANTUM COMPUTER INTERCONNECTS INTEGRATION

SPCC Presentation Chandler/AZ, 17-October 2022

Dr. Alexander M. Breul (CTO)
Karl-Heine-Straße 99
04229 Leipzig, Germany
+49 341 319 68 10 30
+49 176 621 457 43
breul@intelligent-fluids.com
www.intelligent-fluids.com

OUTLINE

1. ***Qubits for quantum computing***
2. ***Demand for high cleaning efficiency***
3. ***MATQu project & the challenge***
4. ***Technological approach***
5. ***TSV cleaning optimization***
   a) Screening
   b) Benchmarking
   c) Characterization
6. ***Summary & outlook***
7. ***Acknowledgements***

QUBITS FOR QUANTUM COMPUTING

Josephson junction (JJ) is an S-I-S junction

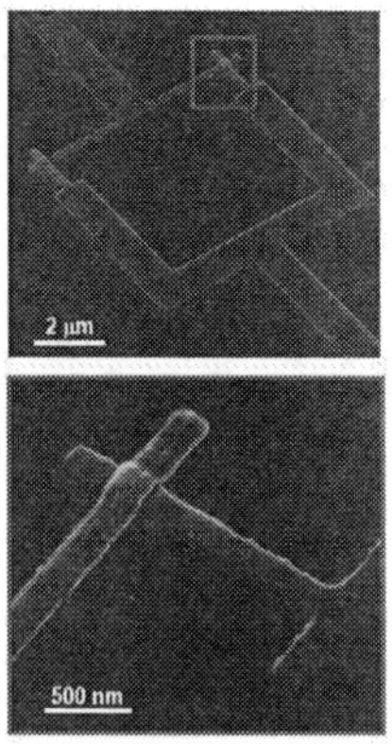

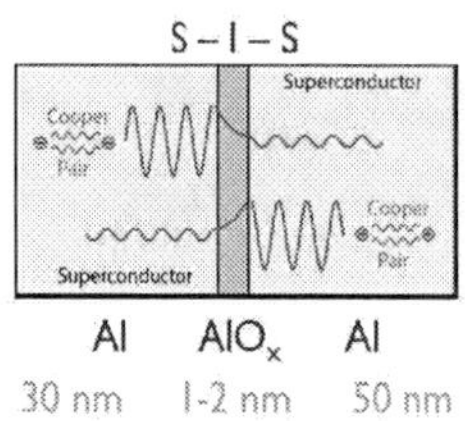

Symbol:

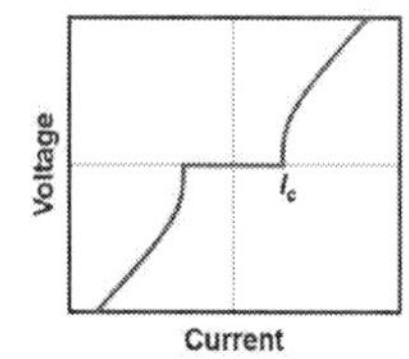

Josephson equations:

$$I(t) = I_c \sin(\varphi(t))$$

$$\frac{\partial \varphi}{\partial t} = \frac{2eV(t)}{\hbar}$$

Josephson Energy:

$$H = -E_J \cos(\varphi)$$

Superconducting qubit

DEMAND FOR HIGH CLEANING EFFICIENCY

Microwave losses and decoherence

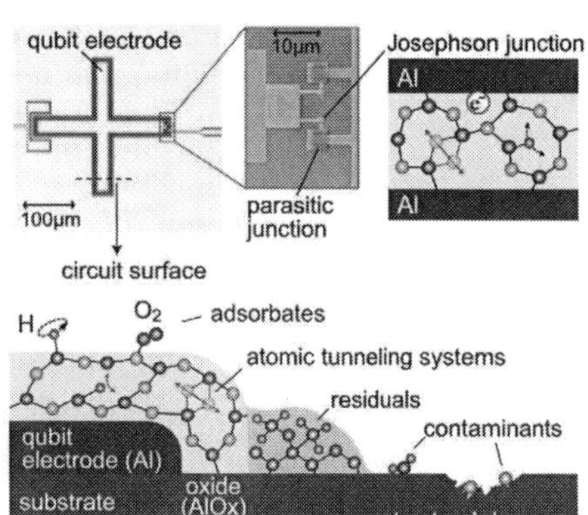

Lisenfeld, *et al.* Npj Quantum Inf. 5, 105 (2019).
Müller *et al.* Rep. Prog. Phys. 82 124501 (2019).

- Two level system loss (TLS) found in amorphous interfaces are main source of dielectric loss
- TLS visible: < 100 mK and fW MW powers
- > 60% of loss in the capacitor

- Search for material with lowest TLS loss tangent
- Search for new deposition conditions

MATQU (MATERIALS FOR QUANTUM COMPUTING)

- MATQu is an ECSEL grant to provide solutions for up scaling quantum computers
- It has different WPs
- Wet cleaning is essential for this application since qubits are very sensitive to residuals, plasma, ...

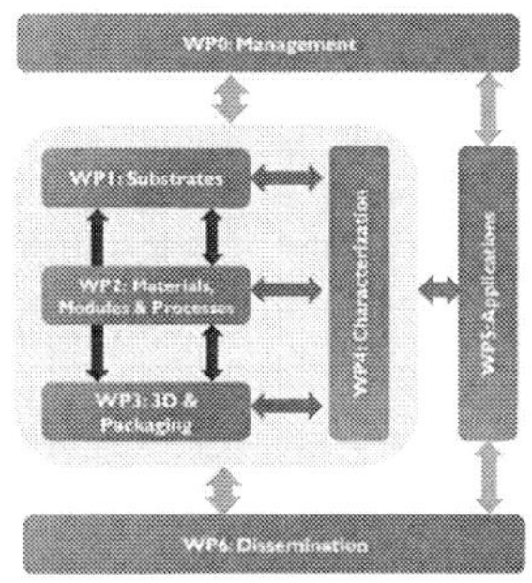

3D stacking

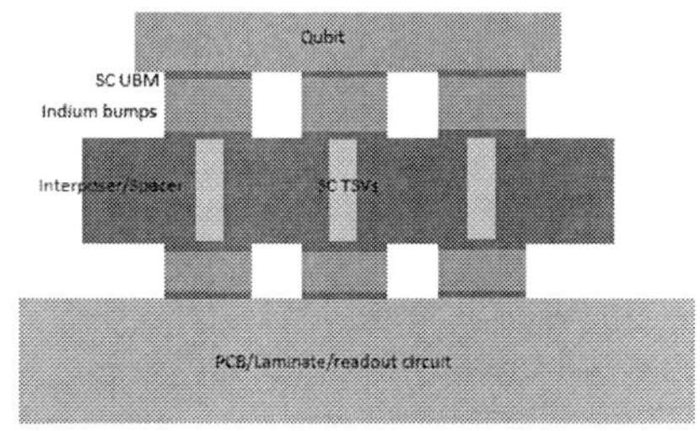

Resonators

junctions

integration

testing

DRIE

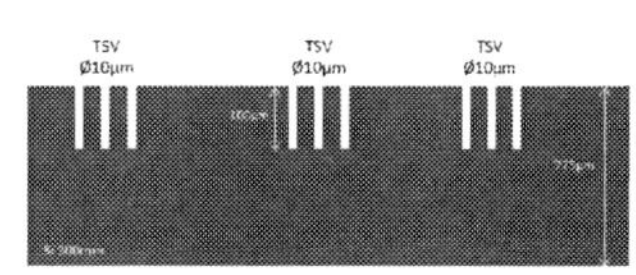

Bosch process:

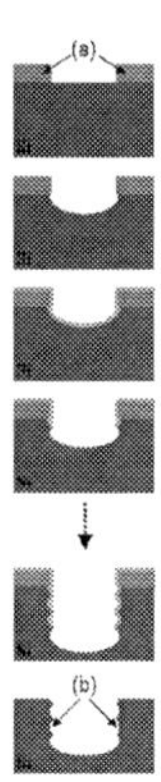

(1) Deposit and pattern masking layer

(2) Etch

(3) Passivation

(4) Etch

(5) Structure after many etch steps

(6) After stripping passivation and mask

Mask

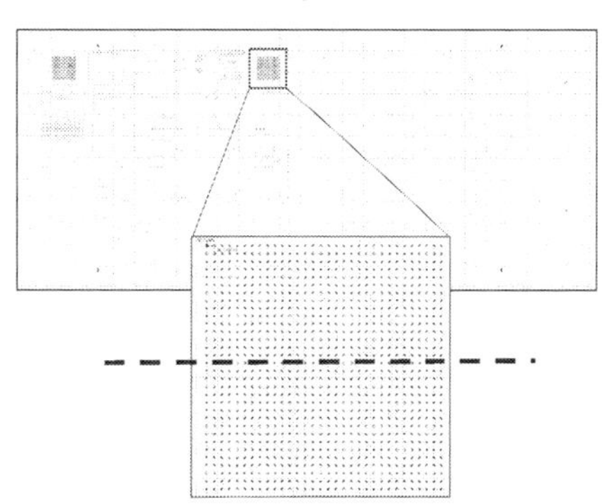

Dense TSV matrices (pitch 35 µm)

THE CHALLENGE

Current industry practice:

DRIE / Bosch Process → Dry Ash → Wet Strip

- Plasma cleaning: source of negative impact on coherence time: can add loss
- NMP-based wet stripping step: petrol-based and toxic

intelligent fluids® cleaning challenge:

DRIE / Bosch Process → Wet Strip

- Removal of fluorinated polymer and PR
- Low stripping time: single-wafer tool compatibility
- Environmentally friendly
- No degradation of the qubit performance
- Low risk for human health

TECHNOLOGY

Comparison of phase diagrams of a microemulsion system and phasefluids

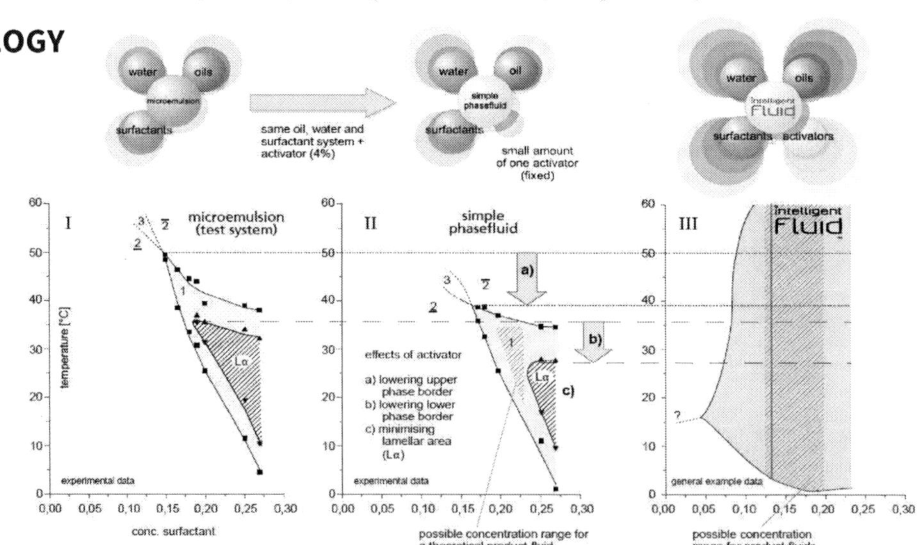

FORMULA INGREDIENTS

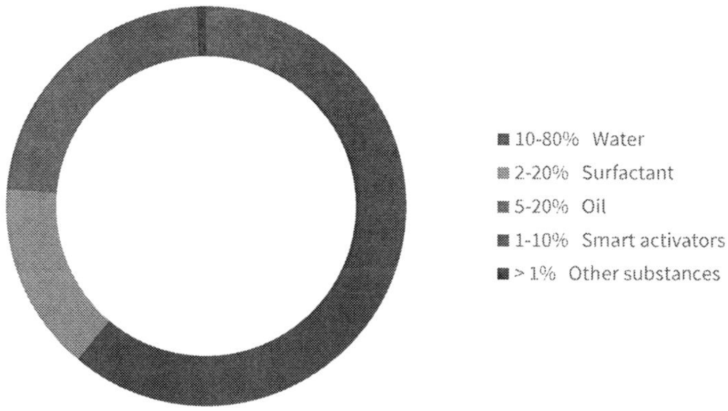

- All ingredients readily biodegradable according to OECD standards
- Flash-Point: > 60 °C (Pensky-Martens)
- No harmful ingredients

INGREDIENT MOLAR MASS VS. PERFORMANCE*

Benchmarking of PR-stripping

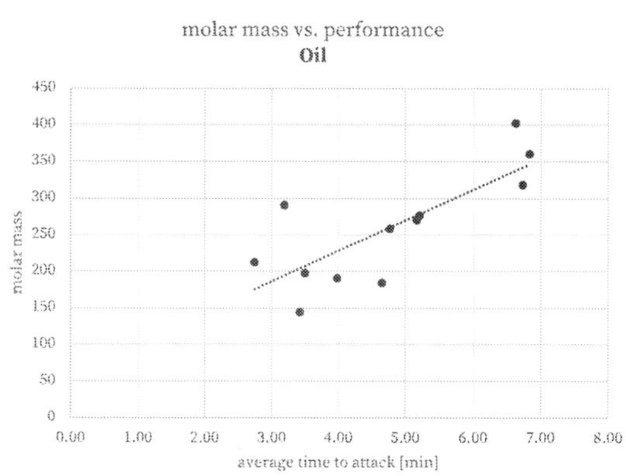

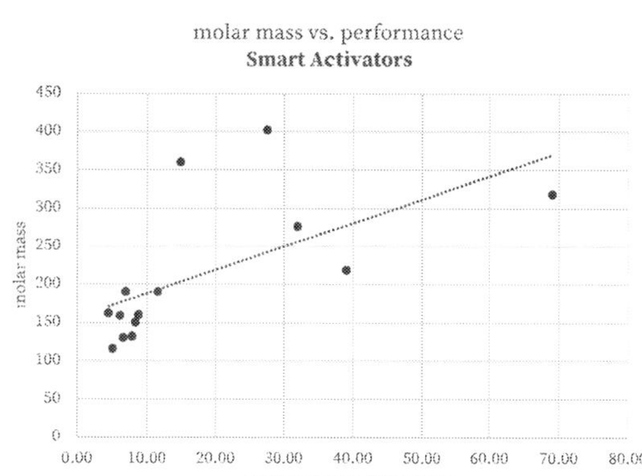

*Performance measured as stripping time on internal benchmarking standards. For details of the benchmarking setup, please see supporting information

FORMULATION WATER CONTENT VS. PERFORMANCE*

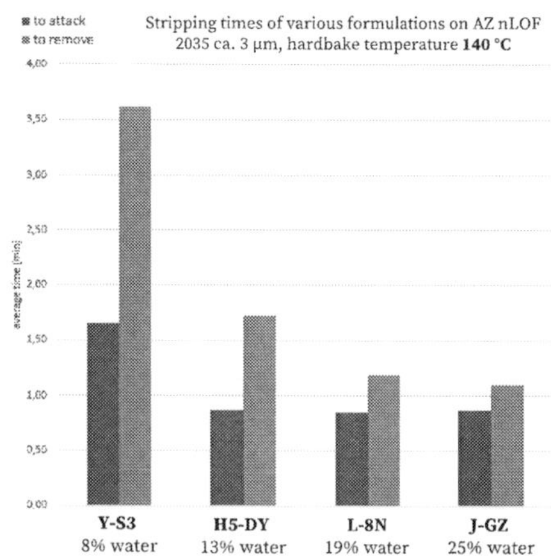

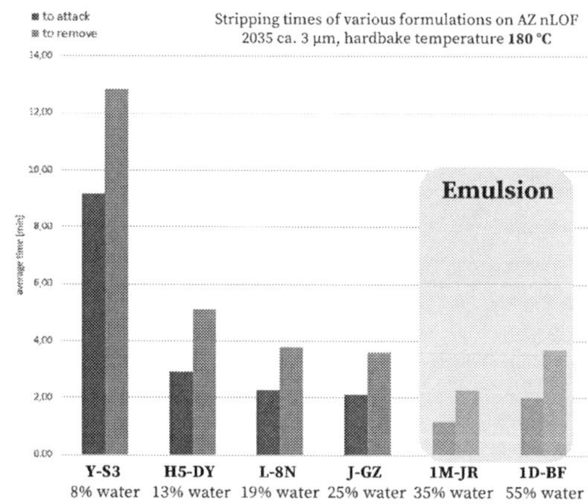

*Performance measured as stripping time on internal benchmarking standards. For details of the benchmarking setup, please see supporting information

INITIAL FORMULATION SCREENING: 45 MIN, 50 °C

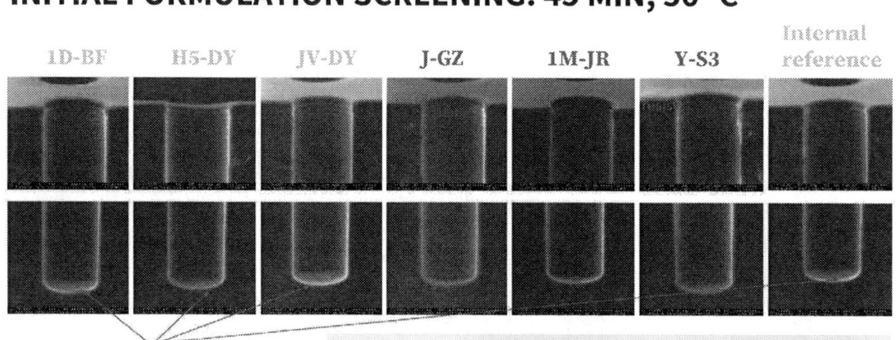

Inspection unclear: (e.g., Lab particles, PR residues or fluorinated polymer residues), → TOFSIMS analysis carried out

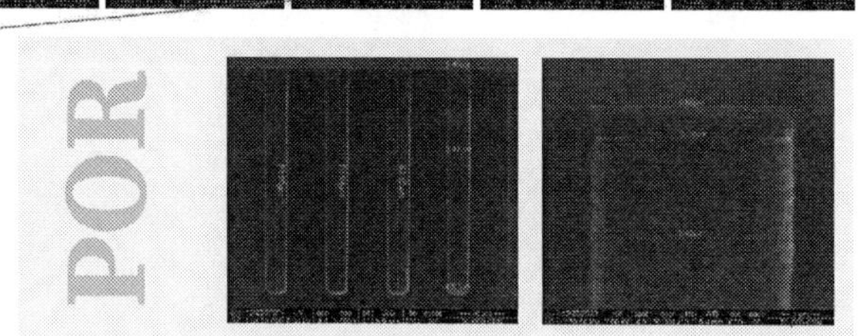

TOFSIMS RESULTS: BLANK, POR & TEST FORMULATIONS

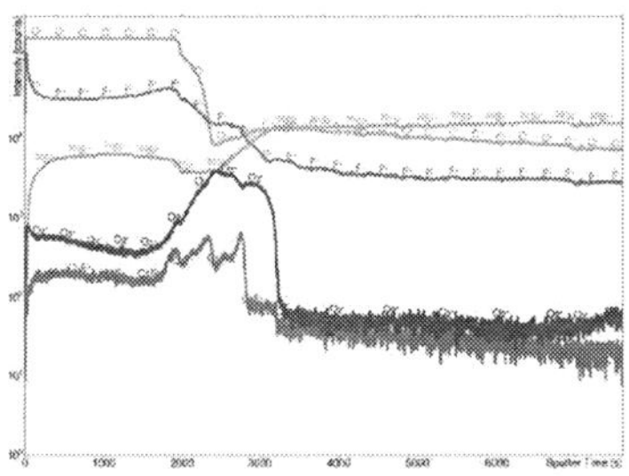

Dept profile of blank sample (uncleaned):

- High amount of C & F atoms
- **~ 10^4 counts**

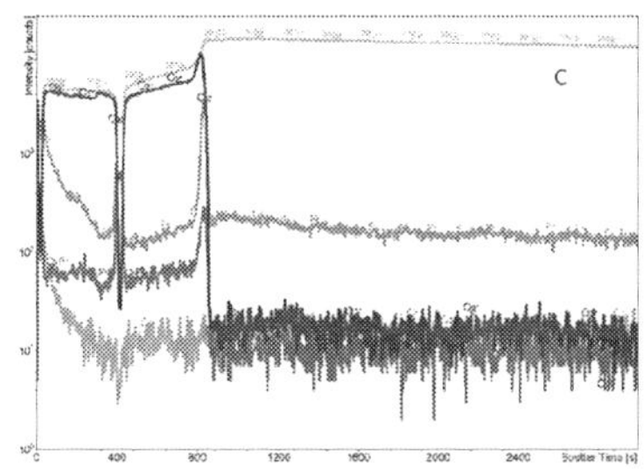

Dept profile of POR sample (cleaned):

- Very low amount of C & F atoms
- **~ 10^2 counts**

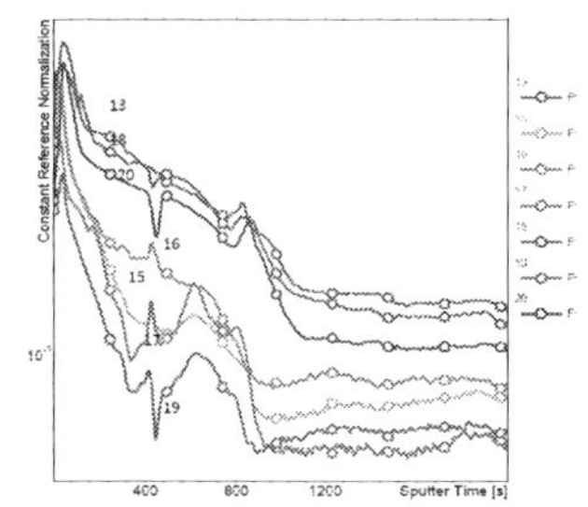

Dept profile of Formulations (cleaned):

- extremely low amount of C & F atoms
- **~ 10^{-1} counts → approximately 2 magnitudes of order lower than POR!**

SURFACE PITTING EFFECTS

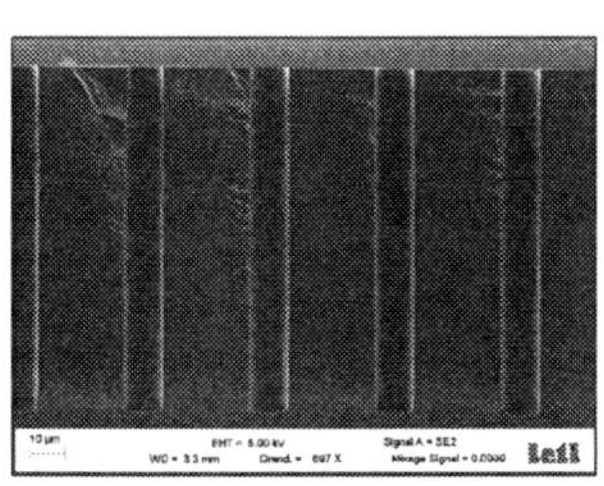

Sample	Effect
Reference	30% H_2O
Y-S3	8% H_2O
JV-DY	13% H_2O
L-8N	19% H_2O
J-GZ	25% H_2O
1M-JR	35% H_2O

Optimum?

Surface pitting observed on the TSV sidewalls*

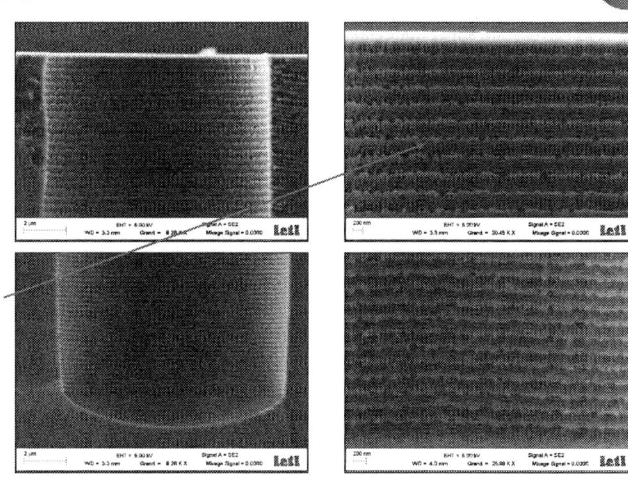

*Investigation still ongoing: other potential influence parameters: plasma artefacts

VARIATION SURFACTANT CONTENT & TYPE

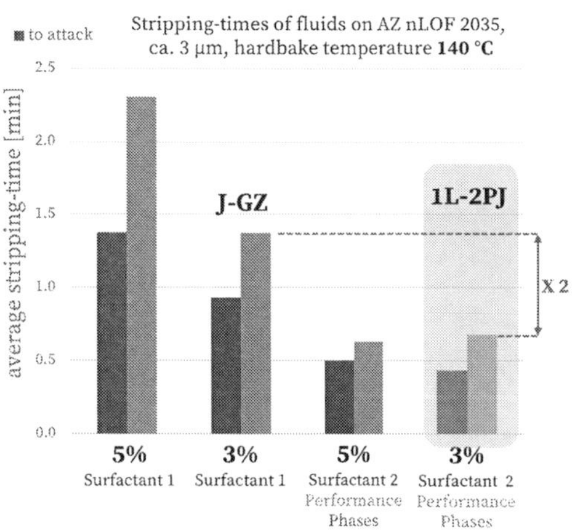

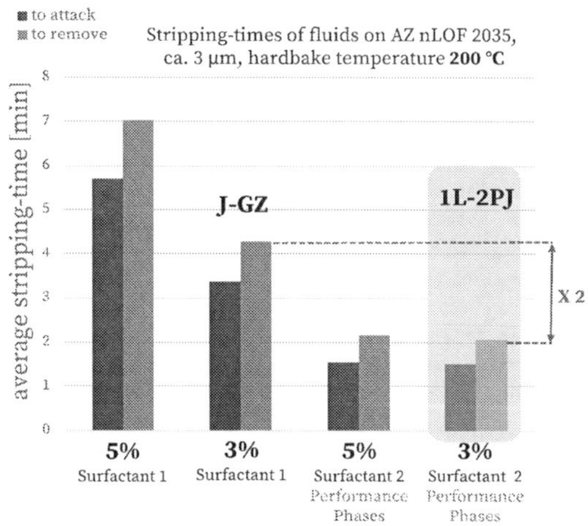

FORMULATION 1L-2PJ, 5 MIN, 50 °C

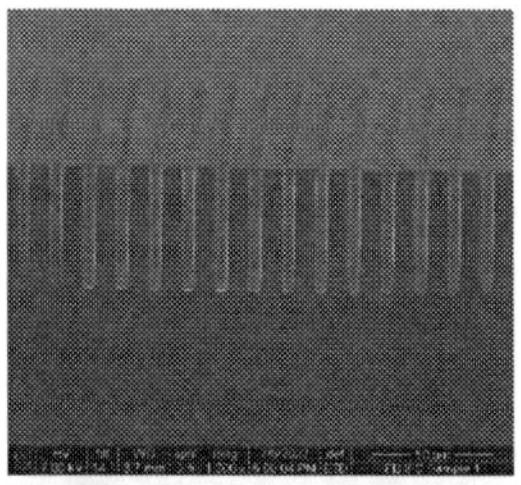

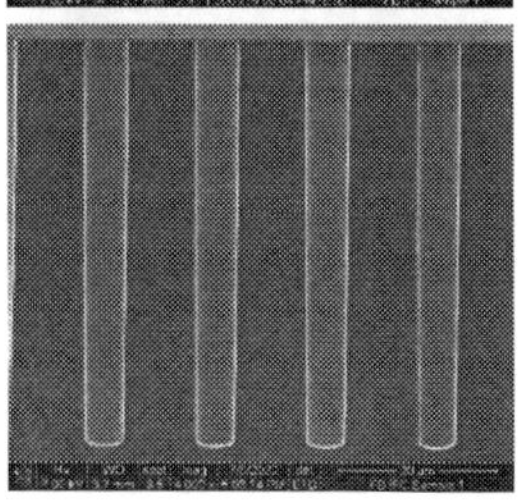

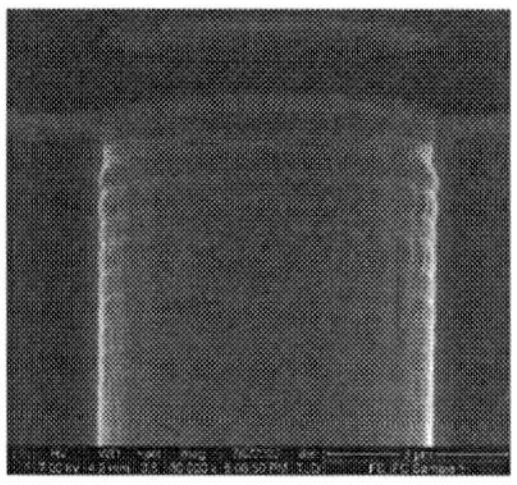

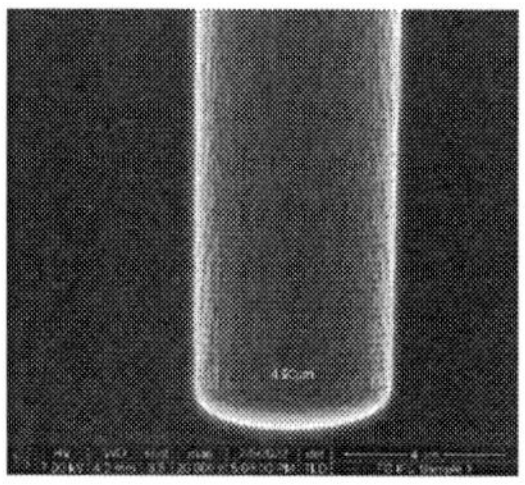

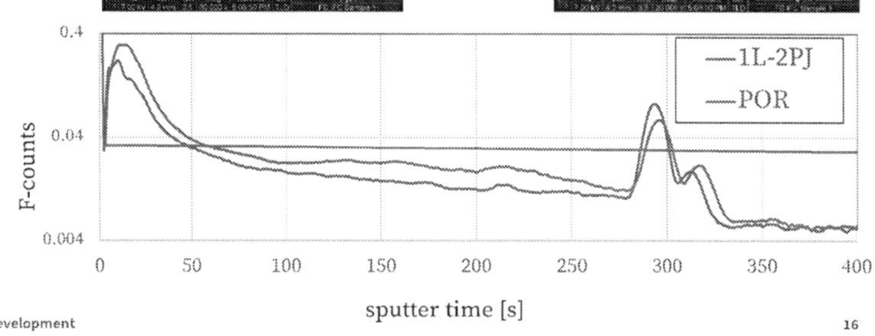

SUMMARY & OUTLOOK

- ✓ Photoresist & fluoropolymers successfully removed after DRIE process
- ✓ High efficiency/capacity, proven by SEM & TOFSIMS investigations
- ✓ Waterbased cleaning fluid:
  - ➢ Environmentally friendly and non-toxic alternative to conventional solvents (e.g., NMP)
  - ➢ Potential for lowering carbon footprint compared to petrol-based solvents
- ✓ No pitting for selected samples: potential H_2O content dependency
- ✓ Ready-to-use mixture for single-phase formulation:
  - ✓ Oil & activator components showed molar mass dependencies
  - ✓ Water dependency on PR-stripping behavior
  - ✓ Surfactant influence
- ✓ Flash point > 60 °C - safe handling & storage

- ➢ Process time optimization ongoing (~ 1 min)
- ➢ Tool integration @IMEC planned for 300 mm single-wafer tool

10/25/2022 © intelligent fluid 2022 · Research & Development 17

ACKNOWLEDGEMENTS

10/25/2022 © intelligent fluid 2022 · Research & Development 18

DISCLAIMER

The aforementioned presentation reflects only the author's view. Neither the JU nor the BMBF is responsible for any use that may be made ot the information it contains.

THANK YOU FOR YOUR ATTENTION!

intelligent Fluids GmbH
Dr. Alexander M. Breul (CTO)
Karl-Heine-Straße 99
04229 Leipzig, Germany
+49 341 319 68 10 30
+49 176 621 457 43
breul@intelligent-fluids.com
www.intelligent-fluids.com

SPCC Conference, Oct. 2022

MATQu

Through Silicon Vias Cleaning for Quantum Computer Interconnects Integration

Harold LE TULZO[1*], Loriana CELESTE[1], Inès TENDERO[1], Jaber DERAKHSHANDEH[2], Carine GERETS[2], Jean CHARBONNIER[3], Candice THOMAS[3], Edouard DESCHASEAUX[3], Jérôme DAVIOT[1]

[1] Technic France, 15 rue de la Montjoie, BP 79, 93212 Saint-Denis La Plaine, France

[2] IMEC, Kapeldreef 75, 3001 Leuven, Belgium

[3] CEA-LETI, Univ. Grenoble Alpes, F-38000 Grenoble, France

*harold.letulzo@technic.fr

Outline

MATQu

- Background
  - MATQu project
  - Through Silicon Vias (TSV): function, process and fluoropolymer issue
- **TechniClean D-BOS solutions**
  - Specifications
  - Formulation key breakthroughs
  - Mechanisms study
- **TSV cleaning in MATQu project**
  - SEM & ToF-SIMS results
- Summary

MATQu project

MATQu

- European project with leading companies and RTO (imec, CEA, VTT, Fraunhofer)
- State-of-the-art Qubits based on Josephson junction

Qubit integrated at imec

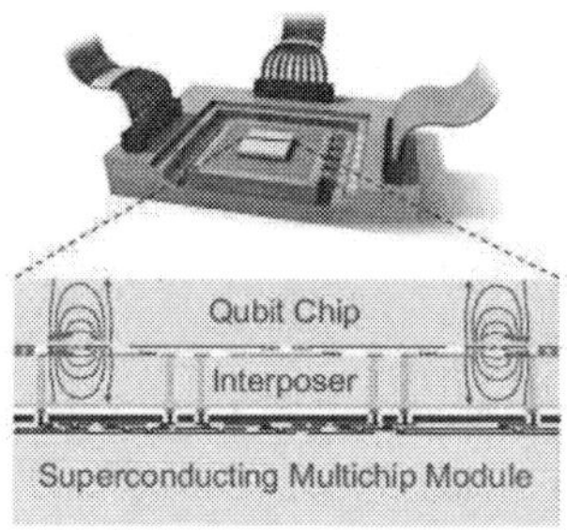

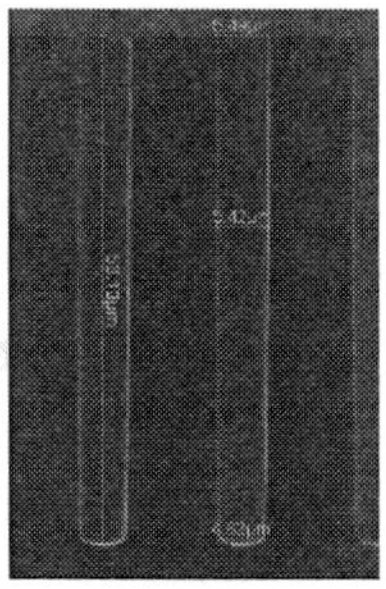

imec

leti
ceatech

TECHNIC

Work Package: « 3D integration and packaging »

- Interposer die development: to interconnect in a 3D multi-stacking manner the qubits dies and the readout wafer [1]
- Through Silicon Vias (TSV) design (diameter = 5 µm), cleaning and filling

Dr H. LE TULZO (Technic) [1] D. R. W. Yost et al., npj Quantum Inf, vol. 6, no. 1, p. 59, Dec. 2020, 8

TSV and Bosch process

MATQu

- TSV are **high aspect ratio deep holes in silicon**, useful in packaging architecture (2.5D, 3D silicon interposer) [1]
- Deep Reactive Ion Etching (DRIE) **Bosch process** is particularly suitable for via-first and via-middle TSV [2]
- Bosch process: cycle with alternative etching and passivation steps [3]
    - Scalloped sidewall profile with a fluorinated polymer (C_xF_y) (<100 nm-thick)
    - Photoresist = protective layer on top

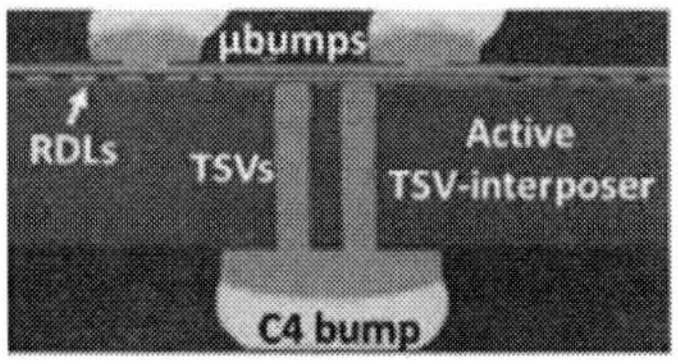

3D Active TSV interposer [1]

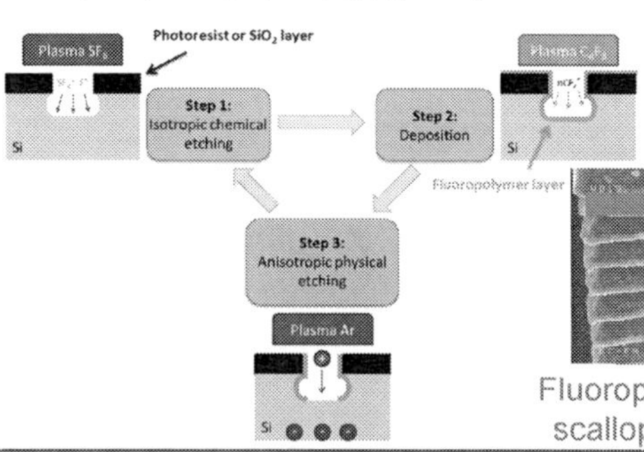

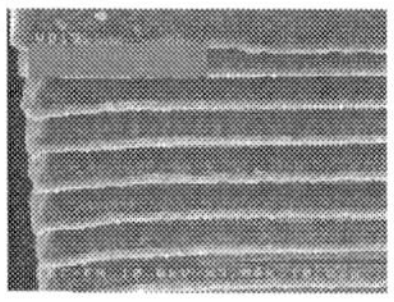

Fluoropolymer on the scalloped sidewalls

Dr H. LE TULZO (Technic)

[1] Yole Développement, « 3DIC & TSV interconnects », Semicon Taiwan, 2012.
[2] J. H. Lau, IEEE Trans. Compon., Packag. Manufact. Technol., vol. 12, nº 2, p. 228-252, févr. 2022.
[3] F. Laermer and A. Urban, Plasma Process Polym, vol. 16, no. 9, p. 1800207, Sep. 2019.

Fluoropolymer issue in TSV

MATQu

TSV possible issues [1; 2]

- Barrier layer growth inhibition
- Barrier layer delamination
- Increased thermal stress (conformality, low thermal resistance)
- Electrical loss mechanisms that can damage coherence and Q factors

→ Reduced device yield

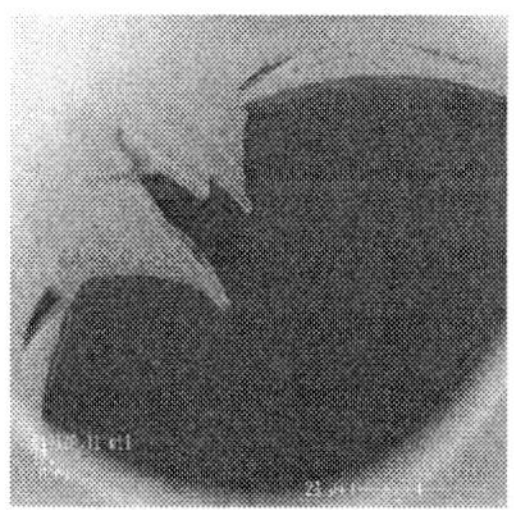

Delamination issue [1]

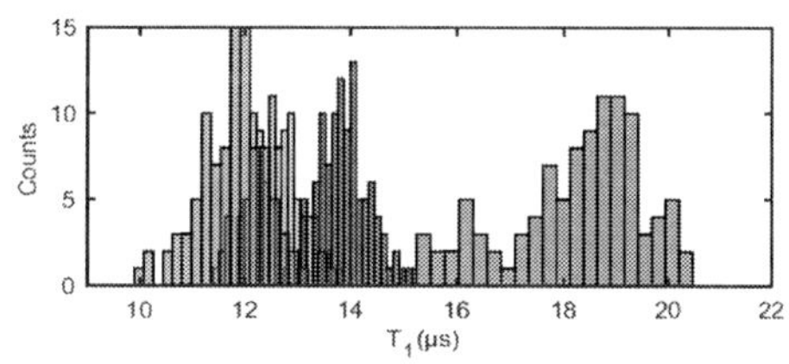

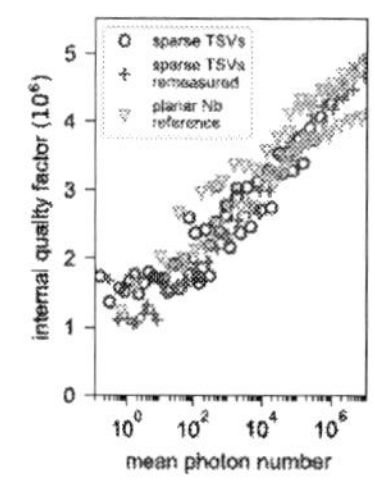

Coherence and Q paramount factors for qubits [3]

[1] J. Kraft and al., in IEEE International Reliability Physics Symposium, April 2008, pp. 506–509.
[2] K. Grigoras and al., arXiv, pp. 7. January 2022.
[3] D. R. W. Yost et al., npj Quantum Inf, vol. 6, no. 1, p. 59, Dec. 2020.

TechniClean D-BOS specifications

MATQu

Current process	TechniClean D-BOS specifications
❖ **Double process:** O_2 ashing + wet cleaning	✓ **One step process:** full wet cleaning Ashing = Throughput bottleneck process
❖ **No photoresist stripping** for some wet cleaning solutions	✓ **Dual functions:** surface photoresist and sidewall fluoropolymer removal in one step
❖ **Aggressive** process, **low selectivity**	✓ **Fully compatible** with exposed materials (via-middle approach)
❖ **Hazardous** chemical components (Toxic, Global Warming Potential (GWP)) [1; 2]	✓ **Clean product**: no bioaccumulating, no CMR*-listed, no GWP chemical components + **not flammable**
❖ **Poorly stable** wet cleaning process	✓ **Long effective bath life** and **stable** during storage
*CMR = Carcinogenic, Mutagenic, Reprotoxic	✓ **Water rinsing**

[1] P. G. Clark et al., in International Conference on Soldering and Reliability, Toronto, 2009, p. 5.
[2] T. Itabashi,in 2009 59th ECTC, San Diego, CA, USA, May 2009, pp. 1759–1763.

Materials & Methods

MATQu

- Development with **plasma-singulated dies**
  - Si substrate etched with Bosch process
    - ✓ **Photoresist (PR)** on surface
    - ✓ **Fluoropolymer (FP)** on the sidewalls
  - Relatively large trenches
    - ✓ Easier to cleave
    - ✓ Sidewalls easier to observe

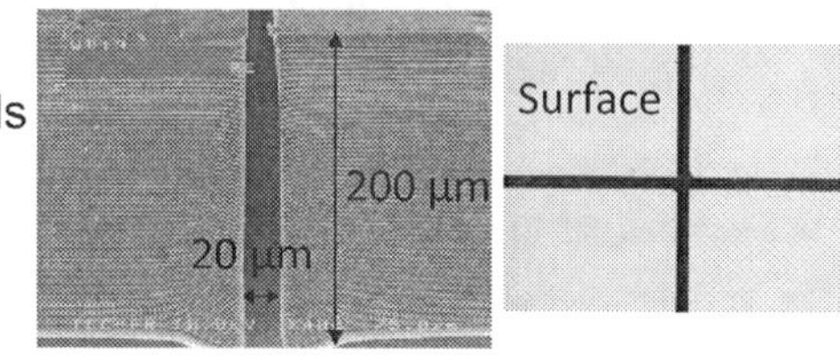

SEM and optical microscope images of plasma-singulated dies (reference)

- **Surface analysis methods**:
  - Optical microscope, SEM and EDS

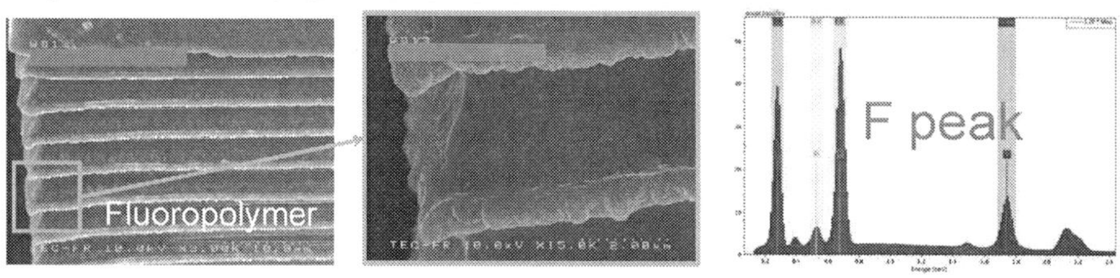

Reference sample (SEM + EDS)

Formulation D-BOS solution

MATQu

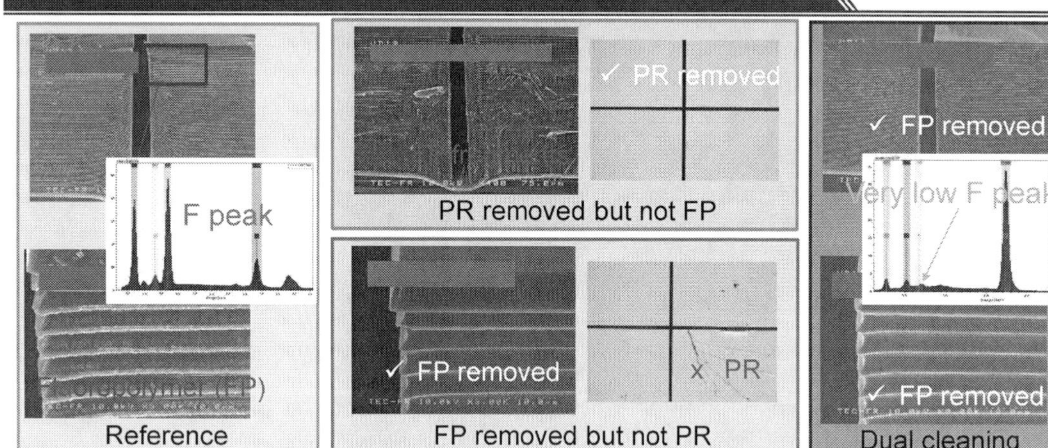

- Depending on chemistry nature and physico-chemical properties:
  - PR removed but not FP
  - FP removed but not PR

  } Compromise
- **Best TechniClean D-BOS solution: PR and FP total removal** (confirmed by EDS) in < 10 min at 75°C with gentle stirring (no ultrasonic waves) and H_2O rinsing

Formulation discovery (1)

MATQu

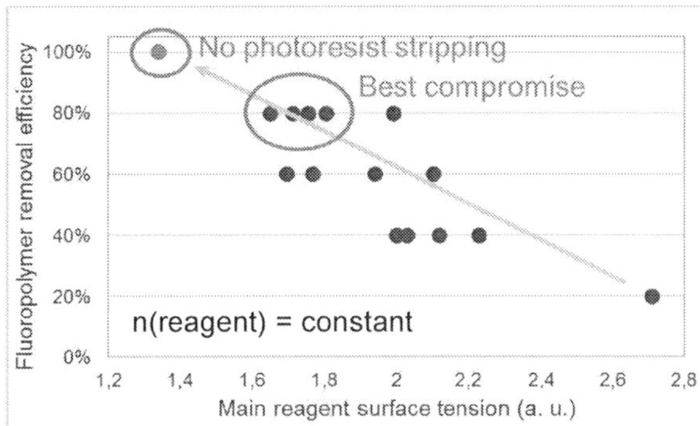

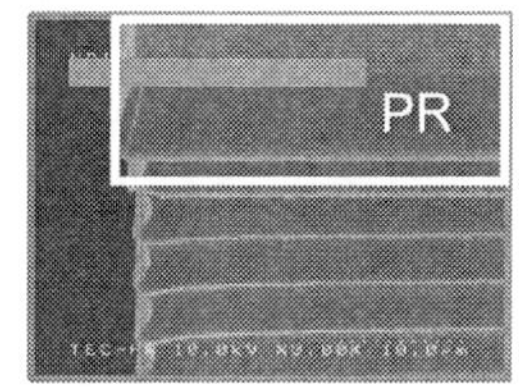

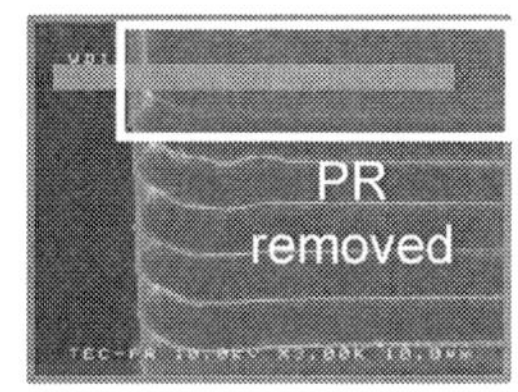

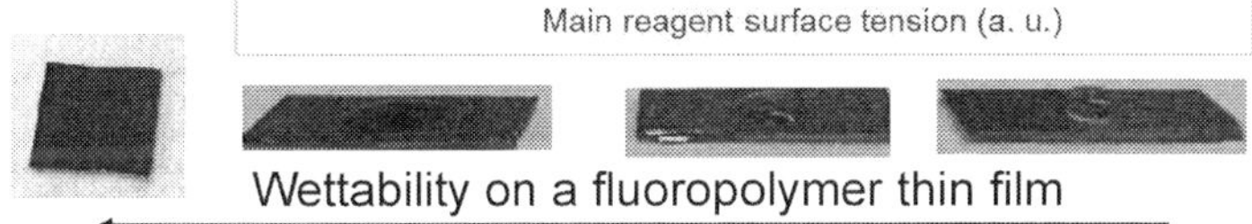

Wettability on a fluoropolymer thin film

Can we improve the FP removal by lowering the surface tension of the main reagent?

- Motivation: wettability enhancement, while FP = strong hydrophobic surface
- Result: Yes, **wettability improvement by lowering surface tension enables a better FP removal**

Formulation discovery (2)

MATQu

- 2nd efficiency improvement driven by **reagent synergy**

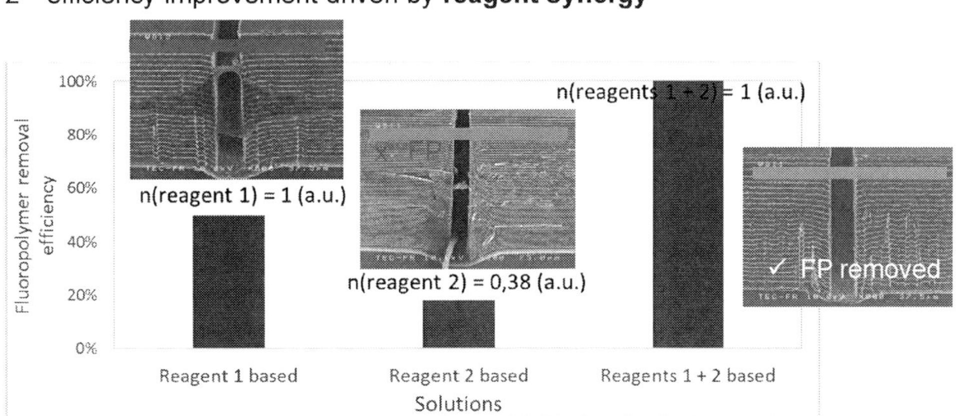

- **TechniClean D-BOS products = Organic nucleophilic based mixture**
  - *Nucleophilic: the tendency of an electron rich species to be attracted to the positive nuclear charge of an electron poor species*
- **Improved FP removal efficiency** compared to legacy products and other Technic's products

Removal mechanisms

MATQu

- After cleaning → no residues left visible in the solution

Question: Is the fluoropolymer dissolved? (C-F bond energy = 485 kJ/mol)

- Ion chromatography has been performed to check [F^-] in TechniClean solution
  - Same solution with various amounts of wafer pieces immersed successively: {0; 3; 6; 9}

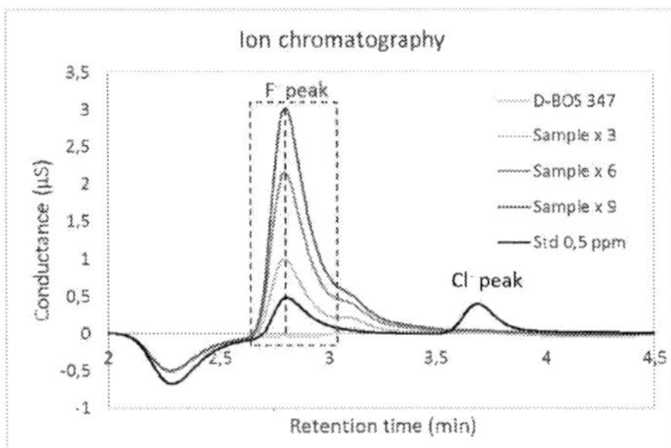

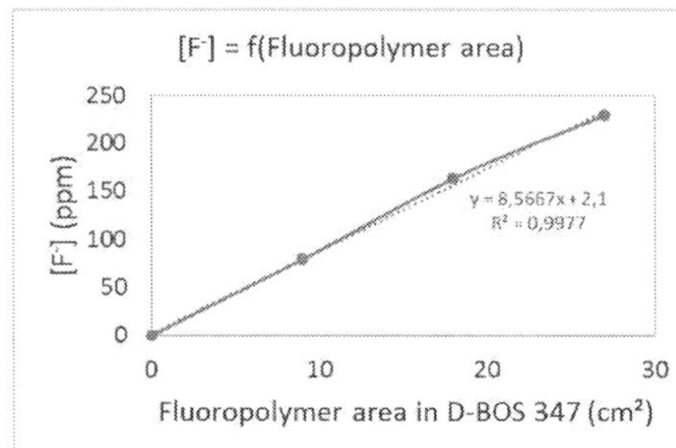

→ **F^- peak is detected in the solution** after fluoropolymer removal
→ Proportionality between [F^-] and the fluoropolymer amount in TechniClean D-BOS 347
→ Evidence of fluoropolymer dissolution

Dr H. LE TULZO (Technic) | 11

Selectivity & EHS

MATQu

Selectivity with metals and oxide

Four point probe measurements

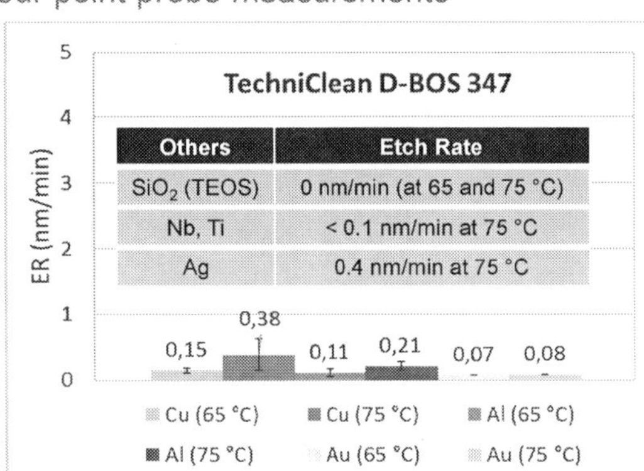

Others	Etch Rate
SiO_2 (TEOS)	0 nm/min (at 65 and 75 °C)
Nb, Ti	< 0.1 nm/min at 75 °C
Ag	0.4 nm/min at 75 °C

- On blanket materials, « ≤ 0.1 nm/min » = noise
- ✓ Very good compatibility with ER_{max}: **≤ 4 Å/min**

→ Corrosion inhibitors validated

EHS

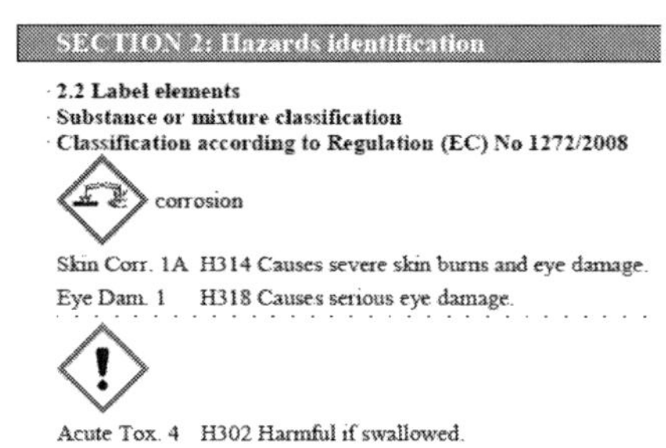

SECTION 2: Hazards identification

2.2 Label elements
Substance or mixture classification
Classification according to Regulation (EC) No 1272/2008

corrosion

Skin Corr. 1A H314 Causes severe skin burns and eye damage.
Eye Dam. 1 H318 Causes serious eye damage.

Acute Tox. 4 H302 Harmful if swallowed.

- ✓ Not flammable
- ✓ Not Toxic, not CMR

→ **Clean chemical**

Dr H. LE TULZO (Technic) | 12

MATQu's TSV – SEM study

MATQu

TSV in MATQu (Si substrate)
- 5 x 50 µm (IMEC)
- 10 x 100 µm (CEA)

TechniClean D-BOS 247:
1st formulation

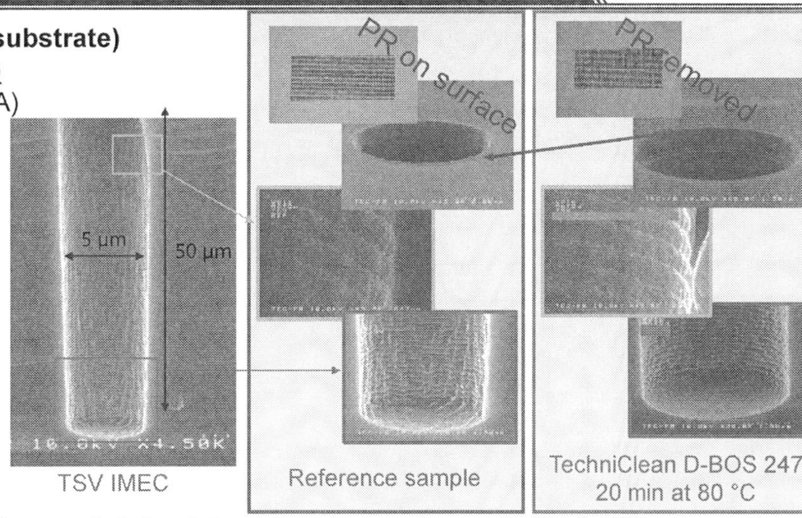

- **Photoresist (PR) completely stripped** on the surface with TechniClean solution
- No clear visual difference in sidewalls at 10 kV (or lower 1-5 kV) with coating

→ Elemental analysis required

ToF-SIMS analyses

MATQu

Why **ToF-SIMS depth** profiling?

✓ Sensitive surface analysis to detect fluoropolymer on the extreme surface of sidewalls

✓ Four elements (F^-, C^{2-}, Si^- and O^-) signals probed in depth with TOF-SIMS IV (IONTOF)

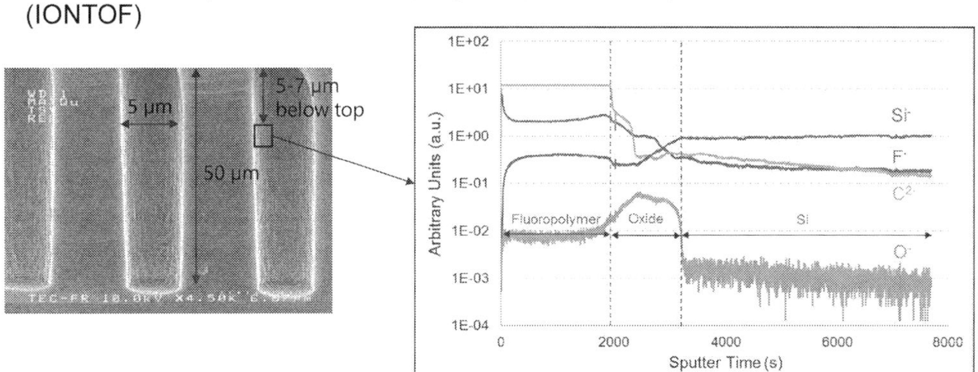

- F^- and C^{2-} signals have higher intensities on the surface where the fluoropolymer is
- O^- concentration is higher at the fluoropolymer/Si interface

ToF-SIMS analyses (2)

MATQu

Cleaning comparison between one-step TechniClean D-BOS 247 and two-step imec POR

- One step TechniClean D-BOS 247 at 80°C in immersion
- Two-step imec POR = O_2 ashing + wet cleaning by single wafer clean tool

Lower F^- intensity on the surface !

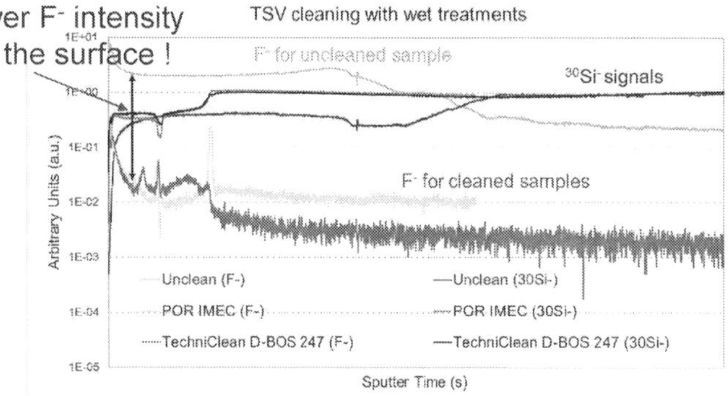

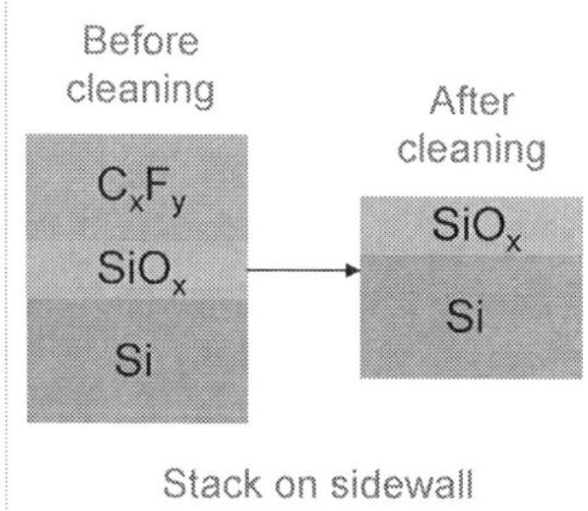

- **TechniClean D-BOS 247 completely removed the fluoropolymer in one step process**
- Next target: Process improvement (new formulation, mechanical assistance)

Summary and Prospects

MATQu

TechniClean D-BOS

- Dual function PR & Fluoropolymer removal
- Very high cleaning efficiency *vs* current wet alternatives
- High selectivity with metals
- Stable (storage, heating)
- Not toxic, Not CMR, Not flammable

- ToF-SIMS analyses have validated **Through Silicon Vias cleaning**
  - **Adhesion enhancer** for subsequent material deposition
  - **Strain/stress reduction** solution

Prospects

- Address shorter process time (<10 min) with mechanical assistance (partnership with OEM) [1]
- New solution dedicated to fluoropolymer removal after plasma singulation process (partnership with glue/tape suppliers) [2]

[1] Fuping Chen et al., in 2015 26th Annual SEMI ASMC, Saratoga Springs, NY, USA, May 2015, pp. 201–203.
[2] D. Lishan et al., International Symposium on Microelectronics, vol. 2014, no. 1, pp. 148-154, Jan. 2014.

Meet us at our booth !!

MATQu

Thank you for your attention!

"This project has received funding from the ECSEL Joint Undertaking (JU) under grant agreement
No 101007322. The JU receives support from the European Union's Horizon 2020 research and innovation
programme and Germany, France, Belgium, Austria, Netherlands, Finland, Israel".

Dr H. LE TULZO (Technic) | 17

Wafer Analysis for Contamination

Victor K.F. Chia, Ph.D.
Air Liquide International Expert

Air Liquide - Balazs NanoAnalysis
46409 Landing Parkway, Fremont, CA 94538

Surface Preparation and Cleaning Conference (SPCC) on October 17-18, 2022

Outline

Wafer Analysis for Contamination

1. Introduction to contamination and analytical techniques
2. Contamination measurements
    - Particles
    - Inorganics/Metals
    - Ionics
    - Organics
3. Summary

2

Introduction to Contamination

3

Contamination in Manufacturing

- Contamination is the primary contributor to most quality issues in manufacturing and can result in lower integrated circuit (IC) fabrication yields from reliability losses
- Contamination can occur at any point during the manufacturing process, and from many possible sources
- Water, chemical, gas and air delivery systems, material handling, process equipment components, manufacturing processes, and cleanroom operation can contribute to contamination related yield failures

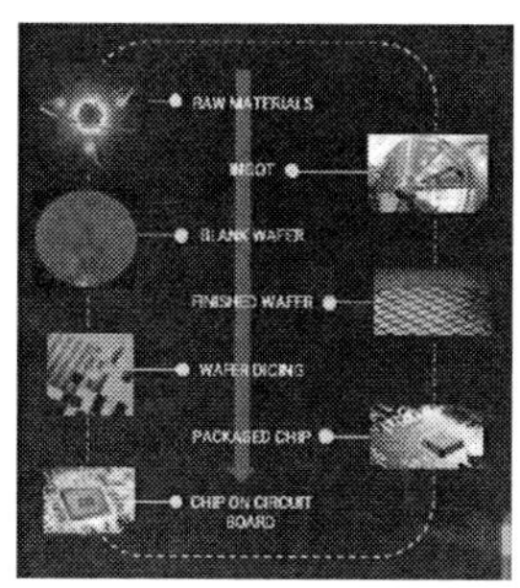

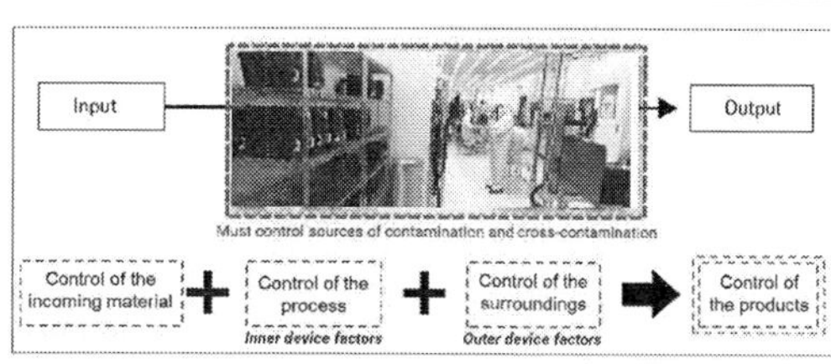

4

Types of Contamination

Environmental (Outer Device Factors)	Surface and In-Depth (Inner Device Factors)
AMC can become SMC	

Airborne molecular contamination (AMC)

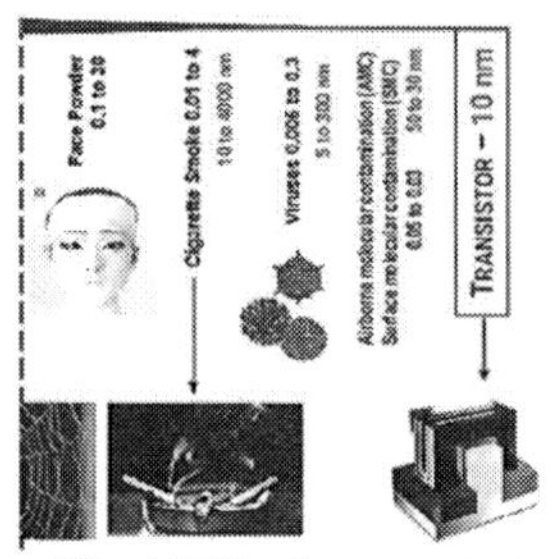

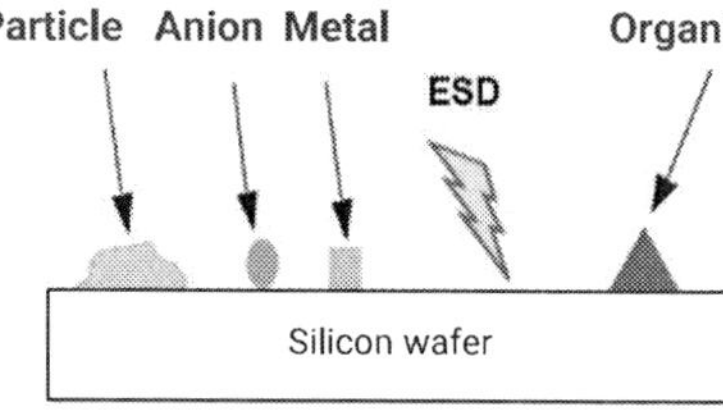

5

Analytical Techniques – Depth of Analysis

1 Surface

Automated Local Scan	Low DL Survey	Medium DL 2 Sources	Low DL Ionic	Chemical State	Org ID Survey	Species ID Survey	Chemical Bond
VPD	ICP-MS	TXRF	IC	XPS	Outgassing	GCMS	NVR-FTIR

2 Film and In-Depth

High Mag CD	Composition Survey	Composition Thickness	Low DL Fast Survey	Survey Fast Profile	Depth Res Sensitivity	Survey Low DL
FE-SEM	XRF	RBS	ICP-MS	GD-OES	SIMS	LA ICP-MS

3 Substrate

Low DL Survey	Low DL Fast Survey	Low DL Fast Profile	Ultra-Low DL Profile
LA ICP-MS	ICP-MS	GD-OES	SIMS

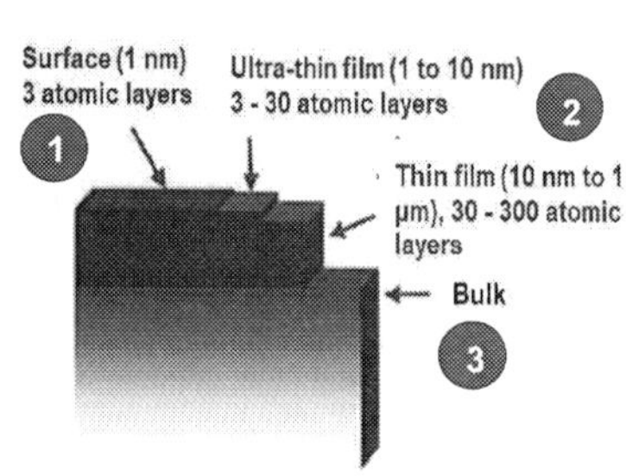

6

Analytical Techniques – Detection Limit

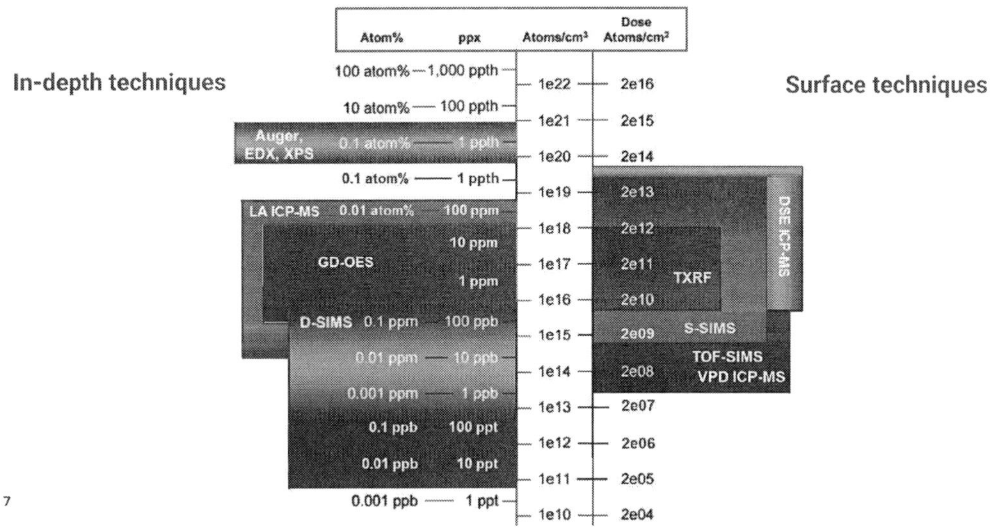

7

Contamination Measurements

Particles

8

Introduction to Particle Measurements

- There have been many studies on identifying the compositions of contaminating particles on the wafers
  - Full Wafer Particle Defect Characterization, C.R. Brundle and Y.S. Uritsky

    Characterization and Metrology for ULSI Technology: 2000 International Conference,
    edited by D.G. Seiler, A.C. Diebold, T.J. Shaffner, R. McDonald, W.M. Bullis, P.J. Smith, and E.M. Secula
    America Institute of Physics 1-56396-967-X/01
  - Investigated the appearance morphology and elemental composition of particles on the wafer surface using SEM/EDS

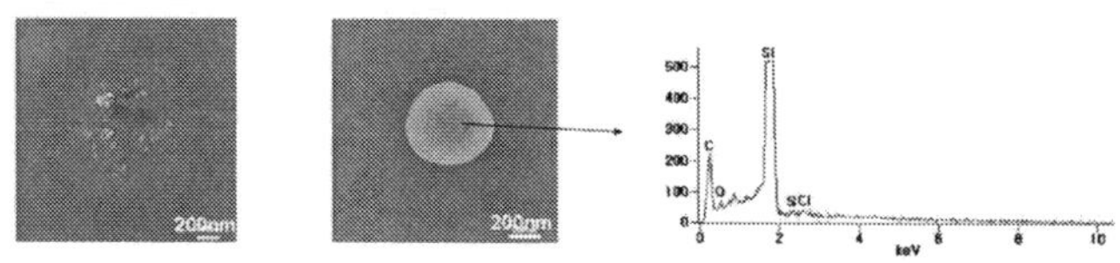

- Organic particles from condensation of organic vapors (AMC-Org) can co-exist with inorganic particles

9

Particle Techniques

Spatial Resolution

TECHNIQUE	ANALYSIS AREA/DIAM.	DETECTION RANGE
VPD ICP-MS	≥ 5 cm	$10^{6\text{-}15}$ at/cm²
TXRF	10 mm	$10^{10\text{-}14}$ at/cm²
TOF-SIMS	≥ 200 μm	$10^{8\text{-}15}$ at/cm²
SIMS	≥ 15 μm	10^{13} at/cc - 5 at%
μ FTIR	≥ 12 μm	100 ppm (5E18 at/cc)
μ-XPS	≥ 10 μm	0.05 – 1 at%
LA ICP-MS	≥ 5 μm	$10^{14\text{-}16}$ at/cm²
μ Raman	≥ 1 μm	100 ppm (5E18 at/cc)
SEM-EDX	≥ 1 μm	100 ppm (5E18 at/cc)
FE-AES	≥ 20 nm	0.1 at% (5E19 at/cc)

Practical specifications

Imaging Capability

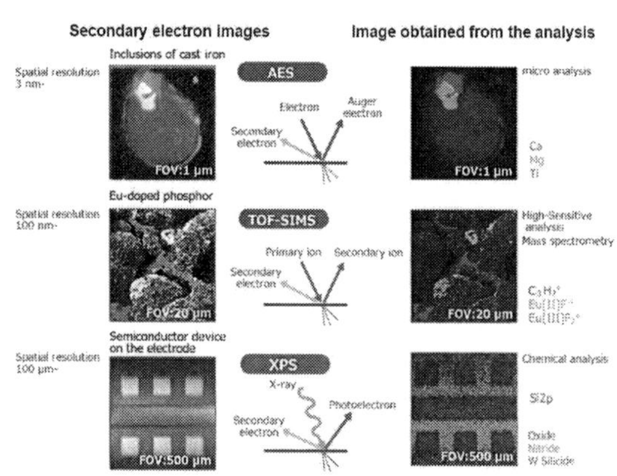

10

Particle Techniques

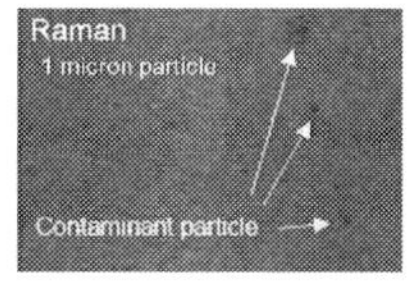

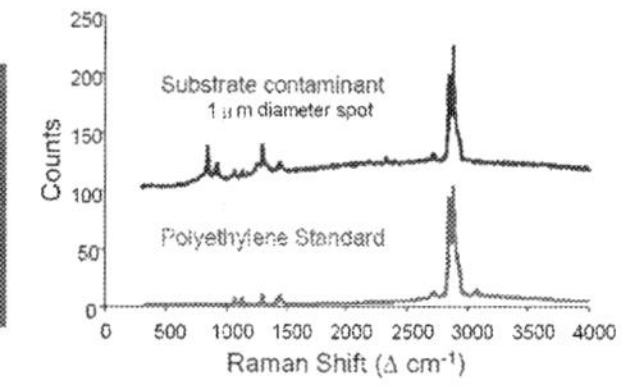

- **Raman Spectroscopy** analysis comparing polyethylene standard and unknown particulate contaminant spectrum yielding a positive match

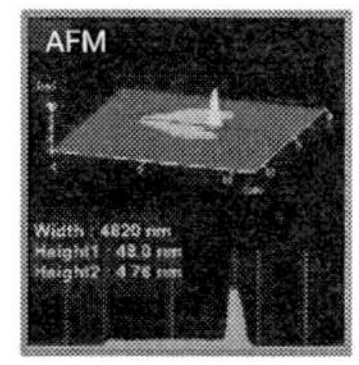

- **AFM** image shows particles with vertical heights ~50 nm above the surface

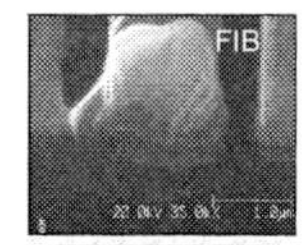

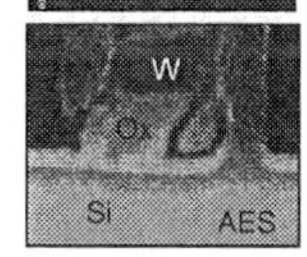

Childs, et al, Characterization and Metrology for ULSI Technology, p. 810, 1998

- Dual-Beam **FIB,** and **Auger**

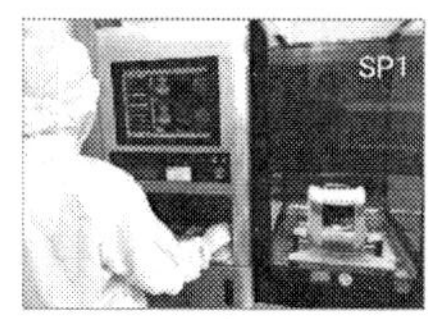

KLA Surfscan at Balazs

- **Wafer defect inspection** to detect particles on wafers and obtain the position coordinates (X, Y) of the particles

11

Contamination Measurements

Inorganics/Metals

12

Surface Techniques

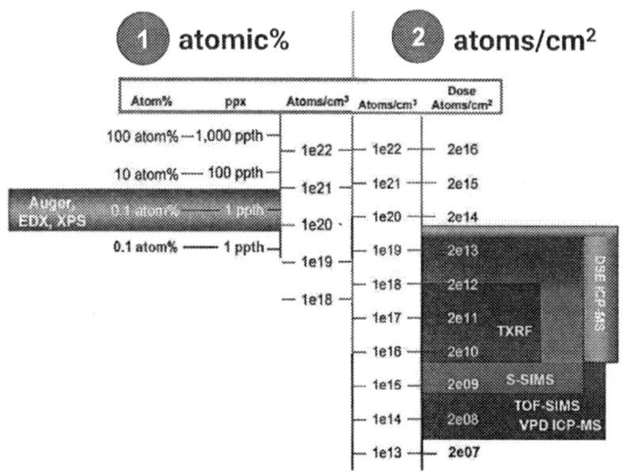

Analytical Summary

1

Techniques	SEM-EDS	AES	XPS
Signal Measured	Backscatter or Secondary Electrons	Auger Electrons	Photoelectrons
Detection Limits	~0.1 Atomic %	0.01 – 0.1 Atomic %	~0.1 Atomic %
Spatial Resolution	~1 micron	~0.3 micron	~10 micron

2

TECHNIQUE ANALYSIS	ANALYSIS	DL	ELEMENTS	
VPD ICP-MS *450 mm* *Non-destructive*	Radial, edge/bevel, whole wafer	$10^{7\text{-}15}$ at/cm²	Metals (not F, Cl) *UPW Leach & IC for F, Cl*	Survey
TOF-SIMS	Localized (200 μm²)	$10^{7\text{-}15}$ at/cm²	Metals, F, Cl, S and organics	Survey
SSIMS	Localized (200 μm²)	$10^{7\text{-}15}$ at/cm²	Metals (alkali, transition)	Element Specific
TXRF *300mm* *Non-destructive*	Localized (10 mm)	$10^{8\text{-}14}$ at/cm²	Metals and F, Cl, S	Survey

13

Surface Techniques

VPD Process

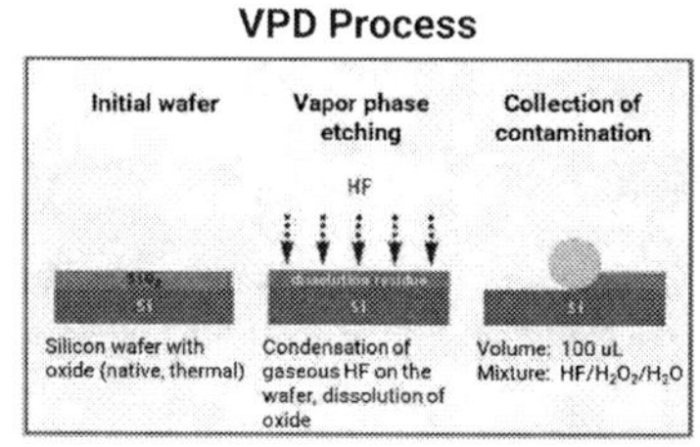

Total surface

- **VPD ICP-MS** involves HF vapor dissolving all oxides on the wafer surface followed by droplet scanning of the surface and ICP-MS of the droplet

Localized

- **SurfaceSIMS** is Dynamic SIMS using oxygen flooding
- **TXRF** uses an X-ray beam directed at the wafer surface at a glancing incident angle resulting in X- ray fluorescence of the surface metals
- **TOF-SIMS** uses a focused, pulsed particle beam (typically Cs, Ga or Au) to produce secondary atomic and molecular ions that are separated during the flight to the detector and detected individually, elemental mapping

SurfaceSIMS

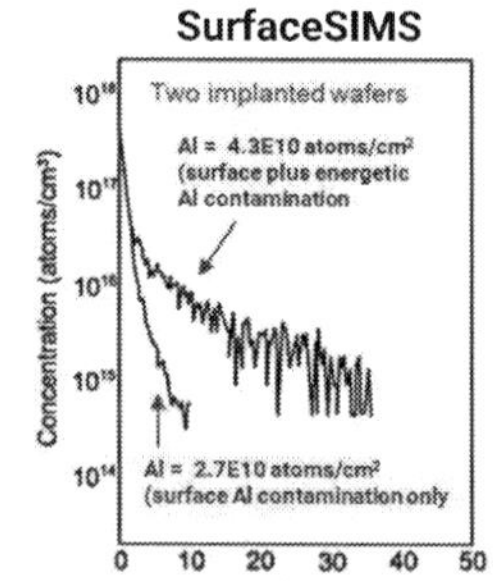

14

Bulk Techniques

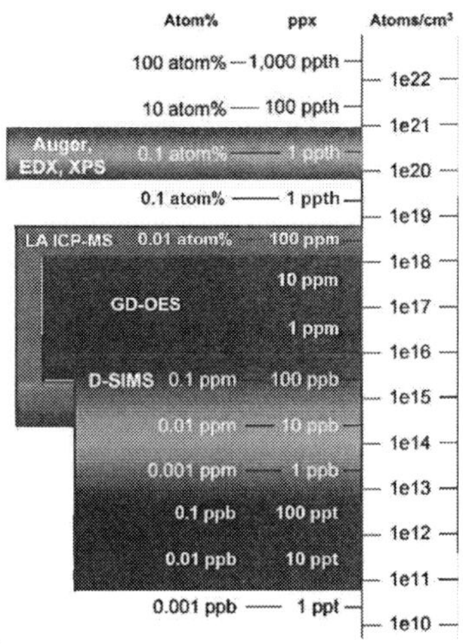

- **LA ICP-MS** and **Acid digestion ICP-MS** for bulk silicon
- **GD-OES** for survey, **SIMS** for best detection limit of Si wafers, film composition, ion implantation dose, and impurities in the film, interface, and in the bulk of the Si wafer

	ADVANTAGE	DISADVANTAGE
GD-EOS	Survey High Sputtering Rate	Develop Standards Large analysis area
LA ICP-MS	Dynamic Range Non-Flat Surface	Depth Resolution No F and Atmospherics
SIMS	Sensitivity Depth Resolution	Impurity Specific Flat-Smooth Surface

15

Bulk Techniques

SIMS

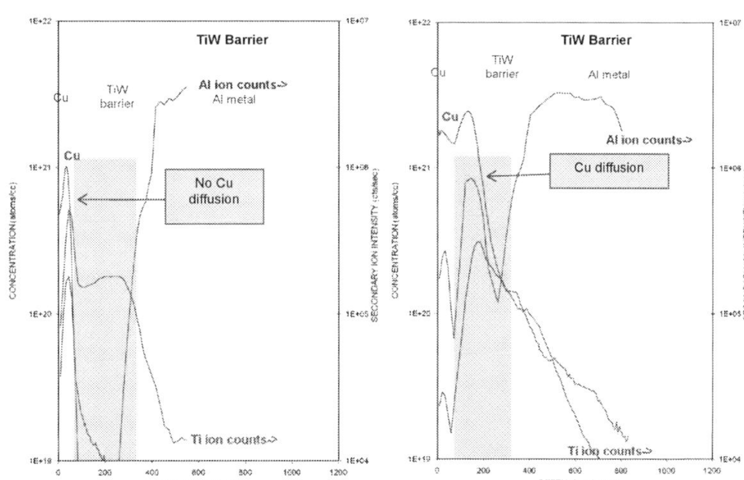

16

Bulk Techniques

LA ICP-MS

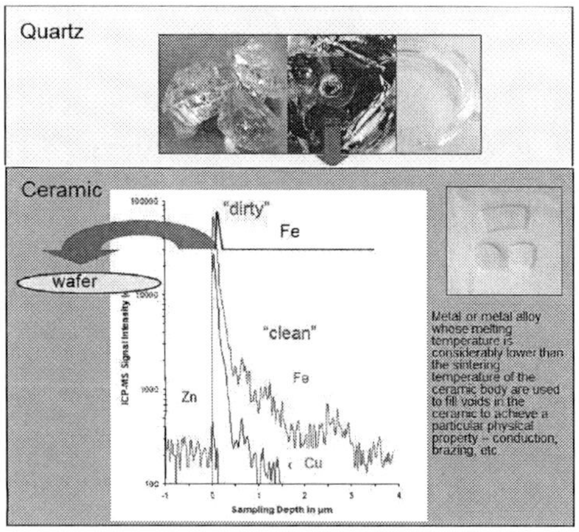

GD-OES

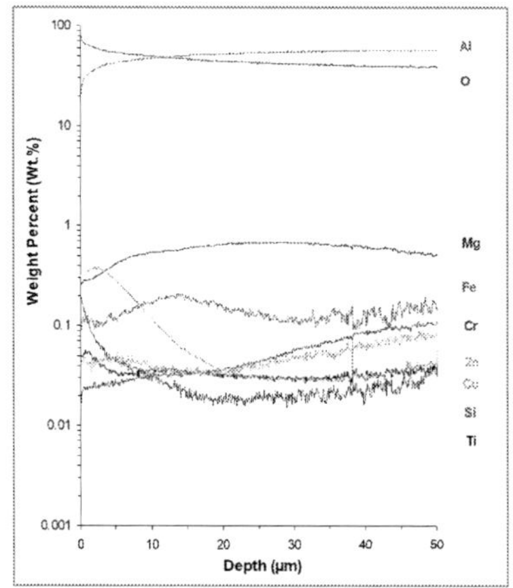

17

Contamination Measurements

Ionics

18

Introduction to Ionic Haze

- Wafer hazing and corrosion are some examples of SMCs
- Major ionic species on the wafer surfaces are **F^-, Cl^-, NO_3^-, SO_4^{2-}, NH_4^+, Na^+, K^+ and Mg^{2+}** because their adsorption rate constants and the sticking coefficients are larger than those of other ionic contaminants
- **Acidic anions** can cause etch rate shifts and metallization corrosion
- **Ammonia** and other basic contaminants can affect photoresist at ppb levels causing T-topping

T-Topping Study Report, University of Pennsylvania

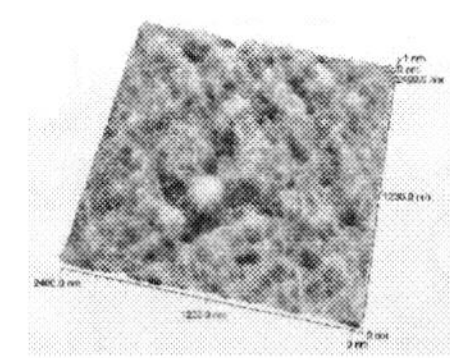

Non-contact image of silicon wafer hazing,- 2.5μm area

19

Introduction to Ionic Haze

- **Cleanroom air humidity** should be kept at 30-50% RH range
  - Tolerances of ± 1 percent in photolithography or deep ultraviolet processing (DUV) areas
  - Relaxing to ± 5 percent in other areas

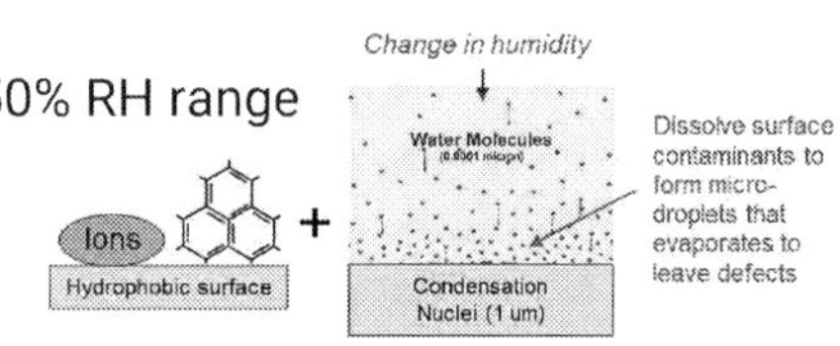

- Surface micro-contamination does not develop into haze without humidity, balance humidity with ESD
- **Ion chromatography** uses an ion exchange column and a dilute ionic solution (eluent), ions travel at different speeds depending on the ion's affinity to the column, arrives one at a time to a conductivity detector
  - UPW leach of the wafer at ambient temperature, 1 h typically, with orbital shaking

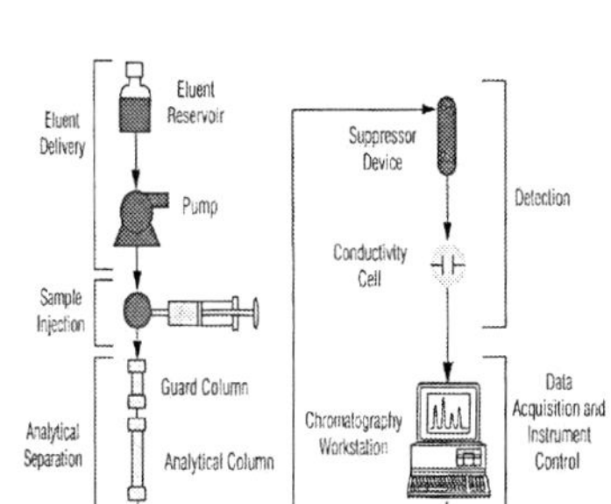

Dionex Handbook: Solutions for the Semiconductor, Disk Drive, and Electronics Industries

20

Surface Ionic Contamination

Time dependent haze (TDH)

- The haze is not stable due to excess NH_4^+ ions, NH_4OH formed is extremely volatile and depends on the temperature and humidity of the wafer environment

Stable and Fluoride haze

- Caused by a high concentration (~10^{14} - 10^{15} atoms/cm^2) of any anions and cations on the wafer surface; for example ammonium chloride or ammonium sulfate residues

Analyte	Reporting Limit	Sample Result
Fluoride (F^-)	6.3E+12	1.4E+13
Chloride (Cl^-)	3.4E+12	1.7E+14
Nitrite (NO_2^-)	2.6E+12	*
Bromide (Br^-)	3.8E+12	*
Nitrate (NO_3^-)	4.9E+12	1.4E+13
Phosphate (HPO_4^{-2})	3.1E+12	*
Sulfate (SO_4^{-2})	3.1E+12	2.1E+13
Ammonium (NH_4^+)	1.7E+13	2.3E+13

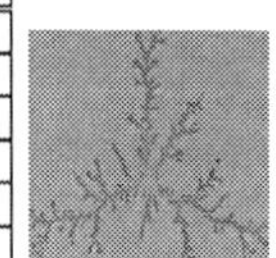

Ammonium sulfate haze

Analyte	Reporting Limit (ng/g)	Sample Results (ng/g)
Fluoride	223	801
Chloride	223	*
Nitrite	223	*
Bromide	134	*
Nitrate	178	*
Phosphate	267	*
Sulfate	178	*

Flouride haze

21

Surface Chemical State Analysis

- **ESCA/XPS** can detect Cations (metals) and Anions on any surfaces, including the surface of wafers, and is the only technique to provide **chemical state information**
- Electrostatic chuck ceramic surface (high purity alumina) has formation of AlOF; can use chemic treatment to remove AlOF using TMAH (tetramethylammonia hydroxide)

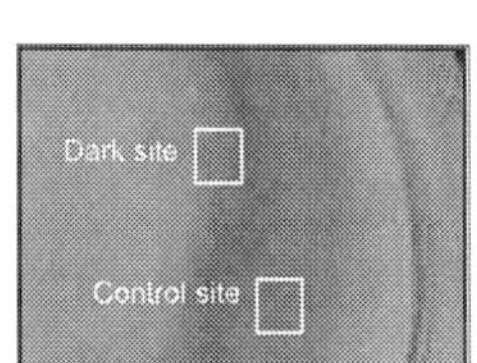

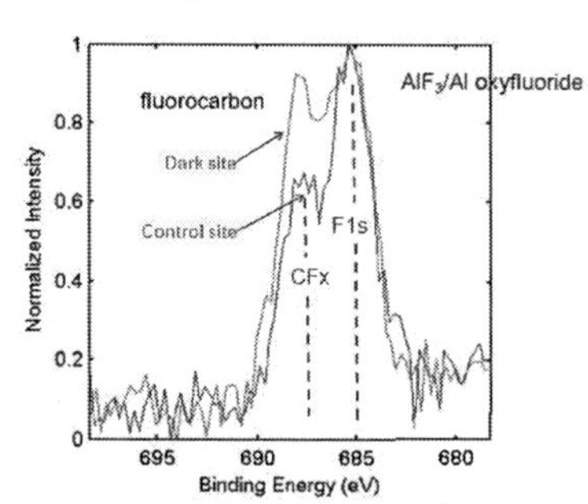

22

Contamination Measurements

Organics

23

Introduction to Organics

- Organic SMC can effect IC wafer processing
  - Can cause delamination or irregular spin-on thickness
  - Vacuum degradation in process tool and inspection tool chambers
  - Organics may carbonize producing graphite, SiC and carbides resulting in electrical shorts

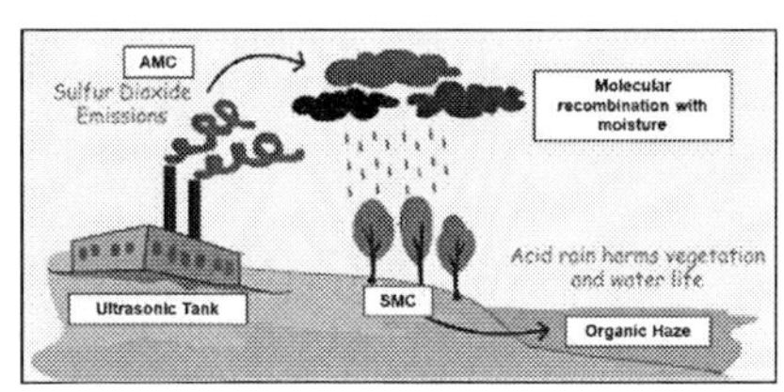

- International Roadmap for Devices and Systems (IRDS) guideline
  - 2 ng/cm^2 for 24 h exposure and reducing to 0.5 ng/cm^2
  - 2 ng/cm^2 is approximately 0.1 monolayer

AMC Class	Sources	Effects
Molecular condensables	Outside air, process chemicals, outgassing from filter, sealants, walls, adhesives, floors, wafer shippers, FOUPs, pods, gaskets, sealing tape, bagging materials, flame retardants	Hazing of exposure tool optics and masks from silicones & HMDS by-products Delamination of PR and ARCs Unwanted n-doping of wafers Interference with thin film metrology

24

Introduction to Organics

Organic SMC has many cleanroom sources

Organic Source	Categories	Identified Compound
Flooring materials and vinyl tiles	Plasticizer Plasticizer Anti-ageing, anti-oxidant Conductive filler	DOP (dioctyl phthalates) TXIB (texanol isobutyrate) BHT (butylated hydroxy toluene) Carbon
Fluid seal (ceiling grid), caulking sealant Cleanroom walls, gaskets	Cyclic siloxanes (silicone bi-component) Anti-ageing, anti-oxidant	Poly dimethyl silicone Hexamethyl tri-silicone Octamethyl tetra-siloxane BHT (butylated hydroxy toluene)
Flexible connectors and ductwork	Crossliking agent Plasticizer Anti-oxidant	Phosphate ester Antimony (Sb) Butyl phthalate
Polyurethane adhesives	Crosslinking agent Plasticizer Anti-oxidant	Amines Ammonium DBP (dibutyl phthalate) BHT (butylated hydroxy toluene)
Paintings, coatings, concrete fillers	Crossliking agent Surfactants	Amines, polyimides
ULPA/HEPA filters (media and potting materials)	Fire retardant Fire retardant Fire retardant Borosilicate fiberglass	TEP (tri-ethyl phosphate) TCEP (tri-chloro ethyl phosphate) TCPP (tri-chloro propyl phosphate) $BF_3B(O\text{-}R)_3$, boron

25

Organic Analytical Techniques

TECHNIQUE	ANALYSIS AREA	DL	COMMENTS
XPS	>30 μm²	0.05 - 1 at%	Surface, survey and high resolution scans, elemental and chemical state, quantitative, insulators
TOF-SIMS	200 μm²	<1 ppm	Surface, survey, organic and elemental information, qualitative for organic, quantitative for metals
TD GC-MS	Full wafer	0.1 ng/cm²	Total surface outgas, survey, comp'd identified
GC-MS survey, organic	Extract area		0.1 ng/cm² Surface, solvent extraction, compounds identified
FTIR	≥10 μm	10^{13} bonds/cm³ or 0.1 - 1 wt%	In-depth, chemical bond information, qualitative with standards, typical standards, typical depth of analysis is 0.1 - 1.0 μm
Raman	≥1 μm	> 1 wt%	Bulk, chemical bond information, qualitative with standards, typical depth of analysis is 1 - 5 μm (depth probed)

26

Organic Outgas Techniques

Full Wafer Thermal Desorption GC-MS, SEMI MF1982-1103

- The whole wafer is heated in a quartz chamber to ≤700ºC and outgassed organic compounds are collected and analyzed by TD GC-MS
- Identifies individual compound that is thermally desorbed off the wafer surface

IEST-RP-CC31: Test Method for Material Outgassing

- GC outgassing temperature of 50 C, 75 C, 100 C, or 150 C for 30 minutes, use the next highest temperature versus the application temperature

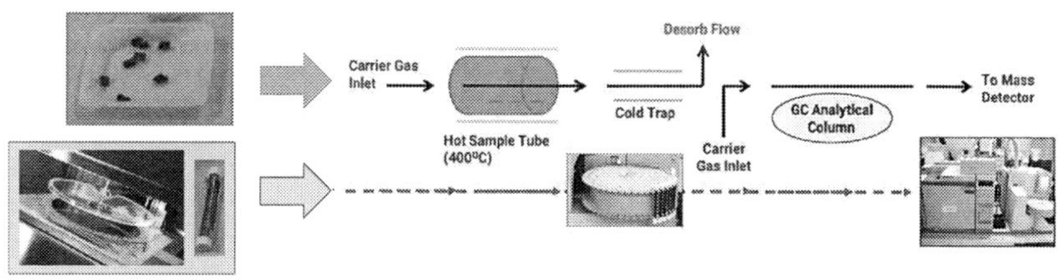

27

Organic Outgas Technique – TD GC-MS

Organics from Full Wafer by TD-GC-MS, SEMI MF 1982-1103 Method-B				
Parameter	RL	Units	CONTROL WAFER SHIPPING BLANK	CHAMBER BASELINE
Low boilers C7-C10	0.1	ng/cm²	*	3.1
Medium boilers >C10-C20	0.1	ng/cm²	*	2.5
High boilers >C20	0.1	ng/cm²	*	18.1
Sum >= C7	0.1	ng/cm²	*	23.7
Semiquantitated levels of the identified organic compounds				
Butoxy ethanol	0.1	ng/cm²	*	0.4
Phenol	0.1	ng/cm²	*	0.2
Ethylhexanol	0.1	ng/cm²	*	0.4
Phthalic anhydride	0.1	ng/cm²	*	0.6
Hexadecanenitrile	0.1	ng/cm²	*	*
Octadecanenitrile	0.1	ng/cm²	*	0.1
Dioctyl adipate	0.1	ng/cm²	*	0.8
Butyl benzyl phthalate	0.1	ng/cm²	*	**0.3**
Dioctyl phthalate	0.1	ng/cm²	*	**5**
Alkyl phthalates	0.1	ng/cm²	*	**3.7**
C8 hydrocarbons	0.1	ng/cm²	*	1.4
Alkyl benzoate	0.1	ng/cm²	*	*
Possible C23-C30 hydrocarbons	0.1	ng/cm²	*	9.3
Butoxyethene	0.1	ng/cm²	*	0.1
Ethyl hexanal	0.1	ng/cm²	*	0.2

Organics from Full Wafer by TD-GC-MS, SEMI MF 1982-1103 Method-B				
Parameter	RL	Units	CONTROL WAFER SHIPPING BLANK	WAFER ROBOT ARM
Low boilers C7-C10	0.1	ng/cm²	*	2.4
Medium boilers >C10-C20	0.1	ng/cm²	*	3.4
High boilers >C20	0.1	ng/cm²	*	17.6
Sum >= C7	0.1	ng/cm²	*	23.4
Semiquantitated levels of the identified organic compounds				
Butoxy ethanol	0.1	ng/cm²	*	0.2
Phenol	0.1	ng/cm²	*	0.1
Ethylhexanol	0.1	ng/cm²	*	0.3
Phthalic anhydride	0.1	ng/cm²	*	0.6
Hexadecanenitrile	0.1	ng/cm²	*	0.1
Octadecanenitrile	0.1	ng/cm²	*	0.2
Dioctyl adipate	0.1	ng/cm²	*	0.7
Butyl benzyl phthalate	0.1	ng/cm²	*	**1**
Dioctyl phthalate	0.1	ng/cm²	*	**2.8**
Alkyl phthalates	0.1	ng/cm²	*	**11.4**
C6-C9 Hydrocarbons	0.1	ng/cm²	*	1.2
C10-20 Hydrocarbons	0.1	ng/cm²	*	1.1
Unknown (m/z: 43,55,71,85,100)	0.1	ng/cm²	*	0.6
Benzoic acid	0.1	ng/cm²	*	0.1
Dibutyl phthalate	0.1	ng/cm²	*	*

28

Surface Organic Techniques

NVR (Non-Volatile Residue)

- NVR is a molecular and particulate residue remaining following the evaporation of a solvent used to extract Organic SMC
- Test methods include:
  - **ASTM E1235-12** "Standard Test Method for Gravimetric Determination of Nonvolatile Residue (NVR) in Environmentally Controlled Areas for Spacecraft"
  - **IDEMA M7-98** "Organic Contamination as Nonvolatile Residue (NVR)"
  - **FTIR** is often used to analyze the NVR
- NVR and FTIR results are essential to validate the cleanliness of the environment, equipment, process, packaging, and operator handling

MIL-STD-1246 NVR Cleanliness

Level	Limit, NVR $\mu g/cm^2$
A/100	0.01
A/50	0.02
A/20	0.05
A/10	0.1
A/5	0.2
A/2	0.5
A	1.0
B	2.0
C	3.0
D	4.0
E	5.0
F	7.0
G	10.0
H	15.0

29

Summary

30

Analytical Technique Selection – Questions to Ask

- What type of data information is required?
- This will dictate the appropriate analytical technique based on the analytical information it provides

Type of contaminant	→	Particle, metal, ionic, organic
Analysis information	→	Inorganic, organic, chemical state
Analysis method	→	Direct or indirect test methods
Concentration	→	Detection limit
	→	Localized or average value
Defect size	→	Spatial resolution
Depth of analysis	→	Surface, near-surface, in-depth
Accuracy	→	Qualitative or quantitative
Precision	→	Low or high precision
Sampling method	→	Bubbler/impinger, witness wafer, adsorption tube, UPW and chemical samplers, gas manifold

31

Analytical Technique Selection – Decision Tree

- One technique may be able to identify a defect and contamination
- But one technique is probably <u>not likely</u> to provide all the information necessary to determine the root source of the contamination

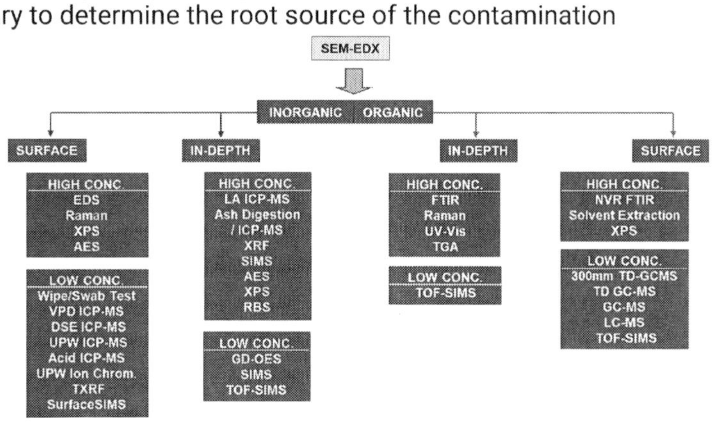

32

Thank you for your attention

Dr. Victor K.F. Chia
International Expert, Surface Contamination

+1 510-825-3701
victor.chia@airliquide.com

33

IDM Perspective of Advanced Nodes Materials, Defectivity And Analytical Metrology Challenges

Presenter
Dr. Archita Sengupta, Principal Engineer, Intel Corporation
Advanced Analytical Metrology & Defectivity Control Program Manager
Manufacturing Supply Chain Organization

Acknowledgement: My Esteemed Colleagues & Partners from Intel and Industry Supply Chain Ecosystem

Intel: Jagannathan Srinivasaraghavan, Kevin Garvin, Saskia Christian and Yossi Revah, Don E Hadder, Jeremie M Moberg, Aidan Hamill, John W O'Sullivan and Many more colleagues!

Industry: Mustafa Badaroglu, Robert McIntosh, Ashutosh Bhabhe, SECC-Critical Component Team Members, Mike Corbett, Ian Brown, Jim O' Neil, and Okechukwu Akpa
Additional Acknowledgement references are on slides

Thank YOU so much to Joel Barnett and SPCC for the invite and opportunity to present

intel

 archita.sengupta@intel.com

Agenda

- ❖Introduction: Perspective
- ❖Advanced Nodes' Process Maturity Vs. Continuing Materials & Defectivity Challenges

- ❖Addressing the Gaps: Reactive vs. Proactive
    - ❖ Holistic Quality Control
    - ❖ Thinking Out of the Box and Asking the Right Questions
    - ❖ Advanced Analytical Metrology Requirement

- ❖Need for Industry Collaboration
    - ❖ Joint Responsibility
    - ❖ Expectations from POR Suppliers

- ❖Optimistic reflection

Advanced Technology Nodes: Disruptive Technologies

Semi Industry is reorienting itself to "more" IOT, Cloud & AI

- ❖ **Goal: More powerful chips:** At scale manufacturing to deliver Process Performance Parity.
  - ❖ To make the transistor **smaller, faster, cheaper, and more energy efficient**
  - ❖ Need **Cost-Effective High Volume Manufacturing** ramp readiness including Supply Chain
- ❖ Future Process Technology will transform Si Process Technology
  - ❖ As we push the **Boundaries of Physics**
- ❖ Process and Packaging Technology innovation happening hand in hand
- ❖ **Product Drive: Performance, Power, Form Factor → Need Velocity, Time to Market, Affordability**

Disruptive Technologies for Advanced Nodes: Challenges in Defect Control

- ❖ **Nontraditional Scaling, 2D-3D mixed architectural changes**
- ❖ **2D Material FET: New Material challenges being added**
- ❖ **Increasing design innovation, integration challenges w/increased process steps, process sensitivity & complexity**
- ❖ **Increased defect sensitivity**
- ❖ **Shrinking feature size**
- ❖ **Challenge of HVM Drivers: Defectivity, Yields and Cost**

- ❖ **Complex Chemistry/Equipment/Process: Compatibility Issues**
  - ❖ **More Defects, New Defect Sources, increase Defect Sensitivity**
  - ❖ **Need unprecedented purity at process maturity**

- ❖ **Metrology techniques of all types are challenged:**
- ❖ **Pushing Fundamental limits of Physics & Sensitivity**
  - ❖ **Supplier Infrastructures still lacking defect detection & *characterization***

Critical Defect Trend

> - Fundamental change to the structure of the transistor translates into new defect mechanisms with major impact on the SOC design and manufacturing
>   - Critical dimensions are significantly smaller than the underlying node dimensions
>   - Complexity of layout and circuit-sensitive defects.
>   - Design variability makes yield a continuing challenge even as the process matures.

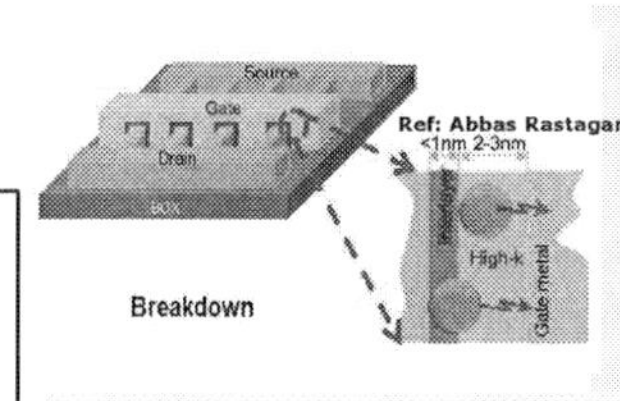

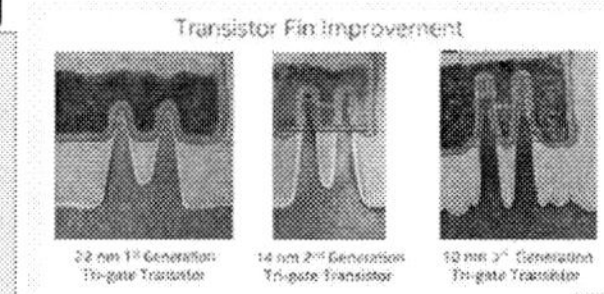

- **Special cleaning formulations, increase # of damage-free cleaning (High aspect ratio structures), precision of patterning and cleaning, unprecedented etch selectivity with atomic level of etch control, more CMP steps, Particle control in ALD, high K deposition/Cleaning challenge**
- **Role of <<5nm conductive particle** for complex topography of advanced 3D gate stack integrity and device reliability
- **Poor signal to noise ratio** (SNR) of localized information
- **HVM EUV towards High NA Readiness: Print even smaller features on Si**
- **Key Measurement and Metrology challenge: Detection and Measurement of <<10nm SEVD process adders and interfacial defects/films (multiple stacks)**

archita.sengupta@intel.com

Defect Control Vs. Process complexity

Defect control – driven by unit processes

- Deposition and etchant materials less likely to change but
  - Non-Cu metallization – Co, Ru
  - New di-electric systems for low-k spacer and self-deposition
  - Si-SiGe heterostructures for nanosheet formation
  - Zero-tolerance to defects in hybrid bonding
- Dimensions getting smaller and higher aspect ratios
  - Taller fins and gates
  - Vertical device
  - More need for conformal deposition and sidewall/bottom cleans
- More material systems and complex structures during deposition & etch
  - Complexity of local interconnect
  - Complex etch selectivity matrix
  - More surface interactions
  - Sidewall damage control
  - More critical loop processes as all cannot be done in-situ
- More reliance on self-alignment and self-deposition
  - Multi-material systems
  - Electrical isolation risks

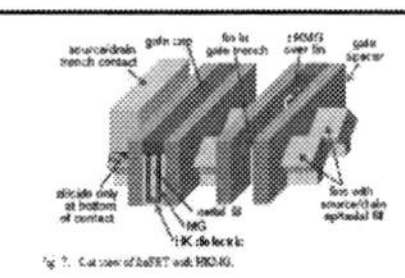

Source: Qualcomm@CICC 2018

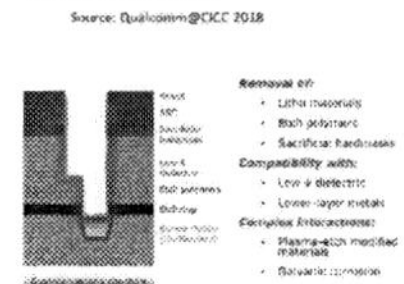

Source: Intel@ECS 2011

IEEE TFRC

Defect control – driven by process complexity

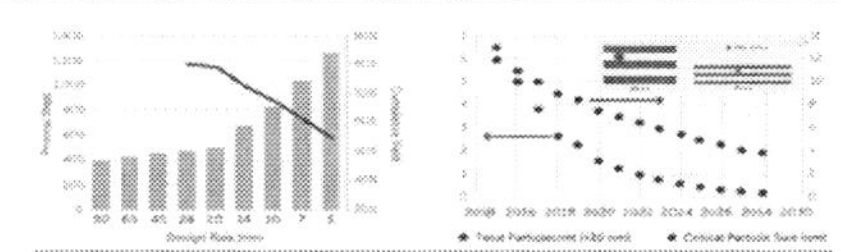

Source: Entegris @ Semiconductor Digest 2019

- Requiring more fault tolerant computing to bridge the gap of infrastructure (detection limits)
- Symbiosis of memory and logic is one potential path forward

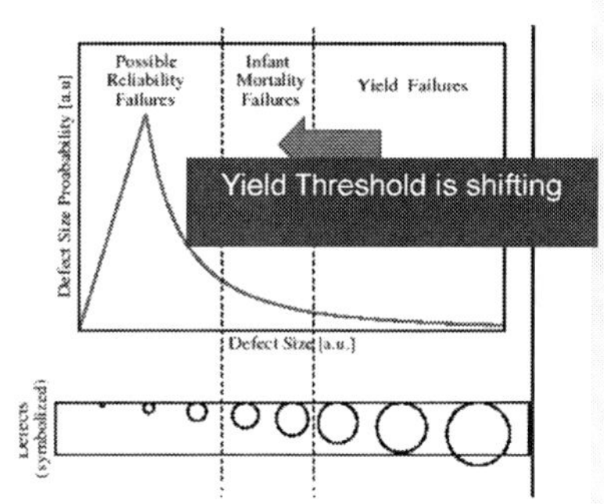

Ref: Mustafa Badaroglu, 2020 IEEE-IRDS Workshop

Need to Redefine "Wafer Environment" with respect to Defects Generations

- ❖New "**INTERACTIVE**" Defects: from complex chemical-component-process interactions
- ❖More possible defects and **"LOWER"** defect tolerance
- ❖Nanoparticles becoming more **"DETECTABLE**" with advanced SCANS at "End Users"
- ❖**"Purity"** is a relative term beyond meeting CofA requirement

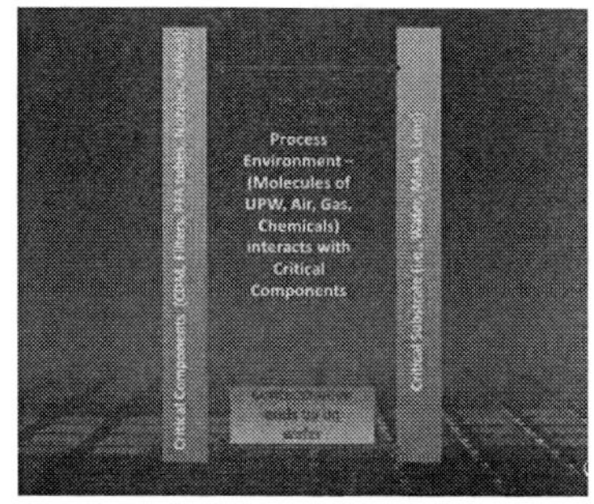

"Total" Wafer Environmental Contamination Control is a must

Wet Clean in Advanced Node HVM Manufacturing

TREND FOR CLEAN/WET-ETCH OPERATIONS

ECI TECHNOLOGY

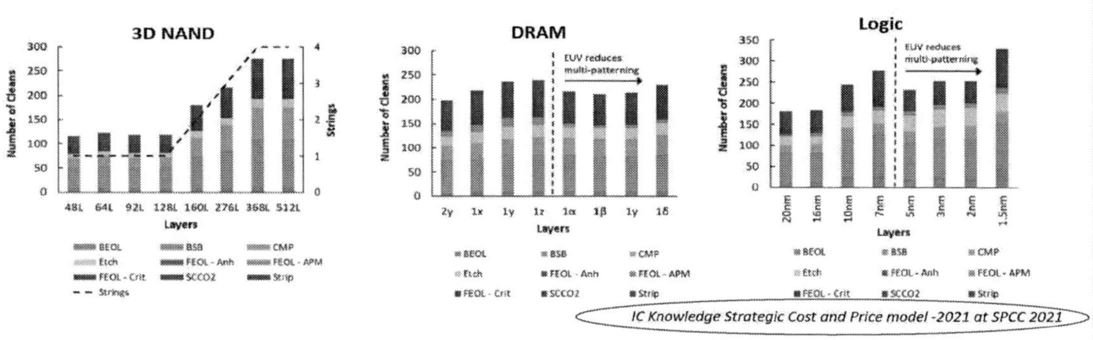

- › Business for formulated chemicals is growing due to new materials, architecture, tolerance of process, etc
- › Bulk/commodity chemicals still have significant shares in number of operations (>60%), yet started to show issues for advanced node/technology

SC1, HF, SPM, IPA, TMAH, NH_4OH

Ref: SPCC 2021, ECI CMC Presentation: JONG WOUNG (JASON) KIM et all

Wet Clean in Advanced Node HVM Manufacturing

TREND FOR CLEAN/WET-ETCH OPERATIONS

TECHNOLOGY

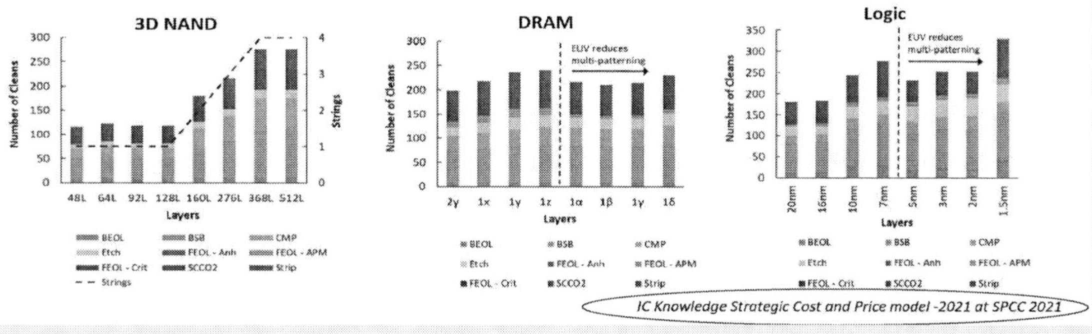

- ❖ **Increase in cleaning demand**
- ❖ **Number of materials it needs to interact with is increasing**
- ❖ **Additional Variables: Measurement, Methods and Human Error, Limitations of Tools**
- ❖ **Different areas of clean impose different challenges.**

Example: Transistor Scaling Cleaning Challenges

SCREEN

A Simplified Audit of Surfaces to be cleaned for different transistor architectures

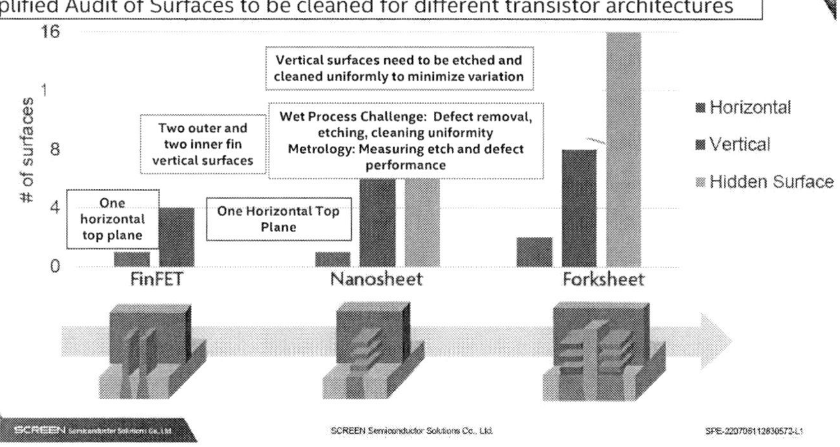

SCREEN Semiconductor Solutions Co., Ltd.

SCREEN Semiconductor Solutions Co., Ltd.

SPE-220708112830572-L1

Slide Acknowledgment: SEMI-West 2022: ian.brown@screen-spe.com

intel. 10

Next Generation Clean Expectation: Next Generation Thinking

- **Narrowing Dimensions:** Complex cleaning needs with fragile structures

- **Increasing Volume demand** with greater qualification sensitivity
- **Better Selectivity**
  - "Remove X, Y, Z without damaging A,B,C"

- **Enhanced Quality Control** : Nothing is inert: Reduce variability at all levels of supply chain
  - Excursion Control **beyond "CofA"**
  - No undesired by-product or residue
  - **Behavior of material reactivity @ High Volume Use (including Environmental Factors)**
  - Advanced Analytical Metrology & Characterization at **"ppq" level**

Some Ref: J. Srinivasaraghavan & A. Sengupta, SPCC 20218

Co$t of Excursions vs. long term Cost of Ownership

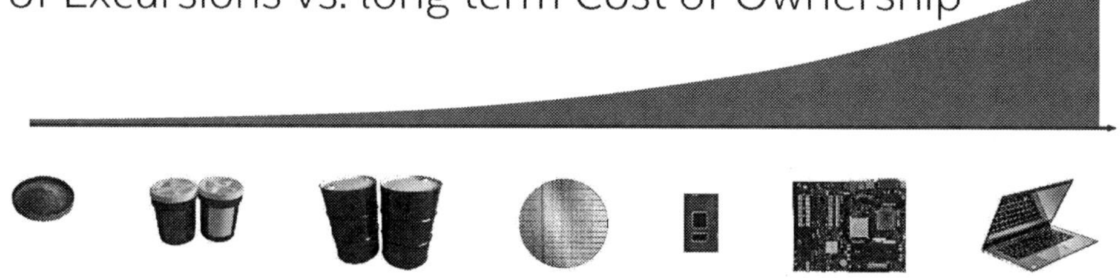

- **Excursions are expensive for everyone**
- **Contaminated raw material impacts finished goods' quality**
- **Factory uses material for several weeks before detection**
- **Earlier Detection → Lowers Impact to Finished Goods**

Small problems not prevented early **increase exponentially** in impact **as value is added** in the supply chain.

For End Users: One issue can have a very large financial impact

Process Yield: Cost vs Defectivity Control
Need to track lifetime of a chemical, gas, AMC, chemical and gas delivery system and tool parts

Defect Traceability & Data Connectivity to start Upstream Proactive Vs. Reactive Quality Control Approach

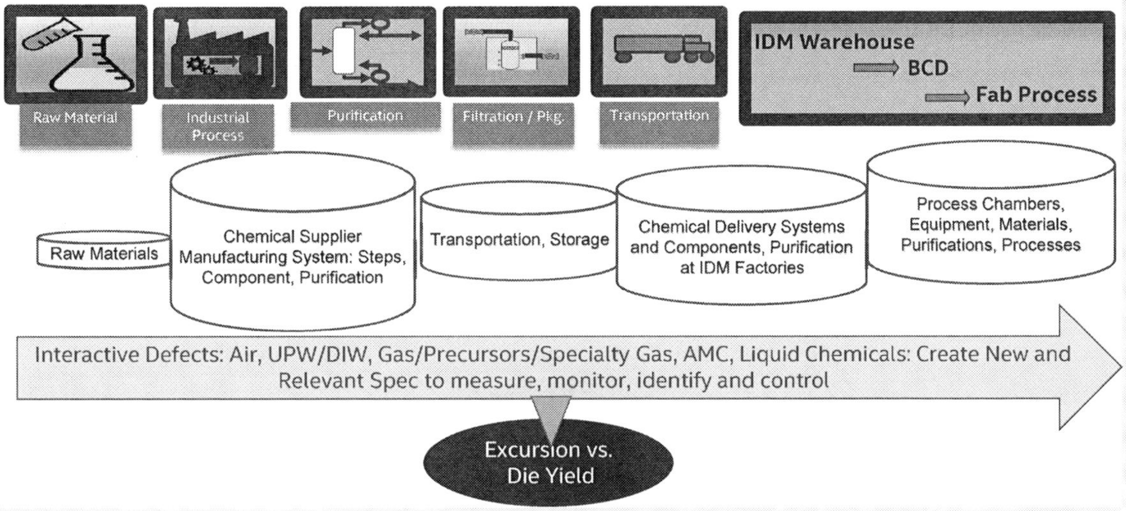

Key to Control Contamination & Maintain Process Stability

- **Each segment of supply chain ecosystem needs to do its due diligence**
- **Without capable and stable metrology, all decisions are flawed.**

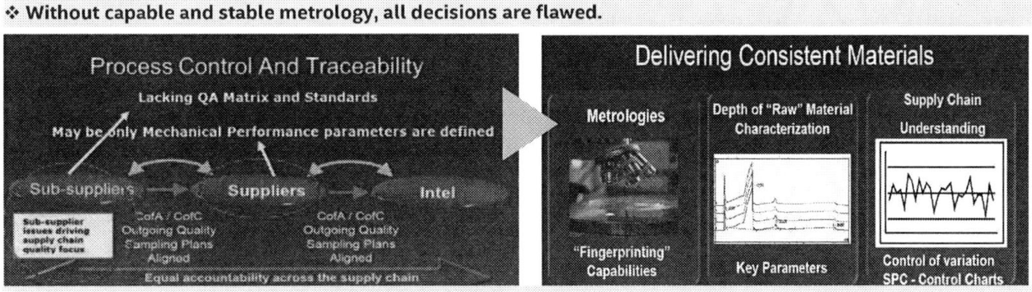

- **Map, Segment, Characterize the contamination sources: Correlate with wafer performance**
- **Redefine ""Relevant Quality Control Matrix" with help from Customer**
- **Redefine control limits for gas/chem/AMC/precursor/UPW/substrate surface**

Strategy at a very high level:
End to End Eco-System Quality Control

- **Think Smart** on where to look "now" and level of sensitive care needed to prevent "Excursion"
- **Every Critical manufacturing step at Suppliers' and at IDM** need:
  - "Measure, Monitor, Maintain and Control" : Enhanced materials and process characterization
- **Detecting, Understanding and Eliminating defect source across supply Line are major keys for HMV yield improvement and keeping cost/transistor down:**
  - Practical and economically viable way
  - Collaborative Advanced Materials/Process Learning
- **Process Control & Role of Critical Analytical Metrology in IC Industry is changing:**
  - Nature of R&D and Pathfinding Technology development
  - Close Collaborative Understanding of the metrology needs
  - Out of the Box thinking: Alternative from outside of IC industry?

Collaboration is the Key

Example of Specific Strategies
Collaboration is Key

- **Advanced Analytical Metrology: talk to Partners and End Users**
- **Blind Spot Monitoring:**
  - Right Parameters, Right Questions, Data Trace and Connect, FMEA
- **Process control:**
  - Minimize unpleasant/costly surprises,
  - Capture normal variability
  - Avoids uncontrolled exploration of 'unchartered' territory
- **Change control:**
  - Reduce/ Eliminate unexpected failure modes: $$$ Saving
  - Business Continuity planning @ qual: Risk Mitigation
- Data Traceability across supply chain is MUST

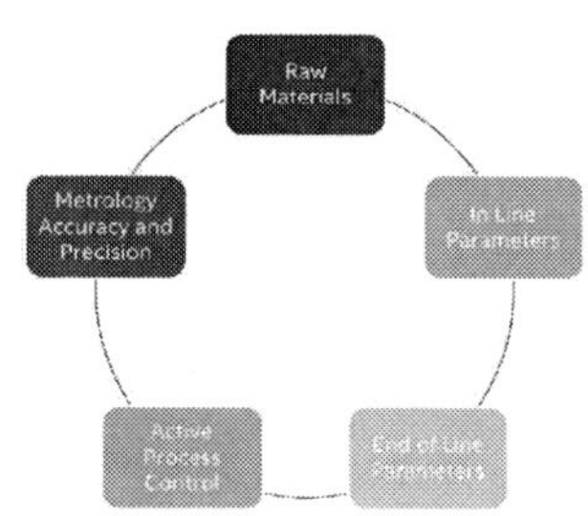

Communication and TRACEABILITY' are "KEY"

Looking Beyond CofA is must

Process Control: Raw Material example

END RESULT:
Product level Spec Violation

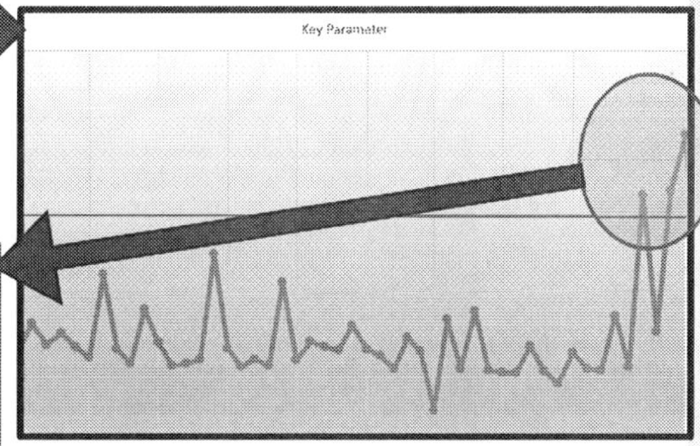

Root Cause:
Lack of statistical scrutiny on RM

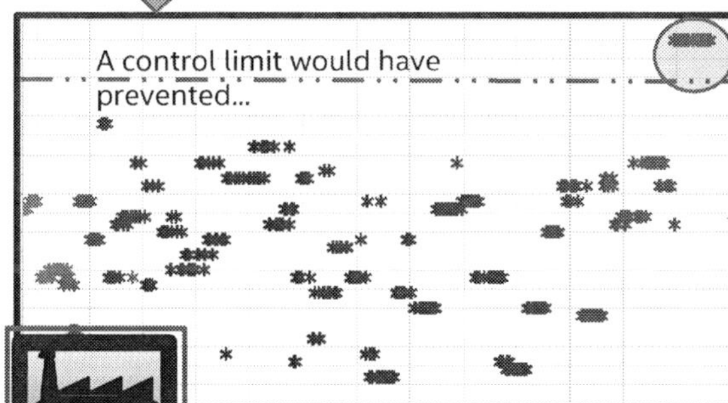

Control incoming raw materials with same criteria as outgoing finished goods
&
Respond to Outliers

Global Sourcing for Equipment & Materials

Reference: jagannathan@srinivasaraghavan@intel.com, J. Srinivasaraghavan and A. Sengupta, SPCC 2018

intel. 17

Process Control: Inline Metrics

END RESULT:
Inline Defect Issue at End-User

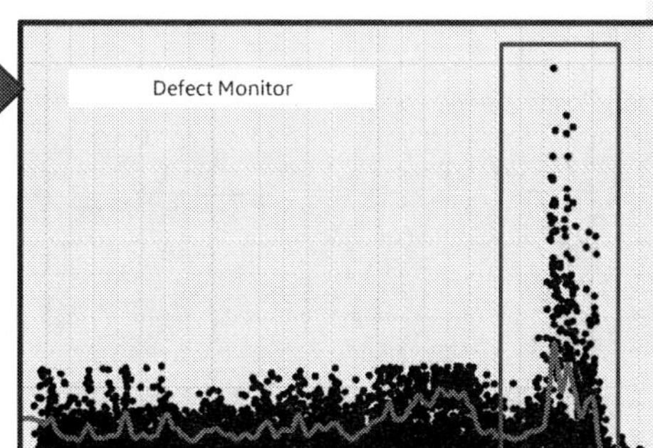

Root Cause:
Lack of statistical scrutiny in sub-supplier Process variables

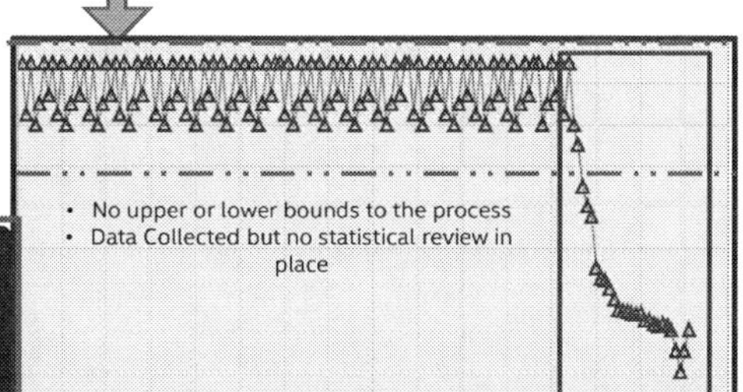

- Manage sub-supplier processes with the same 3 sigma criteria
- Respond to Outliers
- Process variables should be bounded on both sides

Global Sourcing for Equipment & Materials

Reference: jagannathan@srinivasaraghavan@intel.com, J. Srinivasaraghavan and A. Sengupta, SPCC 2018

intel. 18

Filtration Technology is Still Extremely Critical for Defect Scaling

- Customized Filtration is needed to meet "Next Generation Defect Tolerance": Across Supply Chain
- How to remove of <<5nm Metals/Particles/ Dissolved Organics/NVR from Chemicals?
- Ideally Filters should retain and not react!

- Filtration "Beyond" just Pore Size Rating across the pH range and in different solvents of formulations

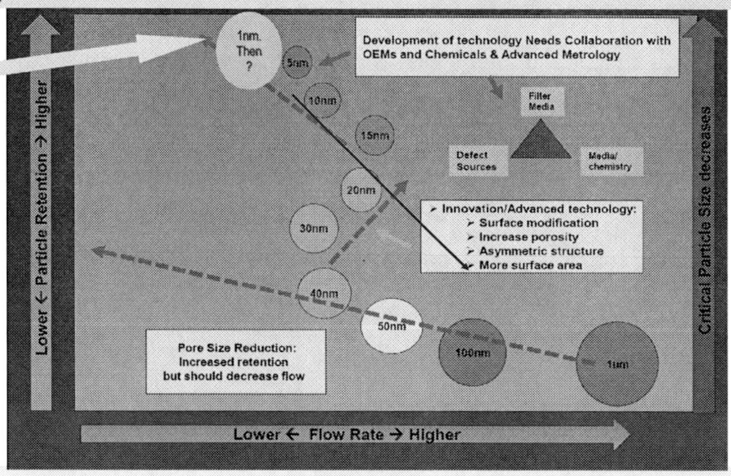

Which Wafer Defects Impact Yield?

- **Environmental and Process Contamination related**
  - **Particles** — Need Control <<10nm and low concentration impact
  - **Metals/Ions** — Need Critical Control in ppq level? Different problem densities (atoms/sq cm) on wafer: Process impact varies
  - **Organics**
  - **NVR** — Need ppq level of control? Need better definitions and detections of DISSOLVED Organics/Particle precursors: Creating thin films and impact on wafer

How are we Monitoring the sources across supply line? → How can we correlate % contribution of such contamination with defects on wafer from various parts of supply chain

- Defects in starting materials
- Printable defects during lithography process
- Process-induced patterning and device defects

Contamination Control in Advanced Node HVM Manufacturing

- ❖ **G**reater qualification sensitivity: Effect of Environmental, Airborne, Chemical, Gas, Ultra-High Purity Components
- ❖ **Enhanced Quality Control** : Nothing is inert: Reduce variability at all levels of supply chain
  - ❖ Excursion Control **beyond "CofA"**
  - ❖ Behavior of surfactant, **dissolved organics**, components reactivity @ High Volume use
  - ❖ **Environmental Factors:** Leaching, Change due to Chemical Reactivity or AMC becoming SMC
  - ❖ **Advanced Analytical Metrology & Characterization at ppq level**

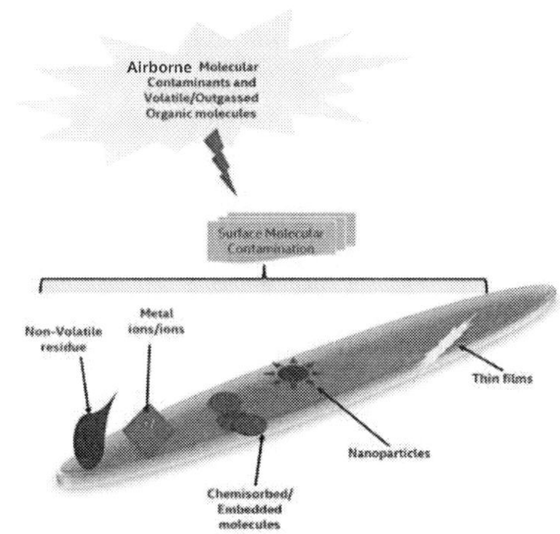

Example: Metrology Challenges: Chemicals, Gasses & Precursors

Material	Major Challenge	Gap in Metrology for Control	Gap in Metrology for Characterization
Wet chemistry, specialty chemistry, Solvents, Litho chemistry	• Bulk/Batch beyond CofA Defect Control: Residues (Trace Metals/organics/Particles), Nanoparticles • Interaction w/critical components, CDM/packaging • Raw Materials quality control	• Main component assay is insufficient for custom blend chemistry • Raw material "Purity & Specs/Grades" Clear definitions • <10nm/dissolved defect detection with high S/N Ratio: Trace metals: sub ppt-ppq detectability in high matrix background • Anionic impurities: sub ppb detectability in highly corrosive matrices	• Organics Detection and Filtration: Interactive Defects • Behavior of surfactant vs. filtration • High resolution, enhanced detectability @ppq level and SPECIATION • Water quality management at suppliers
CMP	• MPS trending <<100nm • Redefine Scratching /Killer particles critical size • Slurries w- Surfactants and new abrasive types • Complex interactions: chemicals/consumables: Filter+ Nanoparticle/Surfactant	• Traditional CofA parameters not sufficient to predict performance • Performance-based monitors required • Normal impurity profile variation of common Industrial-grade additives no longer acceptable: Raw materials batch variation • Non-FIFO raw material management required	• Further Improved analytical metrology to characterize abrasive colloids and nanoparticles behavior (<=20nm sized particle in hetero-dispersed PSD)
Post CMP clean	• Definition of harmful particles: Surfactant vs. Non-Surfactant based.	• Redefine Industry standards • Trace Metals are not necessarily BAD! • Resin byproducts/TOC instead of NVR	• Micelles require a larger size be used to control to prevent counting micelles as harmful particles
UPW	• Reactive vs. non-reactive Silica; Sources/Capture • Silica particles: M+ carrier	• Silica (colloidal silica/silica particles) formation and Sieving filtration: understand colloidal silica behavior.	• Metrology to capture <=10nm size Silica particles: Detect Colloidal Silica (sub ppt) and filtration

Example of Defects

- ❖ **"Common" Chemicals are now "Problematic" due to Stringent Defectivity Baseline requirement**
- ❖ **SEMI Specifications need to have elements added or removed as needed**
- ❖ **Amines/Resin Byproducts/Critical Organics/Surfactants Effects: New methods for measurement/specifications**
- ❖ **Challenge: More non-traditional non-CofA -- sub-10nm adders @ low concentration**
- ❖ **Defects can have affinity toward certain materials/layers**

Examples of Defects in Lithography

➢ Gel Defects:

➢ Metal contamination in photoresist, solvent or filters + cross-linking acrylate polymer molecules → (Upstream/filter plugging or Downstream gel defects on wafer)

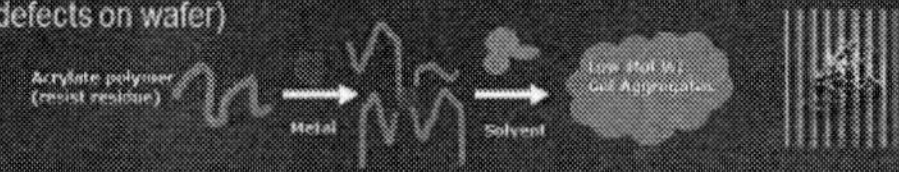

➢ Ppt level of M+ can cause issue: Larger defects through a smaller pore filter: why and How?

– Need "Pore Size Validation"? Quantum Dots? Au Nanoparticles?

Example: Importance of Chemical Purity in WET chemistry

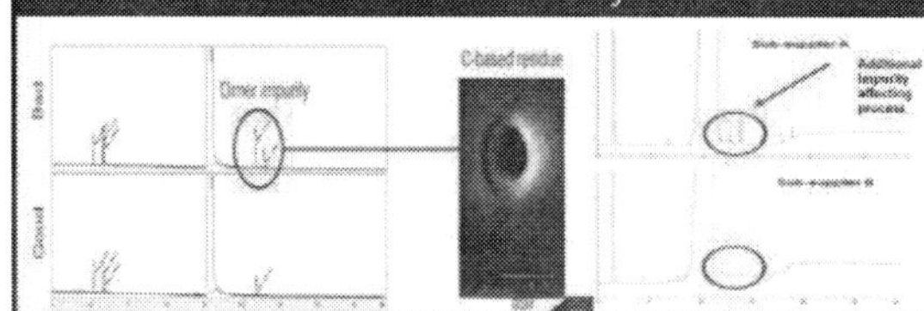

➢ Chemical suppliers need direct process control of raw materials or custom purification: I

➢ Organic impurity detection becoming more critical to defect control

➢ Need "Fingerprint" through Spectroscopic and Chemical methods of higher sensitivity

Interactive Defects caused by Critical Components (Chemical Pass)

- ❖ As chemical travels within any dispense system, different types of contamination is added (leaching and/or reaction with components)
- ❖ PFA/PFDF/SS Critical Components may contain trapped metallic particles (from resins, extrusion process) → May lead to "Metal Leaching"
- ❖ Next Generation SEMI Defect Road map must address the Organics Leaching and Definition of Critical organics

Revision of SEMI C90-1015 standard is happening: Limiting Metals in High Purity Polymeric materials (tube, valves, fittings, resin) used in the semiconductor industry for liquid chemical distribution

Over time:

- Metal Leaching
- Deposition of particles/organics (from hydrodynamic boundary layer)
- Dislodgement of particles

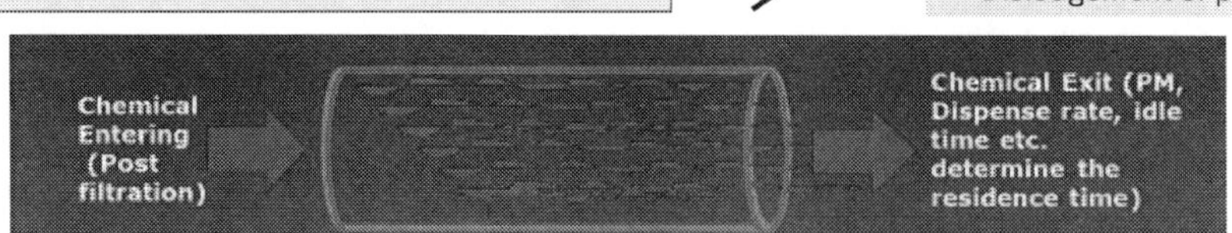

Advanced Metrology: Collaboration is The Key

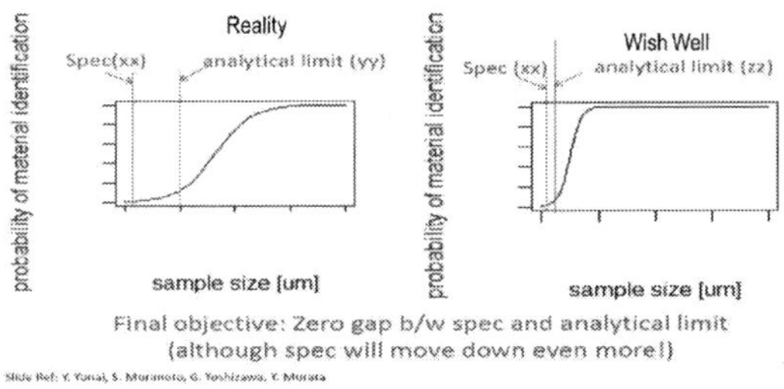

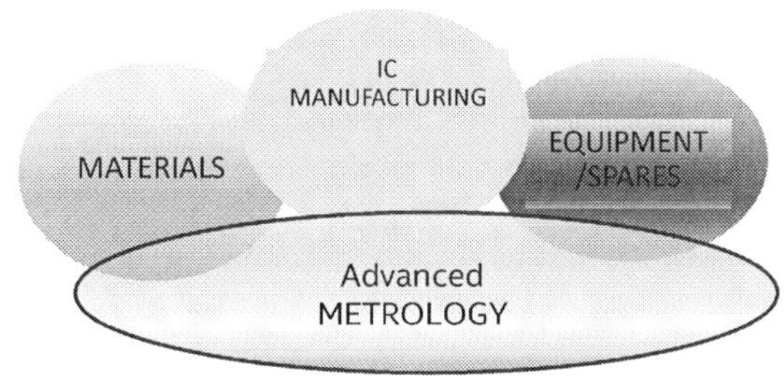

- ❖Partnering with new/ advanced metrology techniques and make it High Volume Ready is imperative
- ❖Continuous improvement in detection limits and characterization need COLLABORATION
- ❖Standard CofA / Spec compliance is 'Necessary' but 'not Sufficient anymore': Must look Beyond

Metrology Challenges
Defect Size Vs. Defect counts Vs. Defect Type

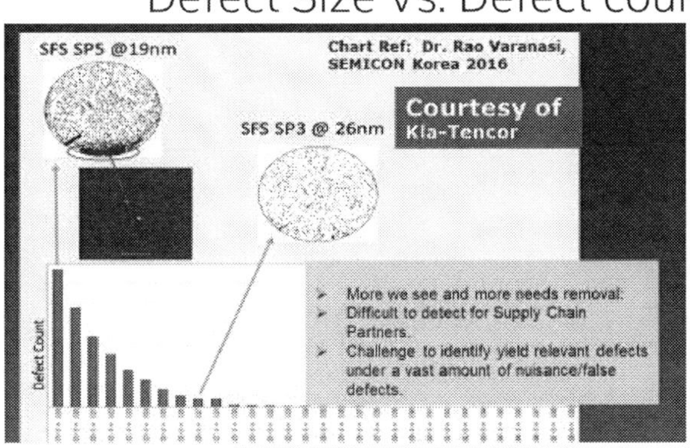

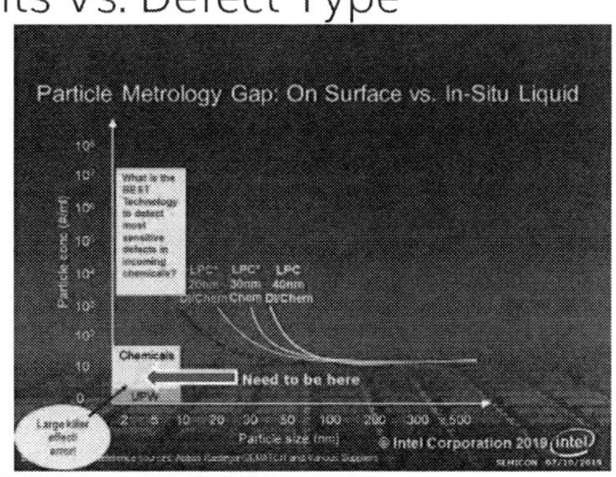

*"Absence of evidence is **not** evidence of absence!"*-- Martin Rees, Astrophysicist

❖ Advanced On Wafer Metrologies are "Not" available across Supply Chain
❖ Reliability, sensitivity, TPT on <10nm Defect Detection for HVM – Still Questionable
- Collaborative "Hybrid Metrology Approach" - IDM + Supply Chain Partners to Work together

Critical Organics from High Purity Critical Component Leaching

- CC and Liquid chem SECC_IRDS_IEEE Team working together
- Fingerprinting PFA and PVDF extracts/residues Via ATR-IR Analysis, Vacuum desorption ATR-IR, SERS, LNS

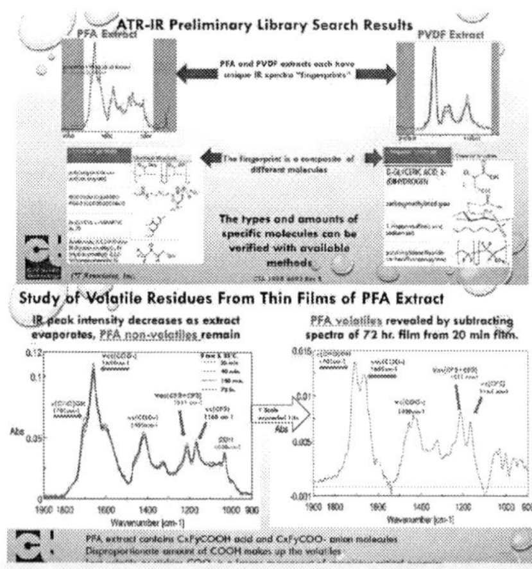

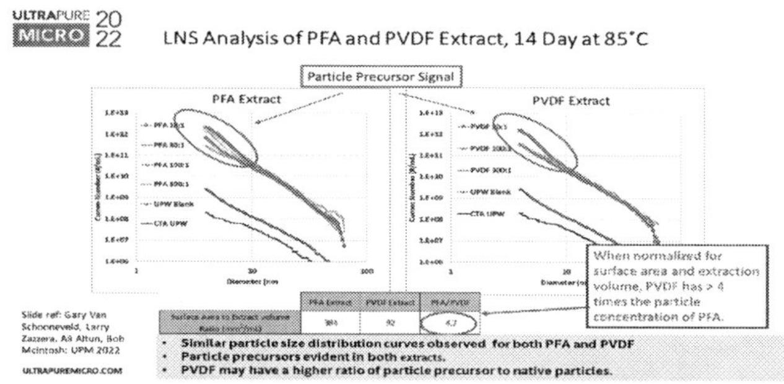

Key Take Away: Multiple Mode of different types of technology needed to understand the contamination

Slide Acknowledgement: @CTAssociates Larry Zazzera and Gary Van Schooneveld, Bob Mcintosh and SECC_IRDS_IEEE CC Team

27

Defect Analysis and Characterization Need Vs. Gap

- ❖Analytical Fingerprinting needed beyond CofA: Higher Resolution Needed
- ❖Reliable Hybrid Metrology Approach with better sensitivity, detection limits and chemical ID
- ❖Combined Quantified Nano-mechanical measurement

Analytical Methods	Availability
Physical Structure	SEM, e-SEM, TEM, AFM, XRD
Chemical/Elemental Composition (solids and Surfaces)	• Raman • FTIR (Qualitative) • Auger, EDS (Elemental) • **SIMS, TOF_SIMS, XPS (Quantitative, Chemical ID)** • EELS, TXRF, XRF • **FCS (Novel)**
Chemical/elemental (Solids, Liquids, Gases)	GCMS, TD_GCMS, ICPMS, VPD-ICPMS, IC, LCMS Auto-filtration, CRDS, FTIR, FCS

In-situ/Inline
- **Particle counters (OPC, CPC)**
- **In-Line ICP-MS**
- **In-line TOC**

Offline
- **ICP-MS, SP ICP-MS**
- **Organics Speciation: GC-MS, LC-MS, GC_FID**
- **Assay (spectroscopic vs. Titrations)**

On-wafer Measurements

Are these enough for <<10nm End to End Supply Chain Defect Characterization?

End Reflections

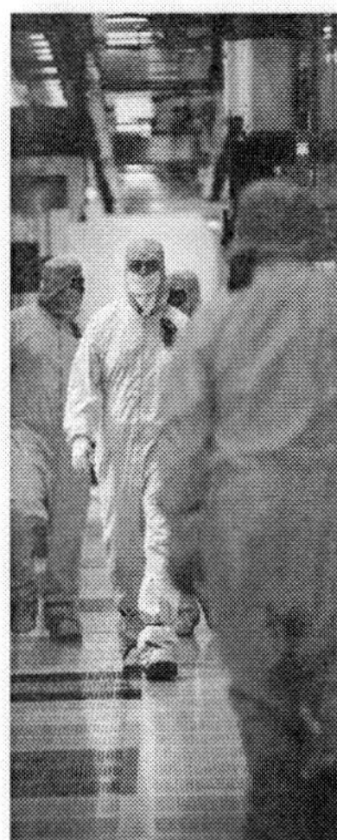

- ❖ Advanced nodes: Paradigm shift in process scaling
- ❖ More waves of unique complications
- ❖ Defectivity challenges vs. high volume yield
  - ❖ **Now "Purity is a relative term"!**
- ❖ Interdisciplinary expertise must work together on Quality and Defect Control

- ❖ Call for actions: To the Supply Chain Eco-System:
  - ❖ Be the Partner of Choice
  - ❖ Invest proactively, reduce total Cost of Ownership and have faster design wins
  - ❖ Secure Business continuity
- ❖ Industry Awareness and Deep Dive in Collaborative Advance Metrology

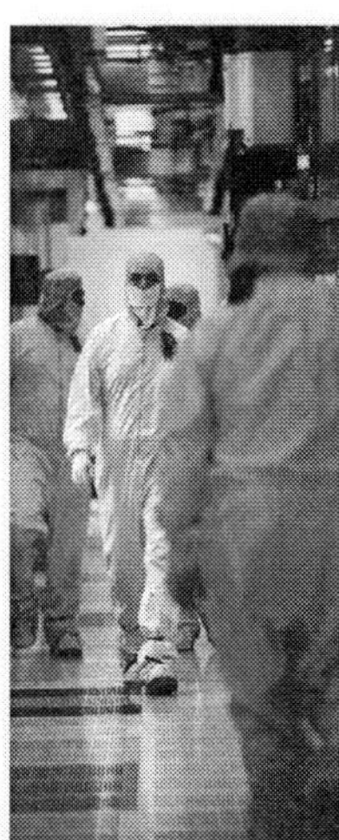

Call for Advanced Metrology Team

- ❖ Last Thought: Must address:
- ❖ Complexity of new CLEAN chemical manufacturing and potential catastrophic Impact
- ❖ Measure Unknown with Advanced Metrology: Look Beyond CofA
- ❖ Conflict of continuous improvement Vs. don't change anything
- ❖ Continuous improvement must be implemented in a very controlled manner

- ❖ Advanced Metrology Suppliers need to be PROACTIVE ECOSYSTEM Partners!
- ❖ Deeper Metrology Discussion in large conference platform is a MUST now!

THANK YOU

Global Sourcing for Equipment & Materials @Intel 2022 archita.sengupta@intel.com intel. 31

Statements in this document that refer to future plans or expectations are forward-looking statements. These statements are based on current expectations and involve many risks and uncertainties that could cause actual results to differ materially from those expressed or implied in such statements. For more information on the factors that could cause actual results to differ materially, see our most recent earnings release and SEC filings at www.intc.com. Any forecasts of goods and services needed for Intel's operations are provided for discussion purposes only. Intel will have no liability to make any purchase in connection with forecasts published in this document.

intel.

Global Sourcing for Equipment & Materials @Intel 2022 intel. 32

SCREEN leti ceatech

life.augmented

Nanolift Particles Removal Process – Polymer film Structure study and Film queuing Influence on Removal

Thomas Mercadier[1,2], Philippe Garnier[1], Raluca Tiron[2], Virginie Loup[2], Song Zhang[3], Shuichi Yasuda[3], Takayoshi Tanaka[3], Ayumi Higuchi[3], Akihisa Iwasaki[3], [4]Naser Belmiloud

[1]STMicroelectronics, Crolles, France
[2]CEA-LETI, MINATEC, Grenoble, France
[3]SCREEN Semiconductor Solutions Co, Ikone, Japan
[4]SCREEN , Ismaning, Germany

Thomas.mercadier@st.com

Outline

- Introduction
- Nanolift process
- Film queuing influence
- Film structure study
- Conclusion

life.augmented

2

Introduction

Wet cleaning facing growing number of constraints

Holes / Trenches cleaning

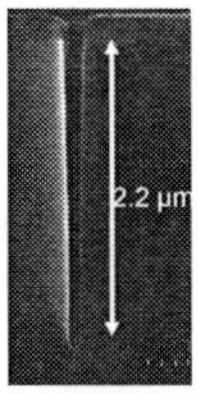

Droplet too large for cleaning

>1µm particles

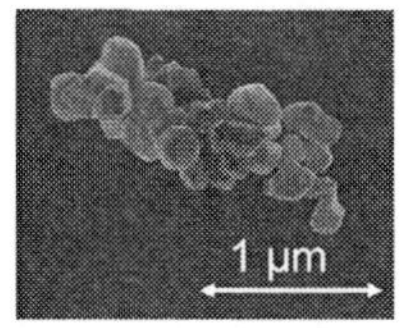

Spray Cleaning example

Nozzle + chemistry

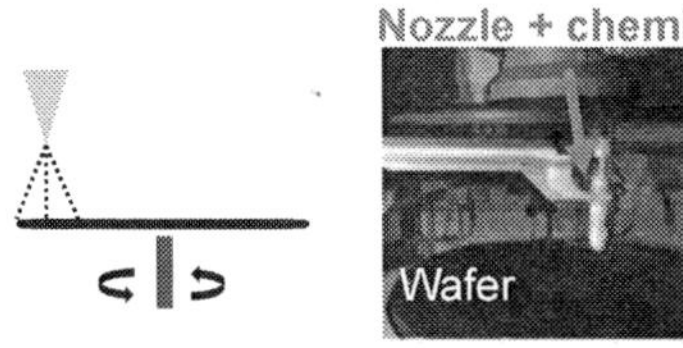

Fragile features

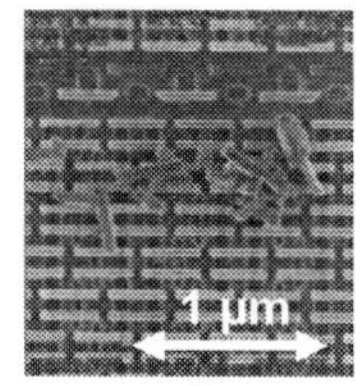

Droplet can damage such surface

➔ Disruptive innovation required as Nanolift process

life.augmented

3

Introduction

➔ Nanolift process = lift off process

Solid Polymer film deposition = 2 resins

Polymer Lift off = particles removal

➔ Promising perspectives

Low material consumption + Compatible with fragile features

Efficiency in Structures

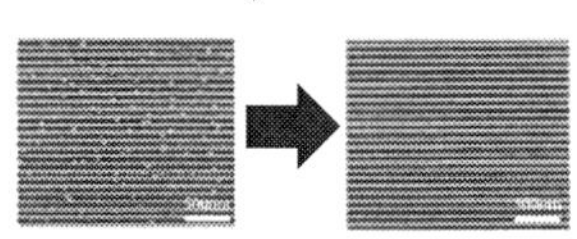

Efficiency on all particles

- Expectation from <20nm to >1µm

Challenges :

- Spatial organization of the Polymer film = Key for process understanding

life.augmented

4

- *Scalable Particle Removal for sub 5-nm Nodes – Yukifumi Yoshida – Solid State Phenomena – V 314 – 2021*
- *Removal of Post Etch Residue on BEOL Low-k with nanolift, Yuka Akanishi -Solid State Phenomena, V 314, 2021*

Outline

- Introduction
- **Nanolift Process**
- Film queuing influence
- Film structure study
- Conclusion

life.augmented

Nanolift Protocol

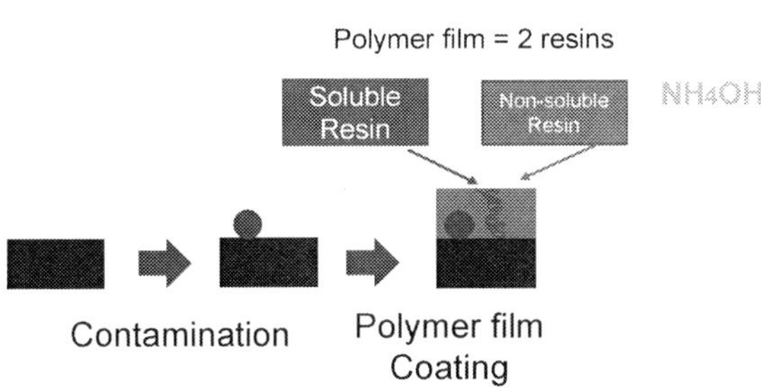

Protocol from Screen	CEA Protocol
One tool used for whole process	Two tools for whole process = Polymer queuing

One tool used for whole process

Single wafer SU3100 from SCREEN

Two tools for whole process = Polymer queuing

- One for coating
- One for peeling

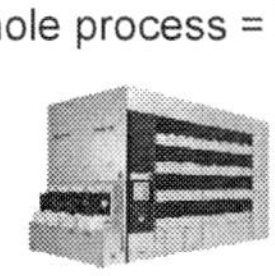

+

Sokudo DUO — Single wafer SU3100

- **Nanolift = Coating + peeling**
- **Two tools used for process = need to validate it**

life.augmented

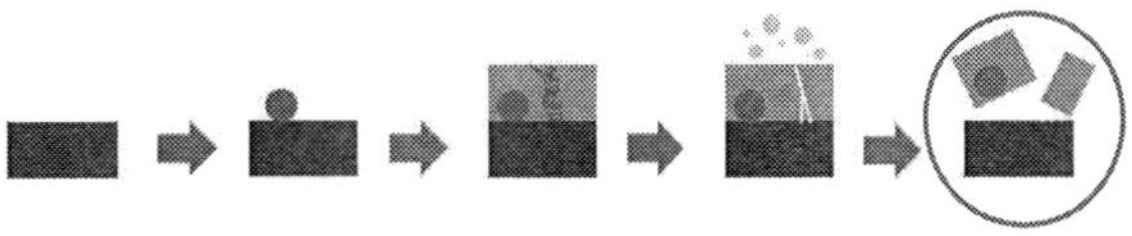

Evaluation on Silicon

Surface	Contamination	Picture	Removal Efficiency (%)
Si (HF-SC1)	Deposited 60nm SiO_2 particles (4 month old)	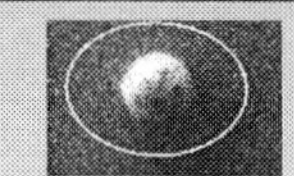 0.1 µm	99

- Protocol validated on Silicon - good efficiency
- Nanolift efficient on Si_3N_4 and SIO_2 particles

7

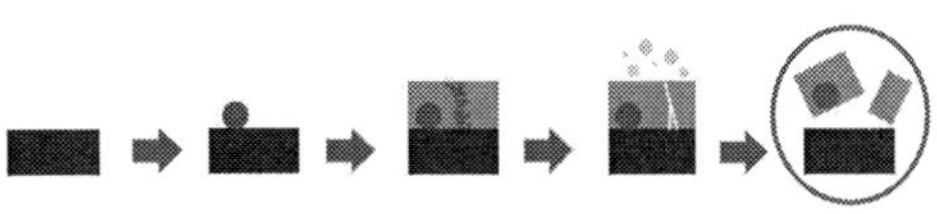

Evaluation on fragile structure

Gates after spacer

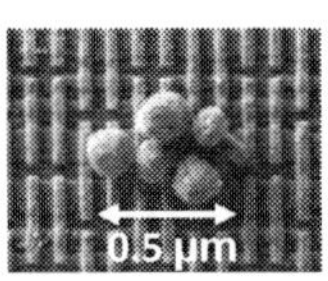

Metallic particles agglomerate

	Strong Clean Single Wafer 80s SPM 120° + SC1 + NS	Nanolift Leti
Pre	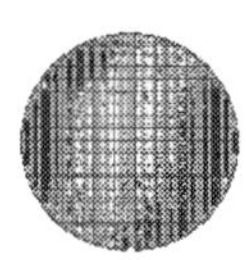 94k	 76k

- **Good efficiency on Industrial Wafers**
- **Strong chemical clean = less efficient**
- **Validate our process**

8

Outline

- Introduction
- Nanolift process
- Film queuing influence
- Film structure study
- Conclusion

Film queuing impact

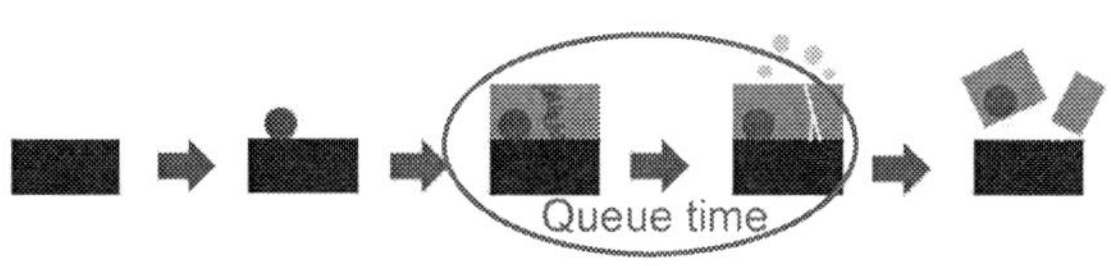

Queuing consequence on Peeling

- Removal recipe : NH_4OH 1/68 – 60s
- Hydrophilic Si (HF-SC1)

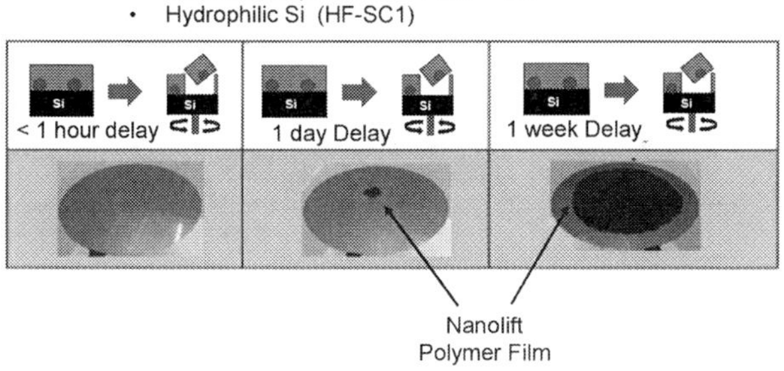

Film thickness evolution with queuing

Ellipsometry

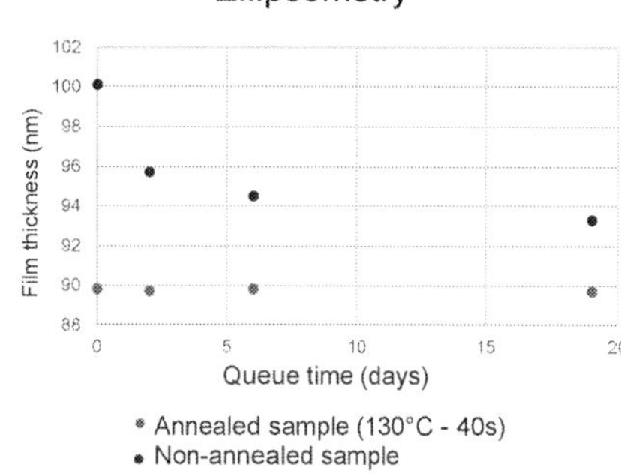

Outline

- Introduction
- Nanolift process
- Film queuing influence
- Film structure study
- Conclusion

life.augmented

11

Film structure study

Results
- Nanolift = good effiency on various cases
- No impact of Film queuing if < few hours

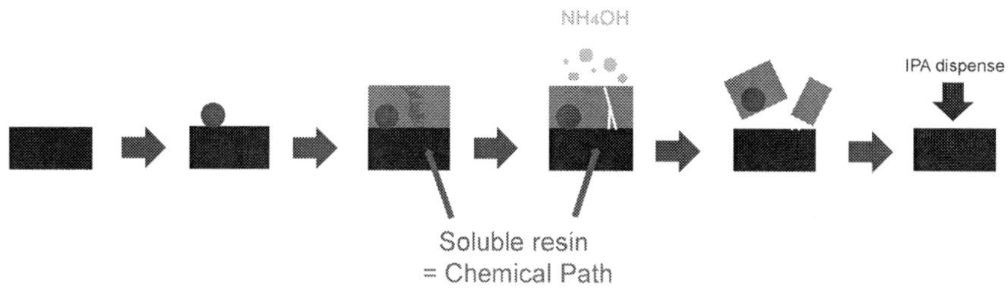

Questions remaining :
- Two resins organisation in Polymer film ?
- Size of chemical paths ?

life.augmented

12

Film structure study

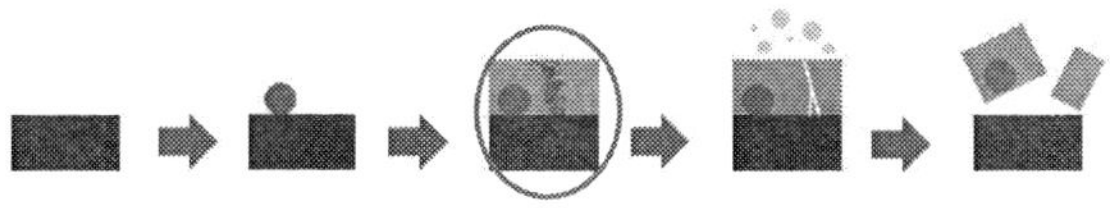

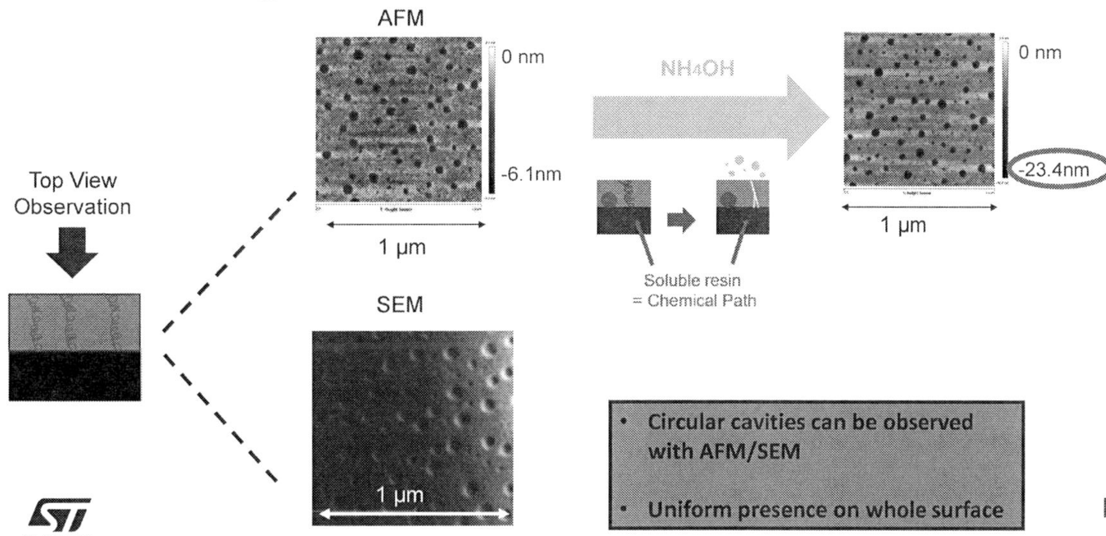

- Circular cavities can be observed with AFM/SEM
- Uniform presence on whole surface

13

Circular cavities study

Soluble resin ratio	SEM observation x10k	AFM scan
Reference 		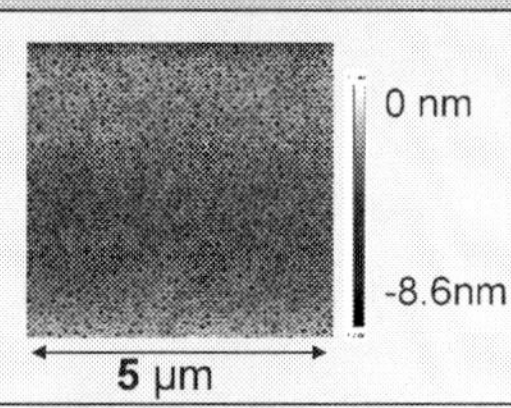
> to reference 		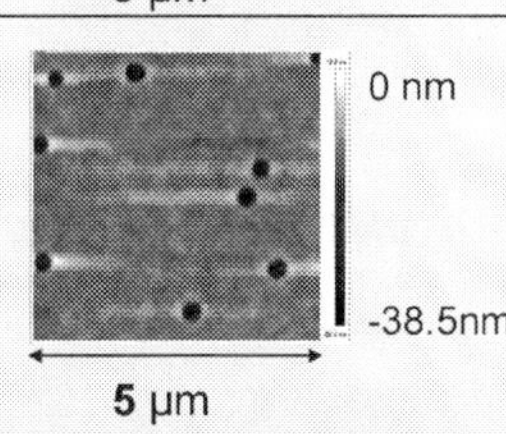

Circular cavities = Presence of soluble resin

14

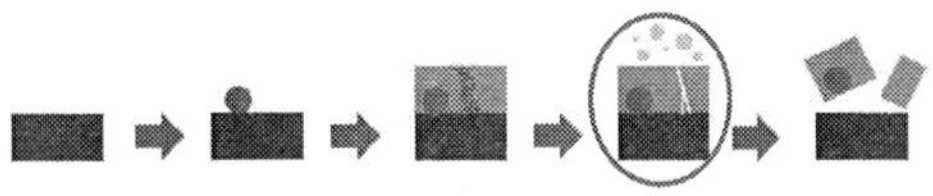

Film Volume organization

Idea = thinning Polymer film

- Chemical attack (DIO3 etch Polymer)

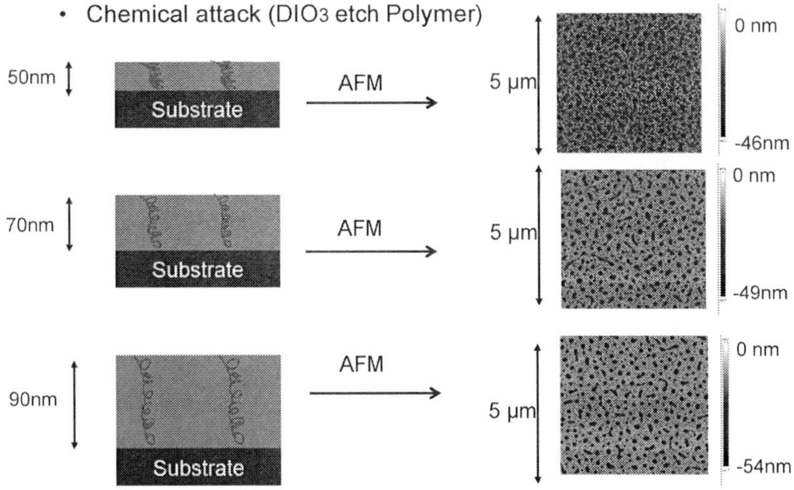

Homogeneous % cavities results on the different film thickness

➔ validate columns organization of soluble polymer

15

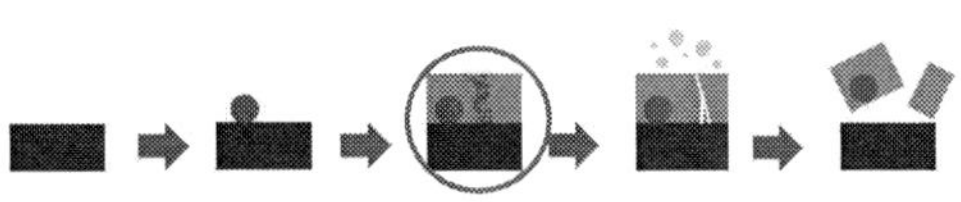

Polymer film Structure : Recap

Resins domains visible at Surface ? ✓

Organized in columns ? ✓

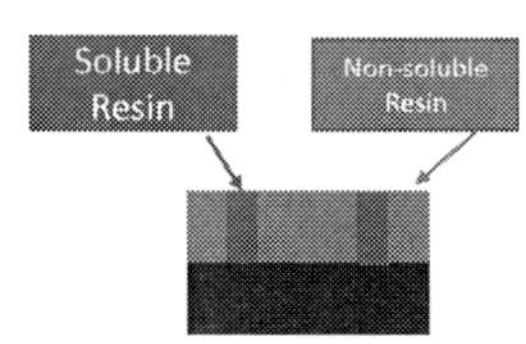

Does this organization depend of the substrate ?

16

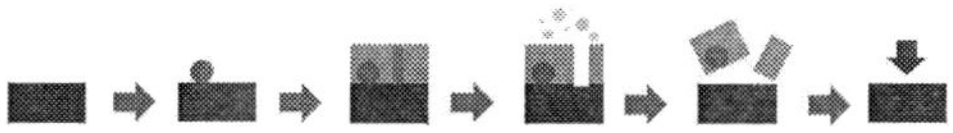

Substrate dependency ?

Substrate	Reference Nanolift Polymer film	Soluble resin ratio superior to reference
	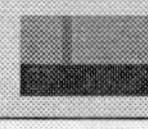	
Silicon HF-SC1	5 µm  0 nm / -6.9nm	5 µm 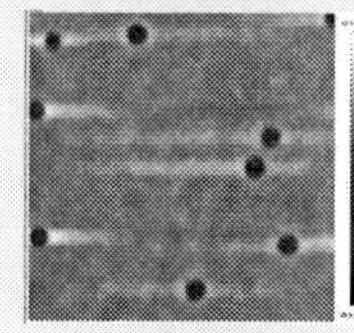 0 nm / -38.5nm
Silicon HF last	5 µm 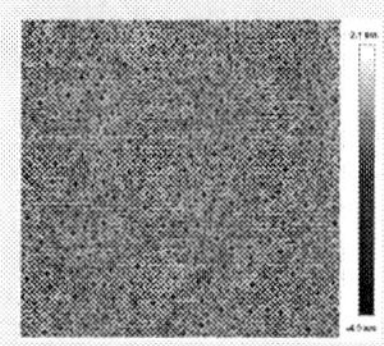 0.0nm / -7.0nm	5 µm 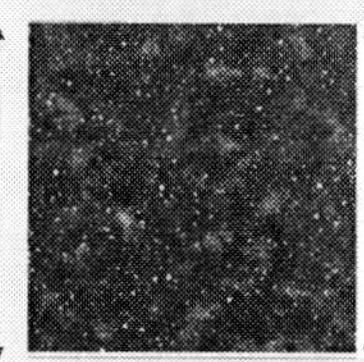 0.0nm / -5.9nm

- Substrate impact film structure when high soluble resin ratio
- May impact reference substrate/film interface

ST life.augmented

17

Outline

- Introduction
- Nanolift process
- Film queuing influence
- Film structure study
- Conclusion

ST life.augmented

18

Summary

1. Nanolift protocol

- → Good PRE on flat Silicon and industrial cases
- Promising results compared to classic technics
- Polymer film queuing = limited influence if <1 hour

Surface	Picture	Removal Efficiency (%)
Si	 0.1 µm 60nm SiO_2 particles	99
Si	 0.1 µm 40-200nm Si_3N_4 particles	90

2. Polymer film spatial organisation :

- Separated areas between two resins
- Columns organization of soluble resin
- Chemical paths dimensions obtained

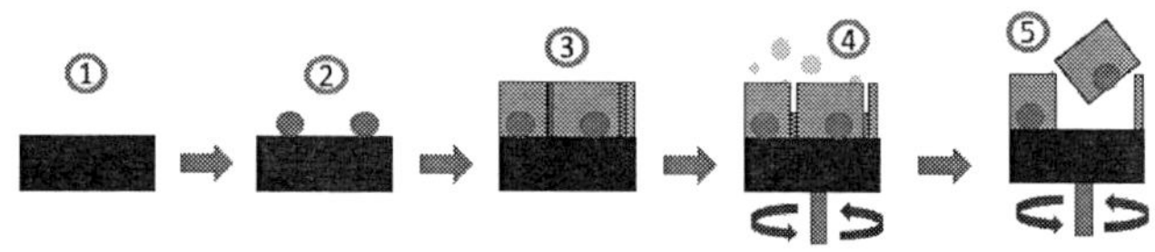

3. Perpectives:

- Substrate dependency of PRE – Film organization ?
- Soluble Resin influence on PRE

life.augmented

19

Thank you

life.augmented

THE SURFACE PREPARATION AND CLEANING CONFERENCE (SPCC)

SPCC 2022 | October 17-18, 2022

EMPL Hanyang University

BASF The Chemical Company

Ti ion contamination and removal mechanism during the W CMP process

Palwasha Jalalzai[1], Ranjith Punathil Meethal[1], Sumit Kumar[1], Tae-Gon Kim[2], Wonseob Cho[3], Andreas Klipp[4], Jin-Goo Park[1*]

[1] Department of Materials Science and Chemical Engineering, Hanyang University, Ansan, Republic of Korea

[2] Department of Smart Convergence Engineering, Hanyang University ERICA, Ansan 15588, Korea,

[3] Electronic Material R&D Center Asia, BASF, Suwon, 16419, Republic of Korea

[4] BASF SE, Ludwigshafen, 67056, Germany

*jgpark@hanyang.ac.kr

The Engine of Korea

Contents

1. Introduction and Motivation

Technology Road Map

❖ Adv. NAND Material Roadmap

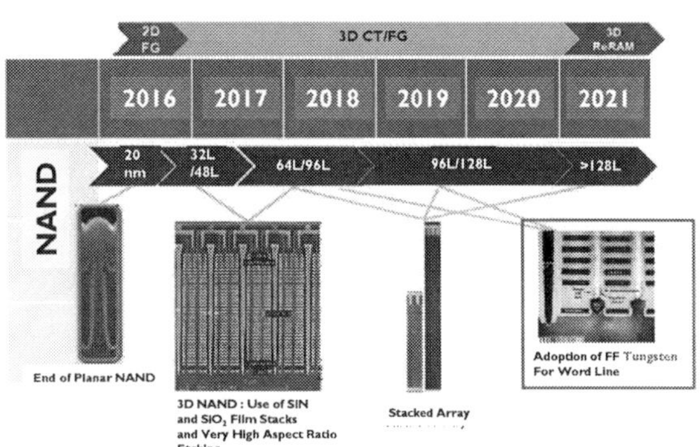

➢ **NAND** : W is used as buried metal line (**$WF_6 \rightarrow W$**)

❖ Adv. DRAM Material Roadmap

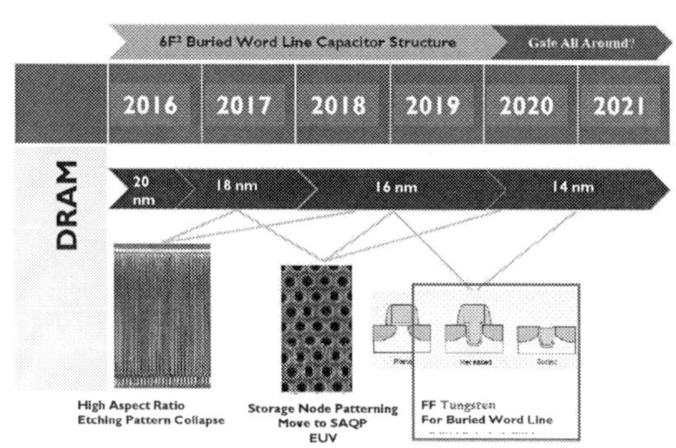

➢ **DRAM** : W is used as buried metal line (**$WF_6 \rightarrow W$**)

Overview of post-CMP cleaning process

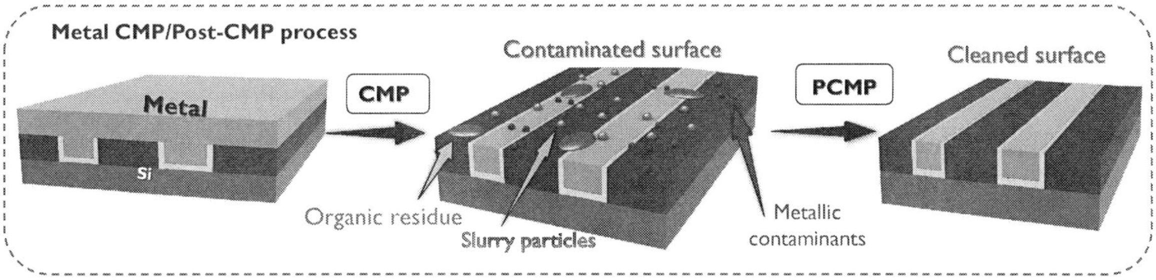

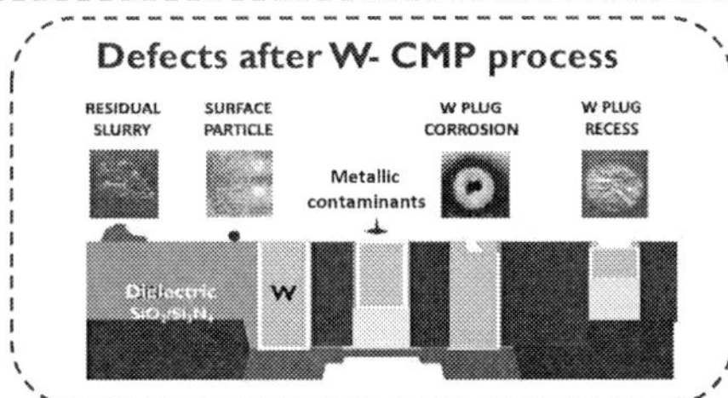

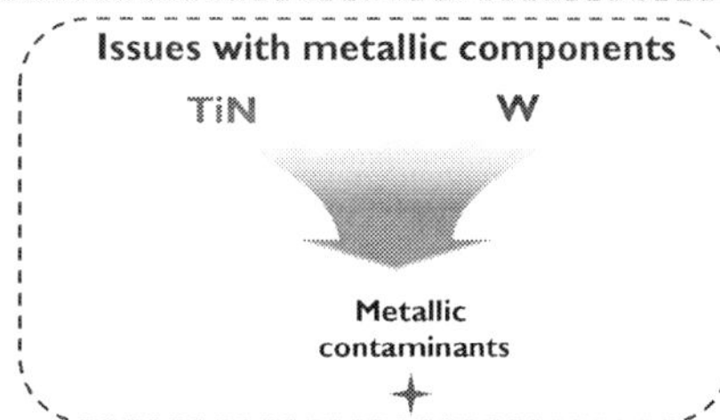

Challenges with common chemistries during W Post-CMP cleaning

DHF cleaning

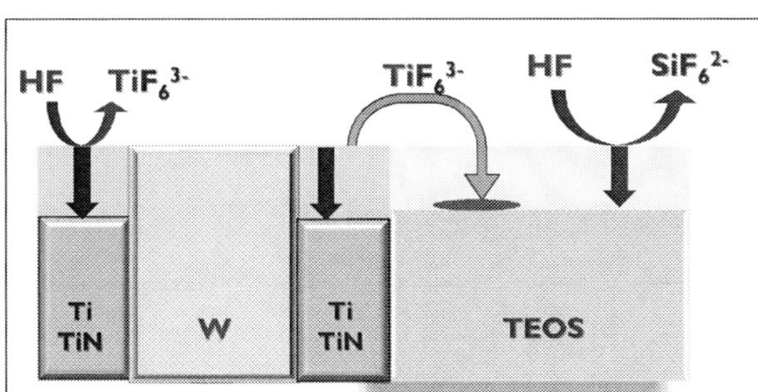

- High etching of Ti and TEOS cause structure damage
- Titanium fluoride recontamination on TEOS causes device failure

Ammonia cleaning

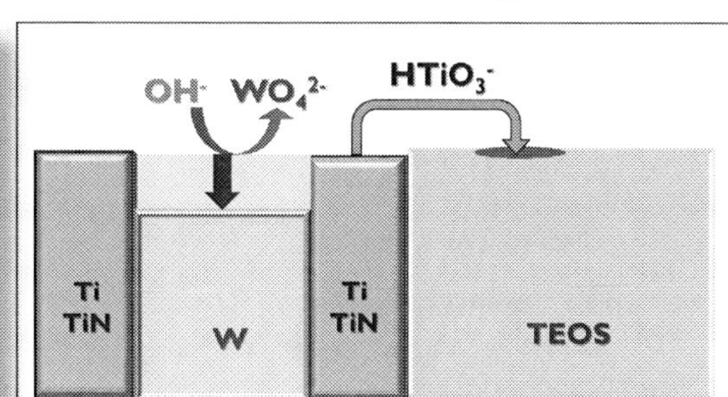

- Severe corrosion of W at alkaline condition
- Low solubility of metal ions results in metal precipitation on oxide surfaces

Major challenges in advanced devices

Contact resistance from W oxidation

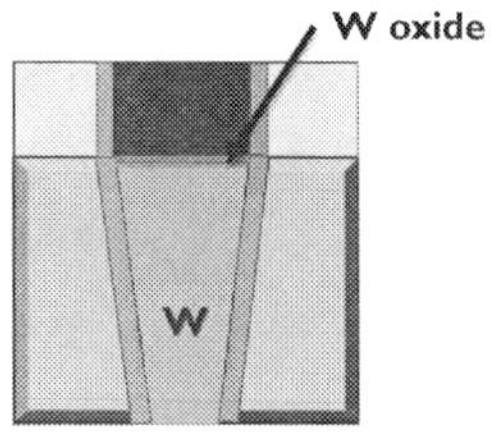

- High contact resistance results poor electrical contact

W voids due to corrosion

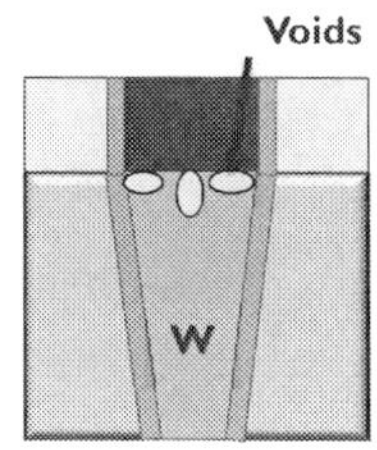

- Poor contact between W plug and metal lines due to voids

Contact shorting or leakage

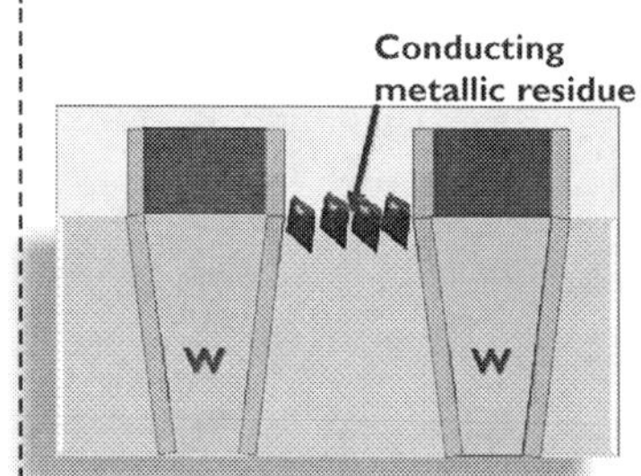

- Failure of devices due to metal contamination

- **Requires formulated chemistries to eliminate the contaminants and to reduce defects**

Objectives

Ti ion contamination and removal

1. **Ti ion interaction with oxide surfaces**
2. **Effect of chelating agents on Ti ions removal**
3. **Particle loading on PVA brushes in presence of Ti ions**

II. Experimental Materials and Procedure

Materials and methods

Materials

Wafer: TEOS

Metal ions: Ti ICP soln

Chelating agent : Citric acid, EDTA, Chem A, Chem B

Equipment

Brush scrubber

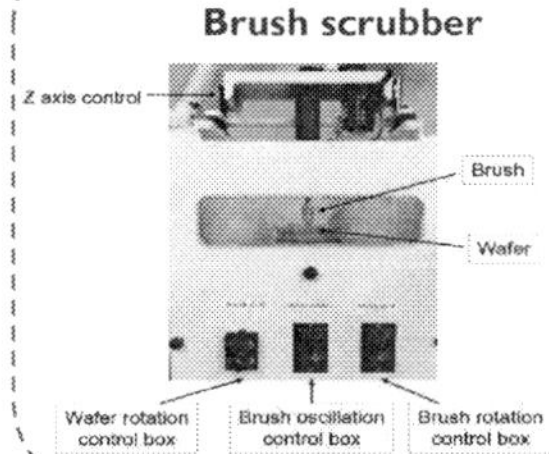

ICP-AES

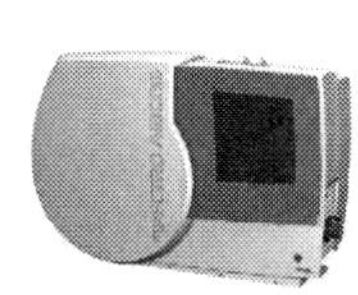

FE-SEM

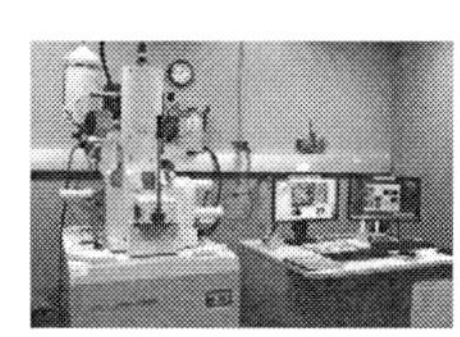

Experimental Conditions	
Brush rpm	60
Wafer rpm	140
Slurry/cleaning solution Flow rate (ml/min)	150
Cleaning time	1 min
Brush gap distance	0mm, -1mm

Effect of chelating agents on Ti ion removal from TEOS: Scrubbing

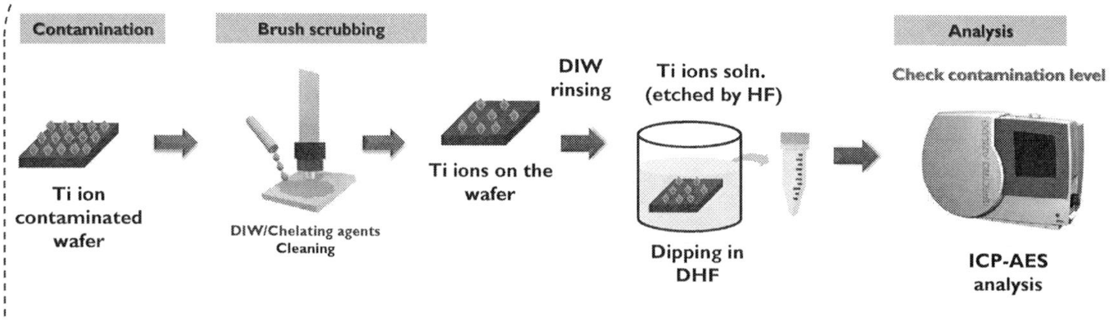

$$Cleaning\ Efficiency\,(\%) = \frac{\text{Initial contamination} - \text{Final contamination}}{\text{Initial contamination}} \times 100$$

Initial Contamination

Ti ions: ~9.6 ppm = 100%

Particle contamination in presence of cleaning additives: By dipping

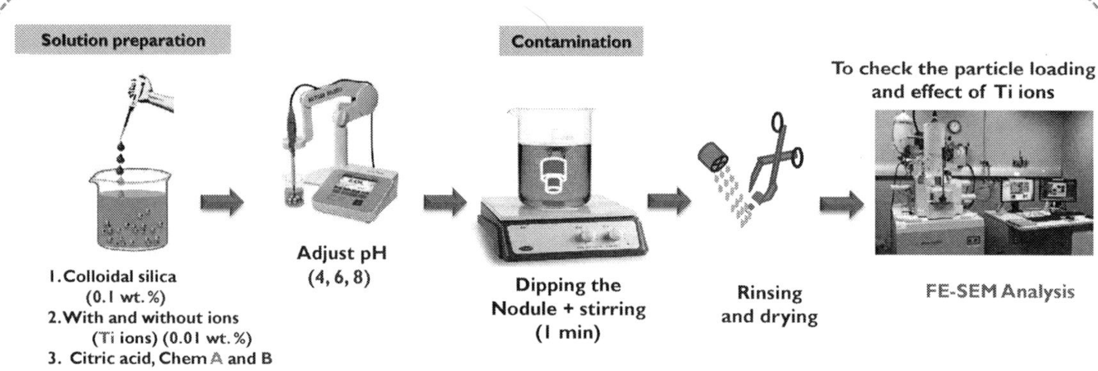

Brush Material - PVA
Brush Type – Commercial

III. Results & Discussion

HANYANG UNIVERSITY

13

Ti ion removal by brush scrubbing

ELECTRONIC MATERIALS AND PROCESSING LABORATORY

14

HANYANG UNIVERSITY

Removal of Ti ions from TEOS : Brush scrubbing

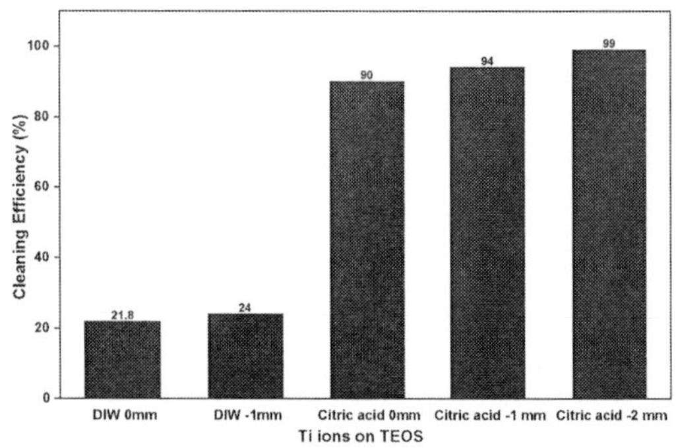

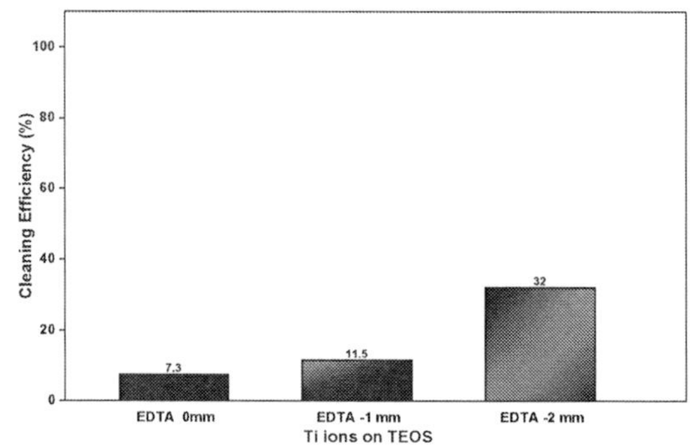

- Citric acid showed excellent cleaning efficiency for the removal of Ti ions
  - EDTA showed poor cleaning efficiency for the removal of Ti ions

Removal of Ti ions from TEOS with commercial chemicals

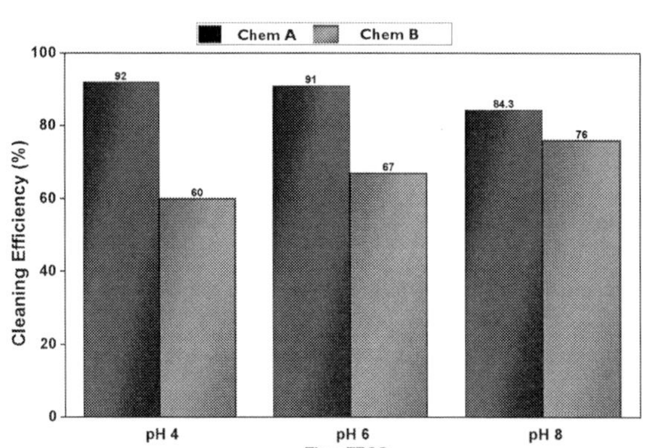

- Chem A showed significant cleaning efficiency for the removal of Ti ions at pH 4 and 6

Mechanism for Ti ion interaction with chelating agents

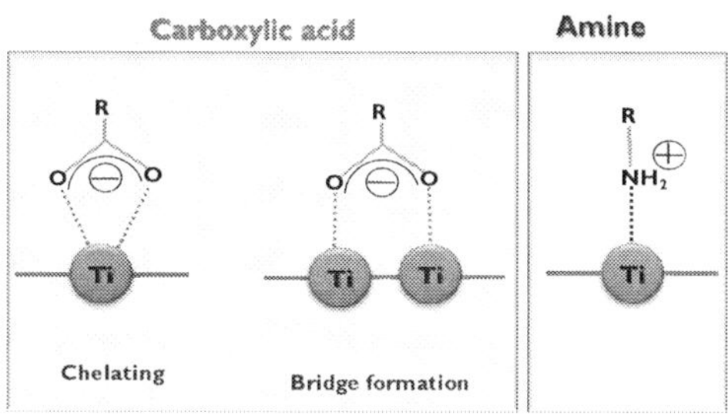

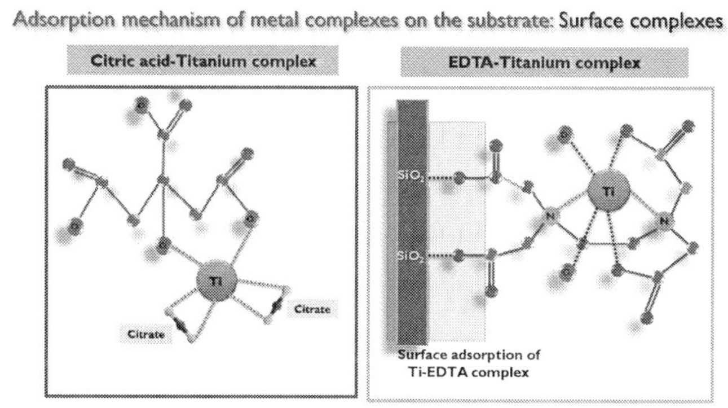

Citric acid complex

↑ **Solution solubility**

↓ **Surface adsorption**

EDTA complex

↓ **Solution solubility**

↑ **Surface adsorption**

Mudunkotuwa IA, Grassian VH. *Citric acid adsorption on TiO2 nanoparticles in aqueous suspensions at acidic and circumneutral pH.* Journal of the American Chemical Society. 2010 Oct 27;132(42):14986-94.(https://doi.org/10.1021/ja106091q)
Nakayama N, Hayashi T. *Preparation of TiO2 nanoparticles surface-modified by both carboxylic acid and amine: Dispersibility and stabilization in organic solvents* Colloids and Surfaces A: Physicochemical and Engineering Aspects. 2008 Mar 20;317(1-3):543-50. (https://doi.org/10.1016/j.colsurfa.2007.11.036)

Effect of Ti ion on brush loading

Effect of Ti ions on the brush loading with particle at different pH

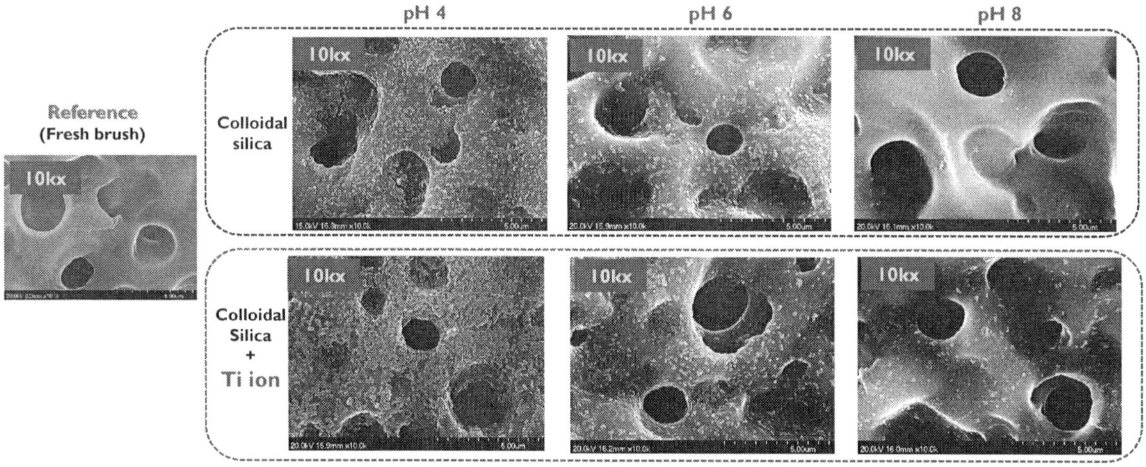

- Very high particle loading at pH 4 and 6: with and without Ti ions
- High particle loading at pH 8 with Ti ions

Effect of chelating agents on the brush loading at different pH

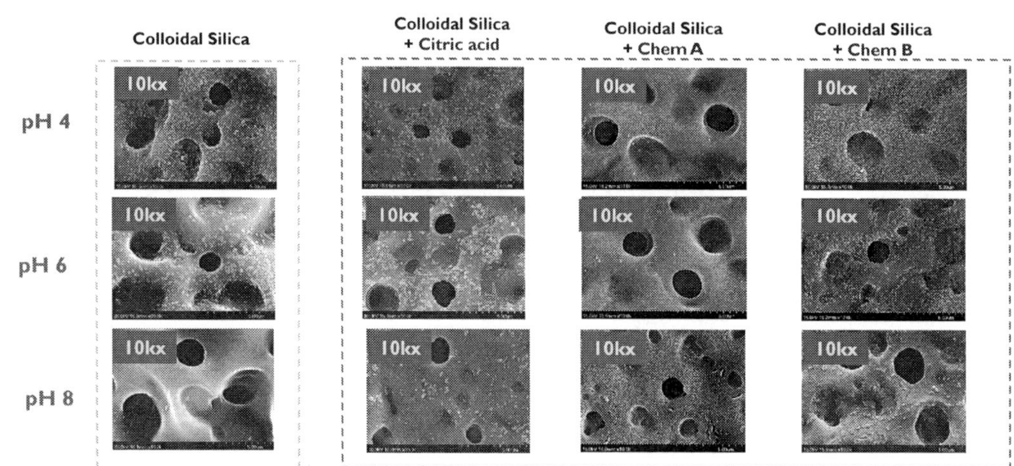

- Citric acid and Chem B showed highest particle loading
- Chem A showed lowest particle contamination on brushes at acidic pH conditions

Effect of chelating agents on the brush loading with Ti ions at different pH

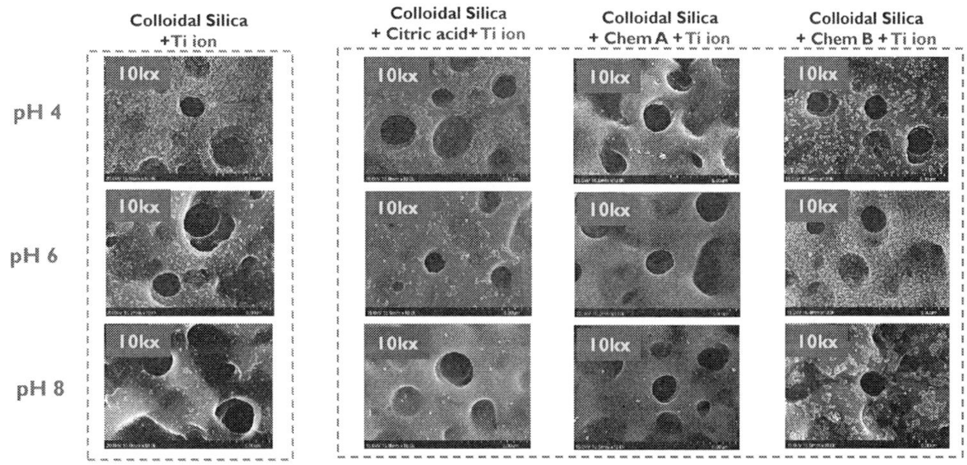

- **Citric acid did not show significant difference on contamination at any pH condition**
- **Chem A showed lowest particle contamination on brushes**

Evaluation of particle coverage on brush at different pH conditions

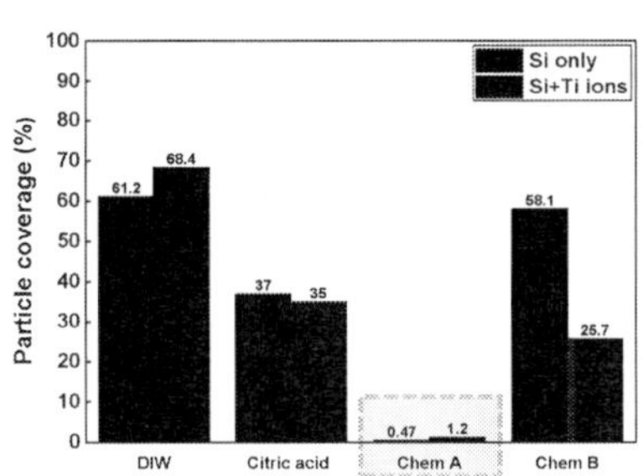

pH 4

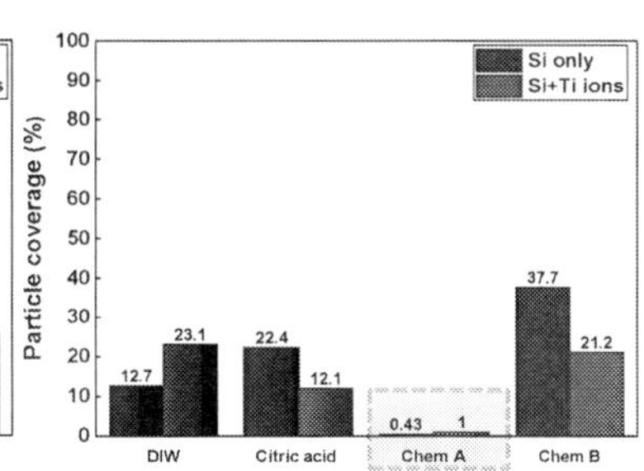

pH 6

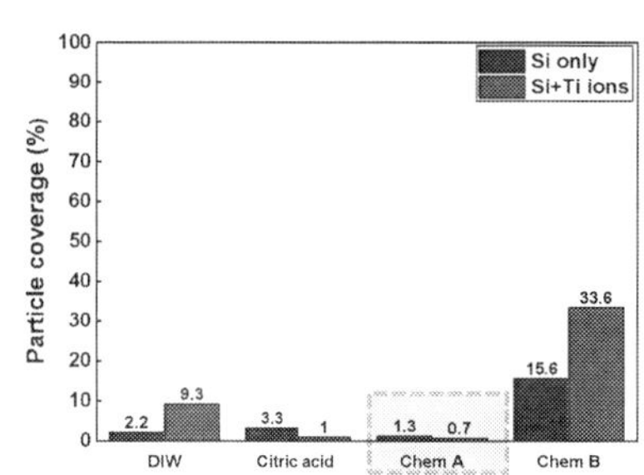

pH 8

- **Chem A showed significant decrease in particle coverage at all pH conditions**

Particle coverage trend of chelating agents: Chem B > Citric acid > Chem A

Mechanism for particle loading on brush in presence of Ti ions

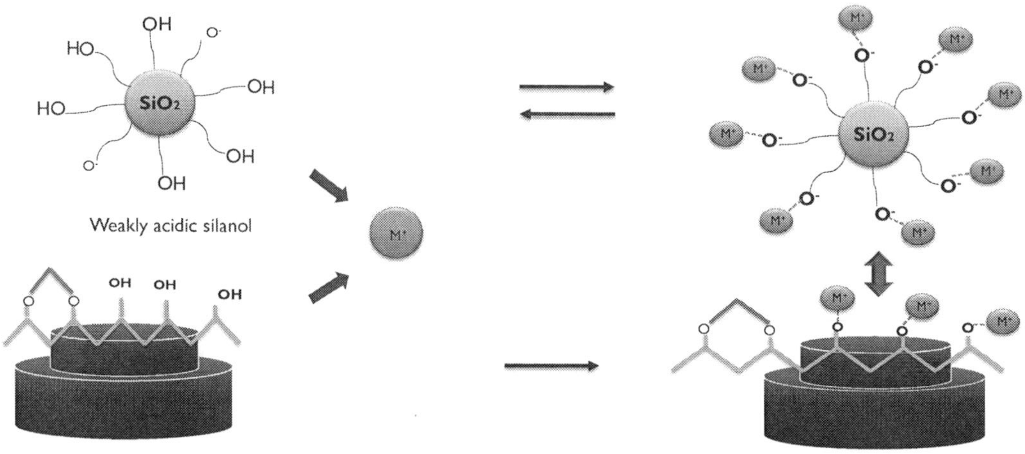

- **Electron pair is provided to the central metal atom and make bonding**
- **Interaction among the complexes can be electrostatic or co-ordination bonding**

Donald L. Dugger et al., *The Exchange of Twenty Metal Ions with the Weakly Acidic Silanol Group of Silica Gel*, The Journal of Physical Chemistry(https://doi.org/10.1021/j100786a007)

IV. Summary

Summary

Ti ion removal from TEOS surfaces

- Cleaning efficiency of different chelating agents has been evaluated
- Ti ions were removed effectively in presence of citric acid
- Chelating agent with carboxylic acid groups co-ordinates strongly with Ti ions

Effect of Ti ion on brush loading

- Ti ions play significant role in increasing the particle loading
- Better chelating agent can decrease the particle loading on brushes

Future study

1. **Reduce the brush loading in the presence citric acid (chelating agents).**
2. **Evaluation of different chelating agents on Ti ion removal and brush loading.**
3. **Confirmation of the mechanism for the contamination and brush loading in presence of Ti ions.**

HANYANG
UNIVERSITY

한양대학교 ERICA 캠퍼스

27

Atomic Layer Etching and Cleaning of Al_2O_3 from Gold Substrates Measured Using *in situ* Auger Electron Spectroscopy

Andrew S. Cavanagh and Steven M. George
Dept. of Chemistry, Univ. of Colorado
Boulder, CO 80309 U.S.A.

University of Colorado
Boulder

Thermal Atomic Layer Etching (ALE)

- Sequential precursor exposure
- Self-limiting surface reactions
- Isotropic material removal
- Digital thickness control

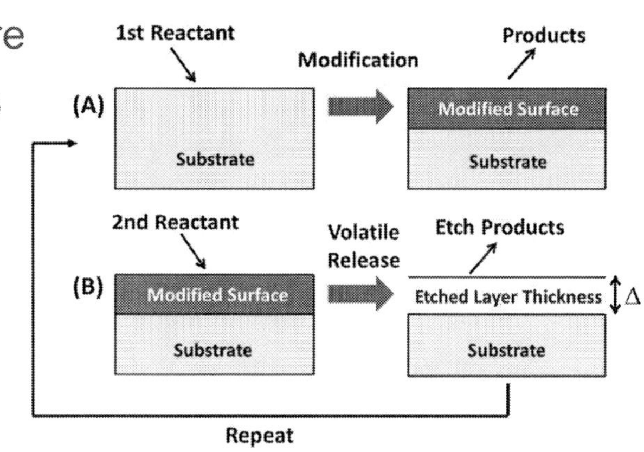

S.M. George, *Accounts of Chemical Research* **2020** *53* (6), 1151-1160

Chemistry for Thermal Al_2O_3 ALE

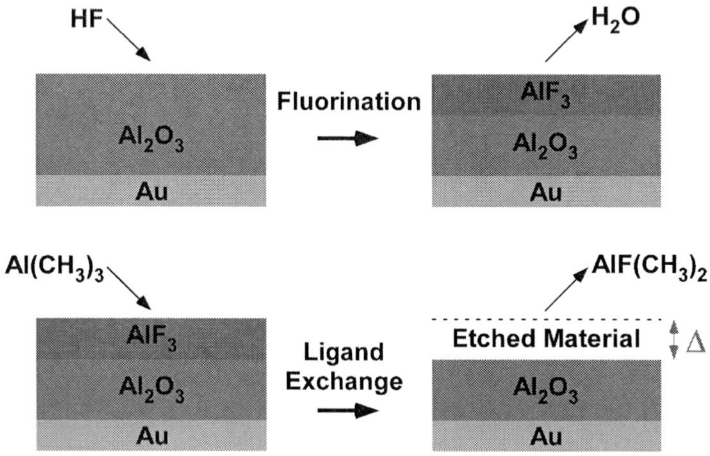

Fluorination of Al_2O_3 to AlF_3 using HF

Removal of AlF_3 by ligand exchange using $Al(CH_3)_3$

Many Possible ALE Chemistries

Oxides: Al_2O_3, Ga_2O_3, HfO_2, $InGaZnO_4$, SiO_2, VO_2, WO_3, ZnO, ZrO_2

Metals: Fe, Co, Mo, Ni, Cu, W

Nitrides: AlN, GaN, Si_3N_4, TaN, TiN

Semiconductors: GaAs, Ge, InAlAs, InGaAs, Si

Other: AlF_3, CoFeB, MoS_2, WS_3

Sensitivity of Auger Electron Spectroscopy (AES)

- Surface sensitive due to short Inelastic Mean Free Path (IMFP) of low energy electrons

- AES detection limit: ~1 part per thousand
  - Well suited to probing surface residues in final cycles of ALE

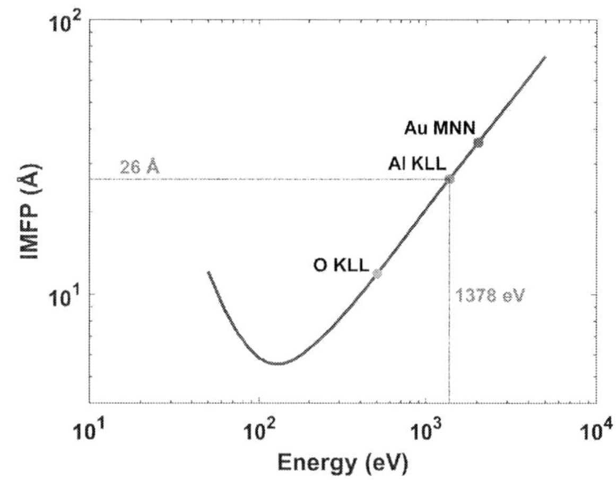

Akkerman et al. Phys. Stat. Sol. (b) 198 (1996) 769.

Monitoring Al_2O_3 ALE on Gold with AES

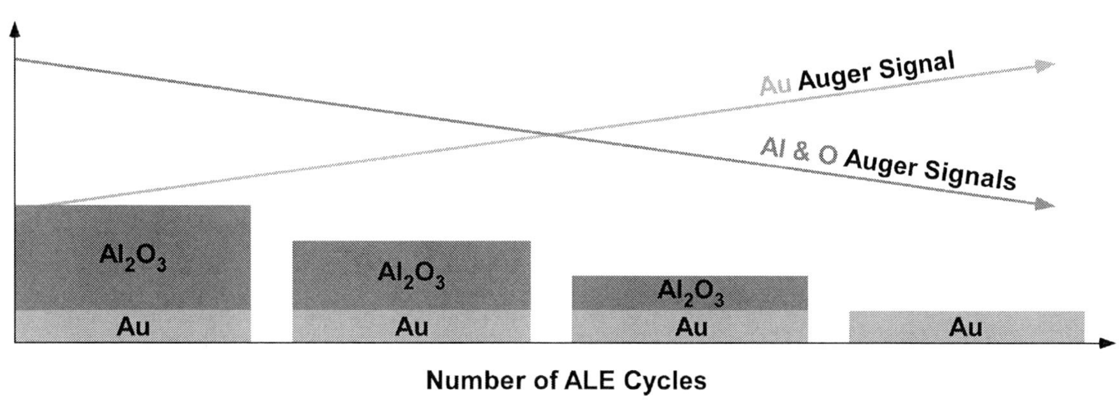

Film Thickness from Holloway Model

$$\frac{I_f}{I_s} = \frac{I_{f,\infty}}{I_{s,\infty}} \left(e^{\frac{t}{\mu_s}} - e^{\frac{t\,(\mu_f - \mu_s)}{\mu_f \mu_s}} \right)$$

I_f = Signal intensity from film

I_s = Signal intensity from substrate

$I_{f,\infty}$ = Signal intensity from a clean infinitely thick film

$I_{s,\infty}$ = Signal intensity from a clean infinitely thick substrate

μ_f = Mean free path of a film AE in film

μ_s = Mean free path of a substrate AE in film

t = Film thickness

Journal of Vacuum Science and Technology 12, 1418 (1975)
https://doi.org/10.1116/1.568553

University of Colorado Boulder

7

Film Thickness from Holloway Model

Intensity ratio cancels systematic variation → $\boxed{\frac{I_f}{I_s}}$

$$\boxed{\frac{I_f}{I_s}} = \frac{I_{f,\infty}}{I_{s,\infty}} \left(e^{\frac{t}{\boxed{\mu_s}}} - e^{\frac{t\,(\mu_f - \mu_s)}{\boxed{\mu_f \mu_s}}} \right)$$

Small IMFP provides high sensitivity

I_f = Signal intensity from film

I_s = Signal intensity from substrate

$I_{f,\infty}$ = Signal intensity from a clean infinitely thick film

$I_{s,\infty}$ = Signal intensity from a clean infinitely thick substrate

μ_f = Mean free path of a film AE in film

μ_s = Mean free path of a substrate AE in film

t = Film thickness

Journal of Vacuum Science and Technology 12, 1418 (1975)
https://doi.org/10.1116/1.568553

University of Colorado Boulder

8

Holloway Model Modified for ALE Cycles

$$\frac{I_f}{I_s} = \frac{I_{f,\infty}}{I_{s,\infty}} \left(e^{\frac{t_0 - N\,\Delta t}{\mu_s}} - e^{\frac{(t_0 - N\,\Delta t)\,(\mu_f - \mu_s)}{\mu_f \mu_s}} \right)$$

Substitute: $t = t_0 - N\,\Delta t$

t_0 = Initial film thickness

N = Number of cycles of ALE

Δt = ALE etch per cycle

When $(t_0 - N\,\Delta t) < 0$
- Holloway model is no longer applicable
- *Surface Clean Region*

University of Colorado Boulder

9

ALE Tool Equipped for *in situ* AES Studies

University of Colorado Boulder

10

Results for Al KLL AES vs Al_2O_3 ALE Cycles

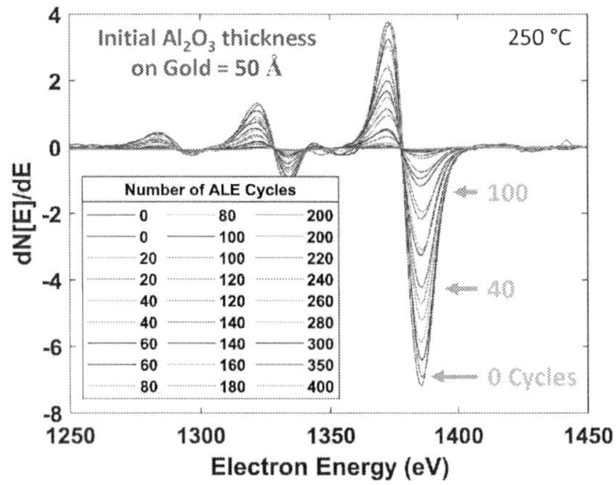

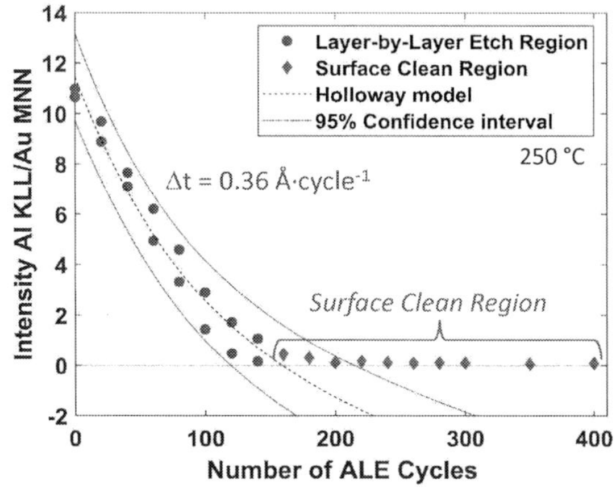

Peaks were aligned to emphasize amplitude variation

Results for O KLL AES vs Al_2O_3 ALE Cycles

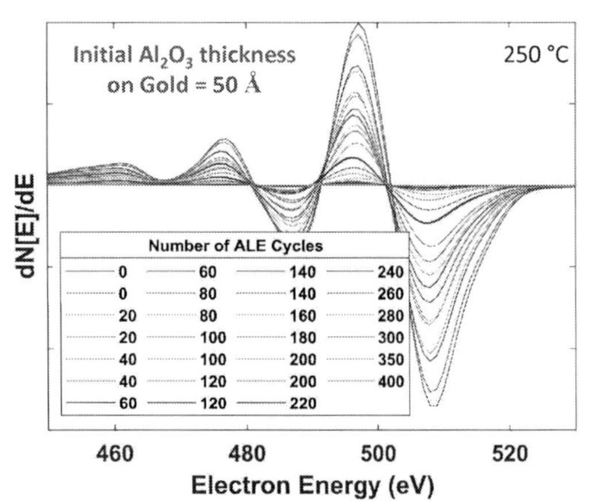

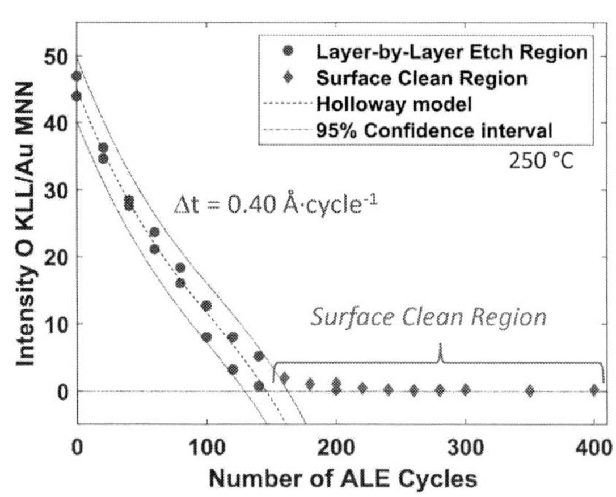

Peaks were aligned to emphasize amplitude variation

Film Growth Modes: *Growth is Reverse of Etch*

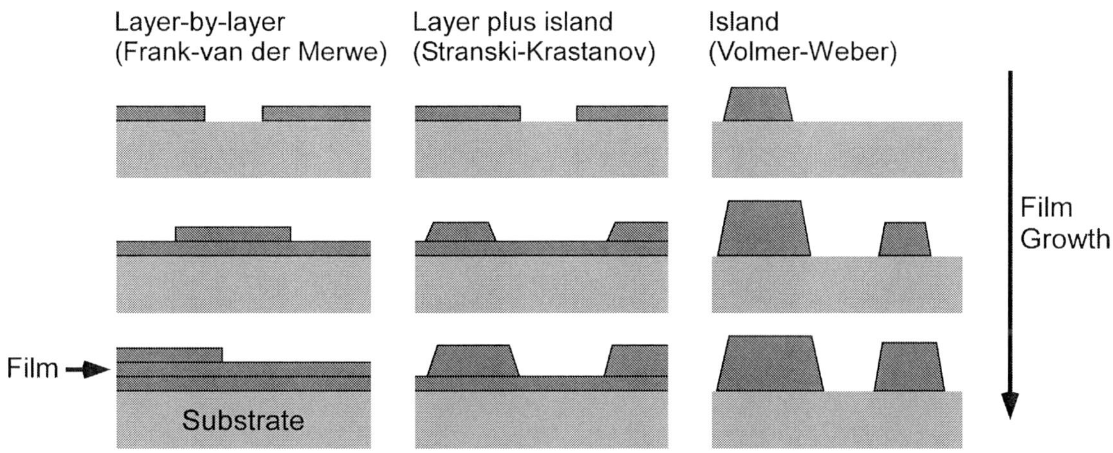

Adapted from: Oura, K. et al. Surface Science: An Introduction, 1st ed.; Springer 2003.

AES of Film Growth: *Growth is Reverse of Etch*

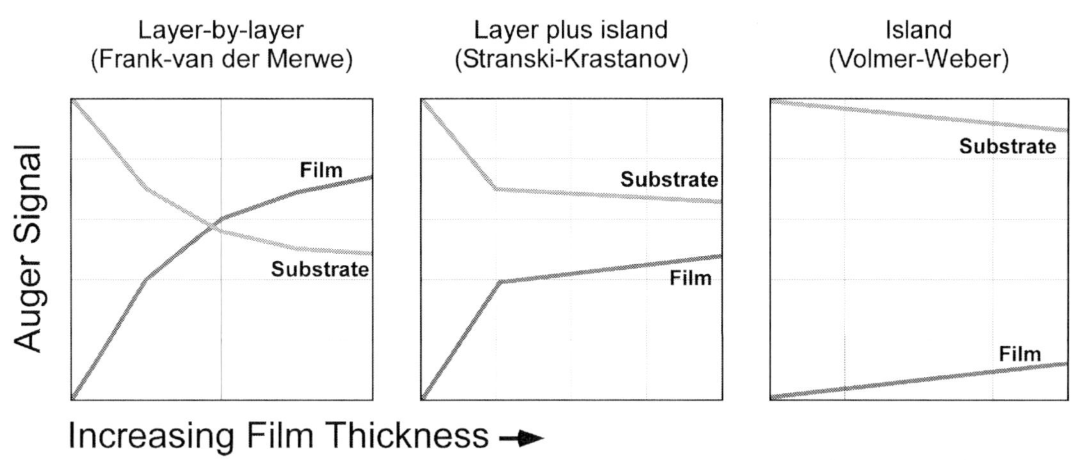

Adapted from: Oura, K. et al. Surface Science: An Introduction, 1st ed.; Springer 2003.

Etch is *Reverse* of Growth

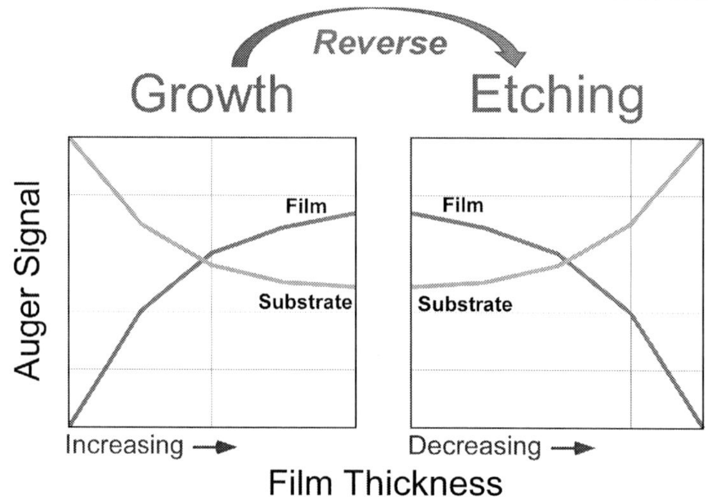

Al KLL & Au MNN in *Layer-by-Layer Etch Region*

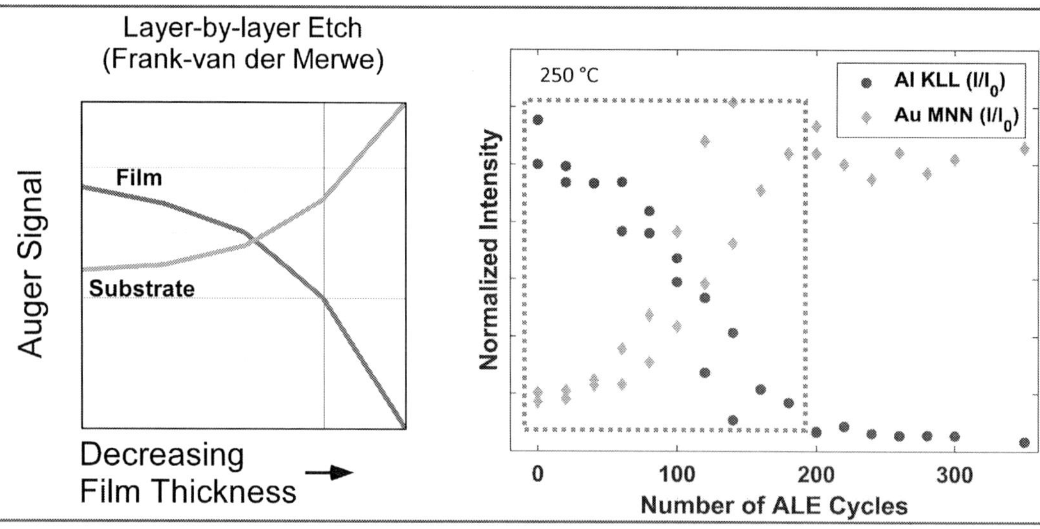

"Island Etch" in *Surface Clean Region*

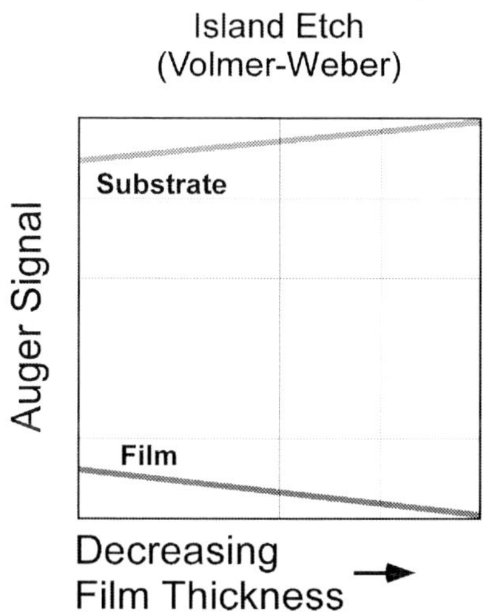

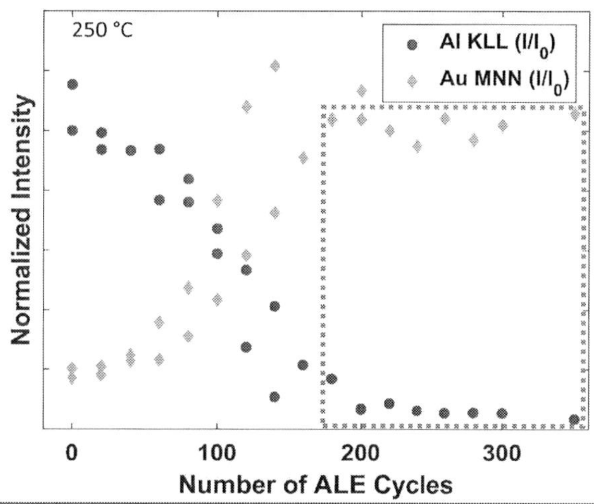

Surface Clean Region (> 150 ALE Cycles)

Thickness calculated from Holloway model in *Surface Clean Region* shows:

- Films are at or below monolayer coverage
- ALE continues to remove material vs ALE cycles
- Etch behavior follows exponential decay with decay constants of 25 – 40 ALE cycles

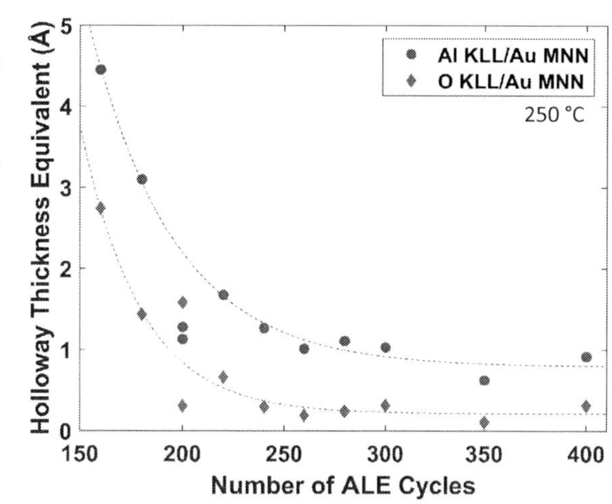

Conclusions

- Al_2O_3 Bulk Etching – Al_2O_3 ALE using TMA & HF etches up to Au interface in layer-by-layer fashion (*Frank-van der Merwe mode)*.
- Surface Clean Region – Residual islands of Al_2O_3 remain at Au interface. These islands are etched more slowly (*Volmer-Weber* mode).

University of Colorado Boulder

TOKYO ELECTRON

Wet Chemical Etching of Si1-xGex in HNO_3: HF: H_2O

October 18, 2022

Henan Zhang, Du Zhang, Shan Hu
TEL Technology Center, America, LLC

Agenda

- Introduction
  - Selective SiGe Removal for Nanowire
  - Chemistry of Si etching by HNO_3 and dHF
- Experimental
  - Evaluation HNO_3 and dHF on blanket film and nanowire
- Results & Discussion
  - Cyclic etching
- Conclusion

Nanosheet Selective Etches

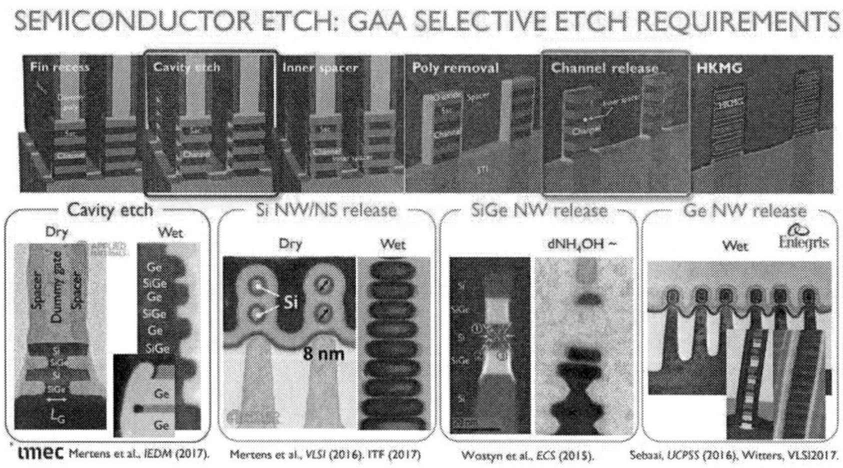

Source: F. Holsteyns, IMEC, SPCC 2018

Nanosheet Selective Etches

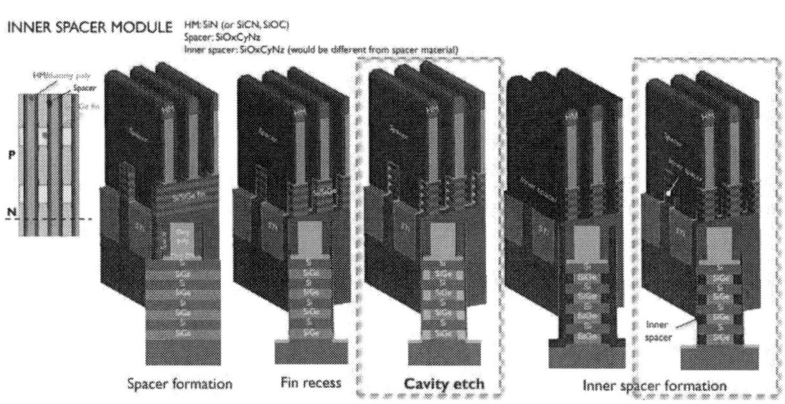

Source: S. Kal, TTCA, SPCC 2018

- To overcome the difficulties of scaling, Silicon Germanium plays a significant role as semiconductor material for the fabrication of the next generation of logic and memory devices

Selective SiGe Removal for Nanowire

- Vertical cross section view of stacked GAA channel, a simplified process flow for SiGe wet removal

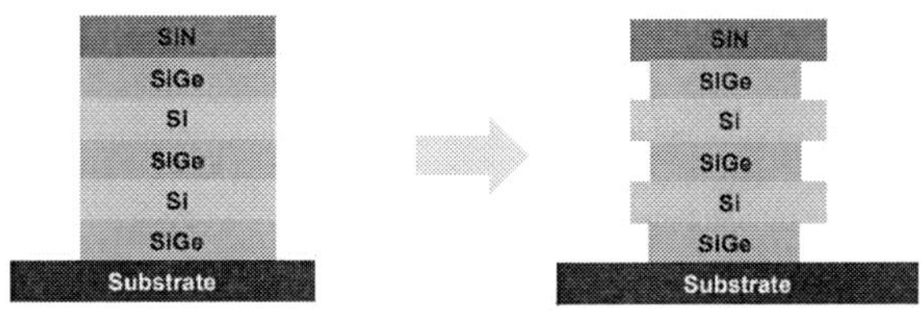

Source: TEL

- Challenges of SiGe Wet removal

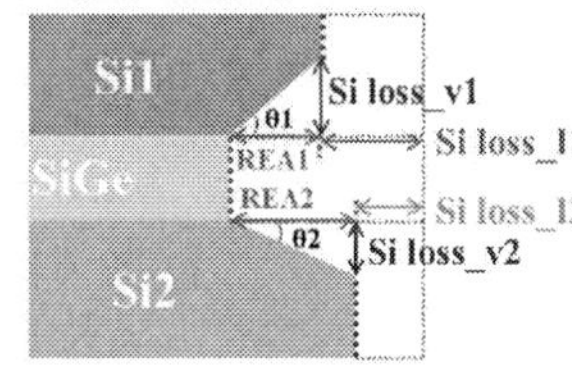

$$selectivity = \frac{(REA + Si\ loss)}{Si\ loss} = 1 + cot\theta$$

Source: Y. Li, Nanomaterials 2021,11,1209

- SiGe etch rate
- Si horizontal loss
- SiGe/Si surface roughness

Chemistry HNO_3 and dHF Etching Si

- Chemical reactions of HNO_3 and dHF etching Si

$$3Si + 4HNO_3 \rightarrow 3SiO_2 + 4NO + 2H_2O$$

$$SiO_2 + 6HF \rightarrow H_2SiF_6 + 2H_2O$$

$$3Si + 4NHO_3 + 18HF \rightarrow 3H_2SiF_6 + 4NO + 8H_2O$$

1. Silicon is oxidized by HNO_3
2. Dissolution of formed SiO_2 by HF
3. Overall reaction

- Nitric Acid has a complex behavior

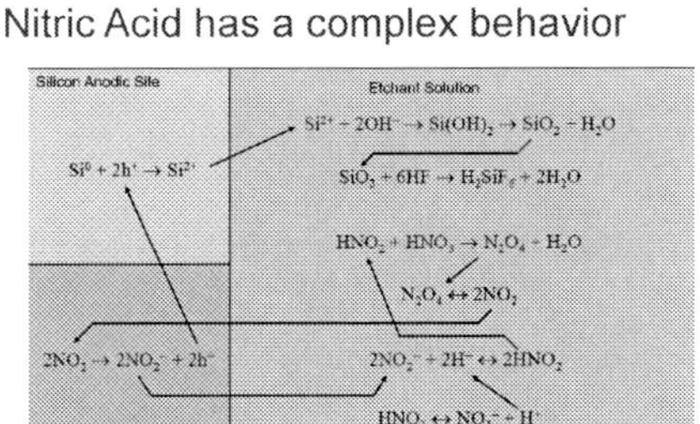

1. Normal dissociation in water (deprotonation)
2. Autocatalytic cycle for generation of holes and HNO2
3. N(III) effectively oxidizes Si
4. HNO_2 is regenerated by the reaction (autocatalytic)

Source: M. Steinert, J. Phys. Chem. C 2006, 110, 23, 2133–11377
A. Rietig, Phys. Chem. Chem. Phys., 2019, 21, 22002

Chemical Etching of Si using HNO_3 and dHF

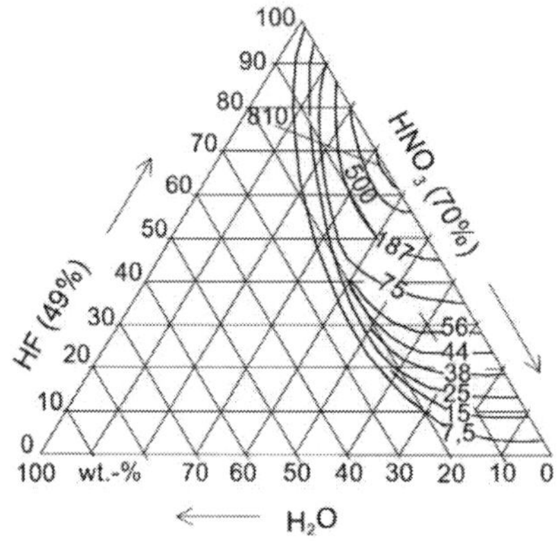

Etch rate [µm/min] of Si surfaces in the system HNO_3:HF:HO_2

Source: Joachim Fruhauf, Shape and Functional Elements of the Bulk Silicon Micro technique: A Manual of Wet-Etched Silicon Structures, 2005

SiGe Etch Rate by HNO_3 and dHF

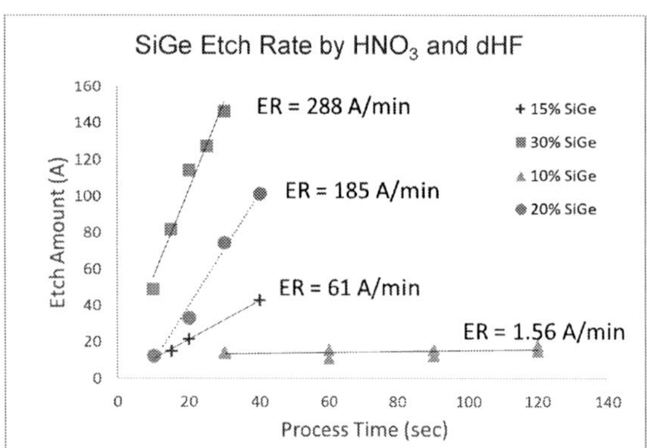

Source: TEL

Film	ER
ALD SiN	~ 2.3 Å/min
EPI Si (SOI)	~ 0 Å/min
SiGe 10%	~ 1.56 Å/min
SiGe 15%	~ 61 Å/min
SiGe 20%	~ 185 Å/min
SiGe 30%	~ 288 Å/min

Note:
1. 0.5% DHF 30s dipping applied to all films
2. Data provided by ellipsometry measurement

- Etch depth as a function of time for SiGe films with different Ge percentage by HNO_3 and dHF system

SiGe Etch Rate by HNO_3 and dHF

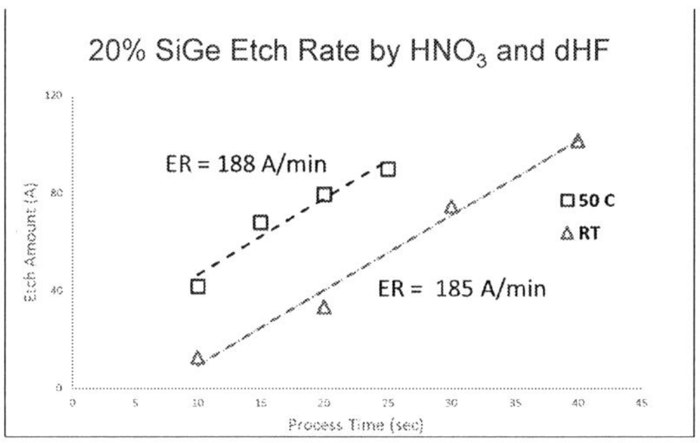

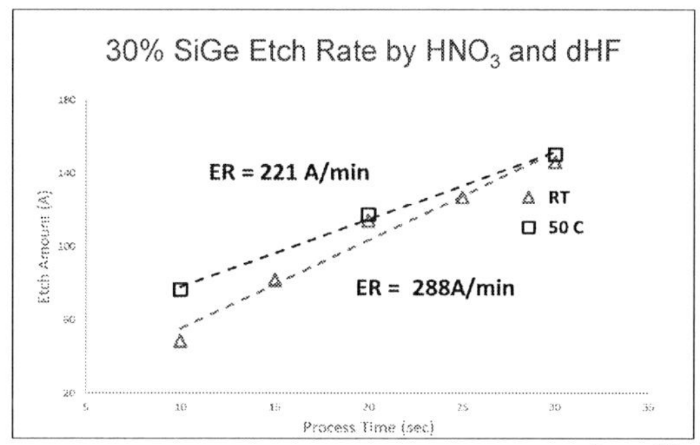

Source: TEL

- Temperature dependencies of HNO_3 and dHF for etching of 20% and 30% SiGe blanket films, respectively

SiGe Etch Rate by HNO_3 and dHF

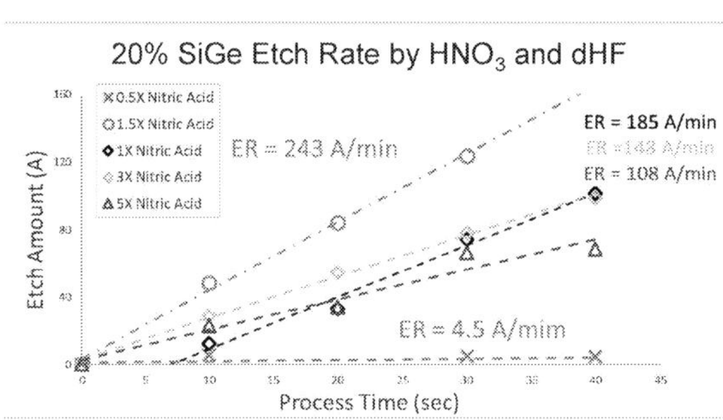

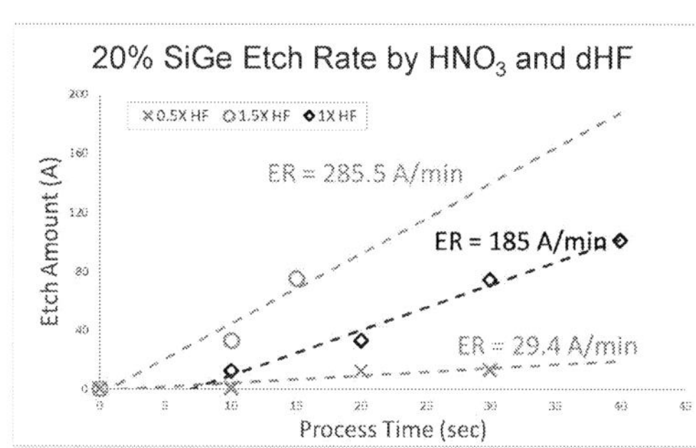

Source: TEL

- Concentration dependencies of HNO_3 and dHF for etching of 20% SiGe blanket film

SiGe Cavity Removal by HNO_3 and dHF

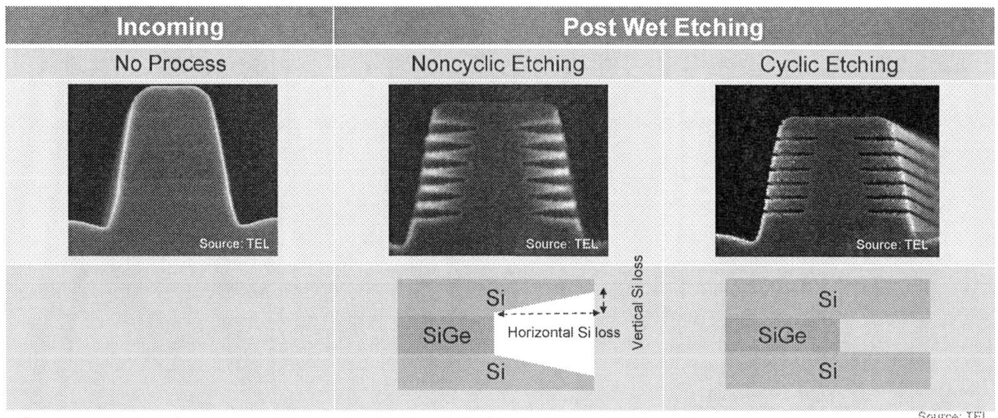

- Cyclic etching improves the selectivity of SiGe to Si, but Si surface roughness remains a challenge

Optimization of HNO_3 and dHF System

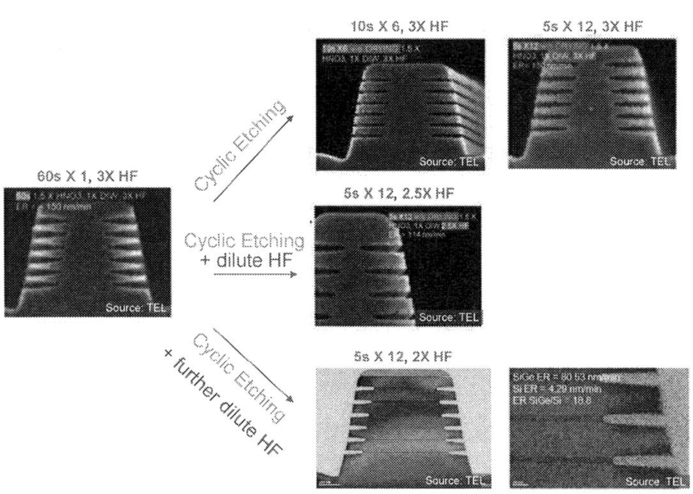

Limitation of cyclic etching

- Cyclic etching solution improves vertical Si loss, but remaining Si surface roughness worsen

Further improve the processing details of cyclic etching

- Cyclic etching with HNO_3 and further dilute HF improves Si loss and Si surface roughness issues, but compensates SiGe ER

SiGe ER = 80.52nm/min
Si ER = 4.29nm/min
Selectivity = 18.8

Mechanism of Cyclic Etching

DIW wash prolongs Si etch induction period

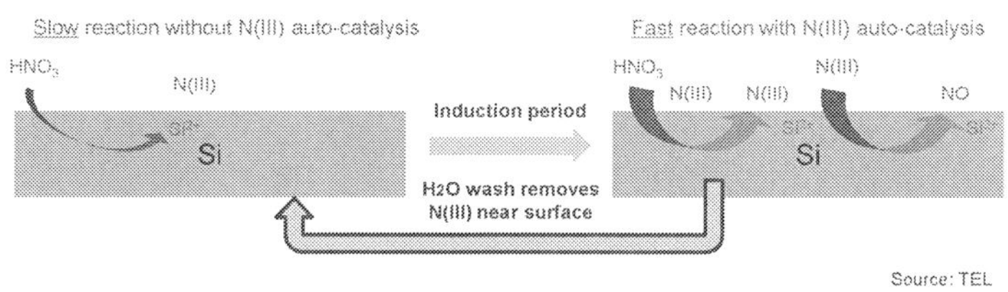

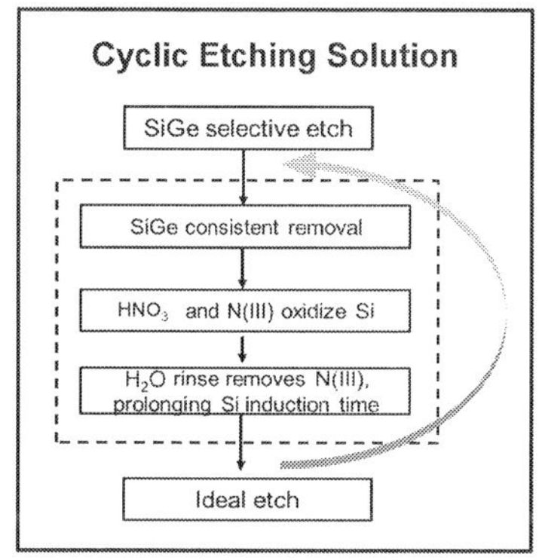

- Si etch has an "induction period" for the oxidation step
- This "induction period" is due to the necessity of N(III) species by-product for autocatalysis
- DIW wash removes N(III) on Si surface and prolongs its "induction period"
- N(III) needs to be formed from the interaction with Si first because "fresh made" does not have it, creating an "induction period" for Si → H_2O wash gets rid of N(III)

Mechanism of Si Porous Surface Formation

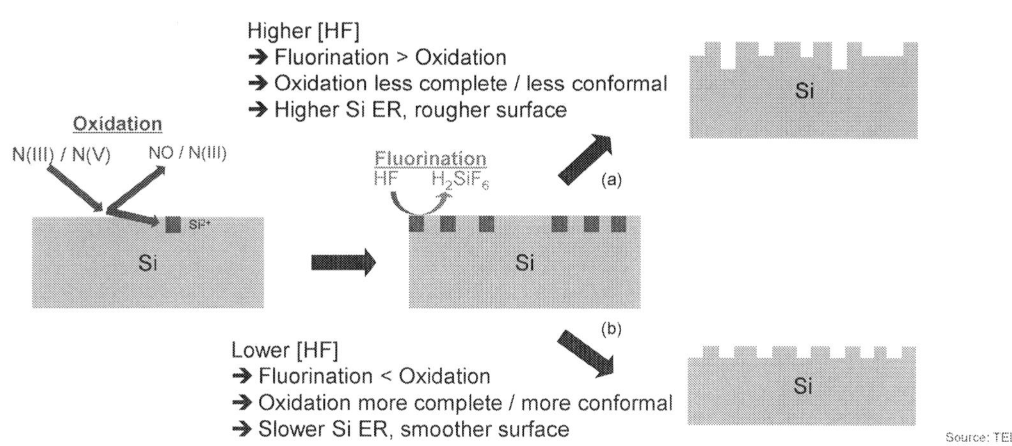

- Si ER and remaining surface roughness dependencies of dHF concentration

Summary

- HNO_3 and dHF selectively etching SiGe for nanowire
- Cyclic etching improves the selectivity between SiGe and Si
- DIW wash prolongs Si etch induction period, enable the potential of further developing the etch performance
- Remaining Si roughness is a challenge

TEL™

TOKYO ELECTRON

Sustainable Value Together

DAICEL

A Novel Selective Adsorption Polymer to Silicon Nitride Enables Etching Selectivity Control in HF and BHF Etching

Kenji Mochida, Tsubasa Miki, Tadashi Teranishi

DAICEL CORPORATION

Etching Selectivity is always a keyword

DAICEL *Sustainable Value Together*

Here are examples of wet-etching with various etchants.

Selective removal of SiO_2
Etchant: BHF

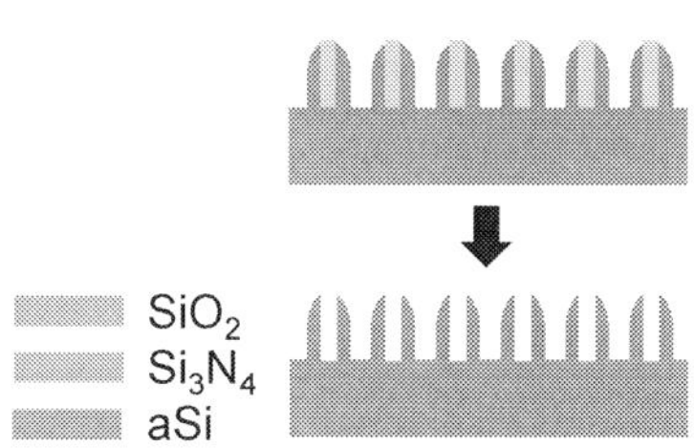

ER (SiO_2) /ER (Si_3N_4)

Selective removal of aSi
Etchant: NaOH

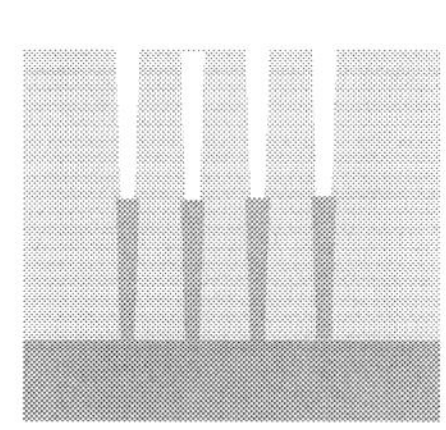

ER (aSi) /ER (SiO_2)

Selective removal of Si_3N_4
Etchant: H_3PO_4

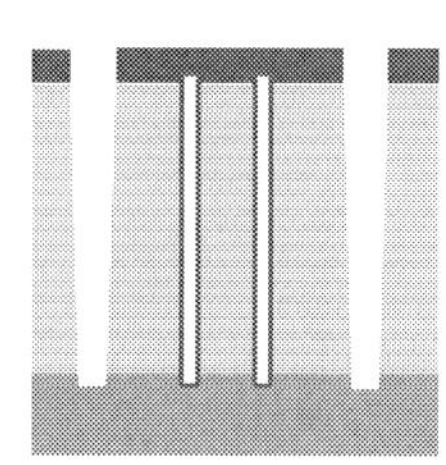

ER (Si_3N_4)/ ER (SiO_2)

How to improve selectivity?

Common Strategy: Add special chemicals

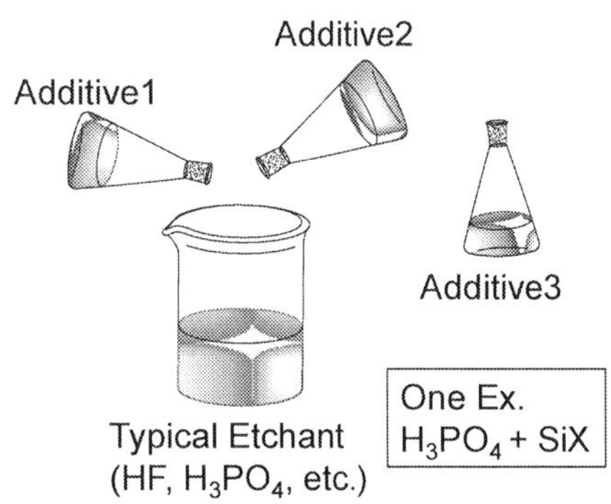

Works Well. High selectivity emerged!!

But most chemicals are supplied by a centralized distribution system

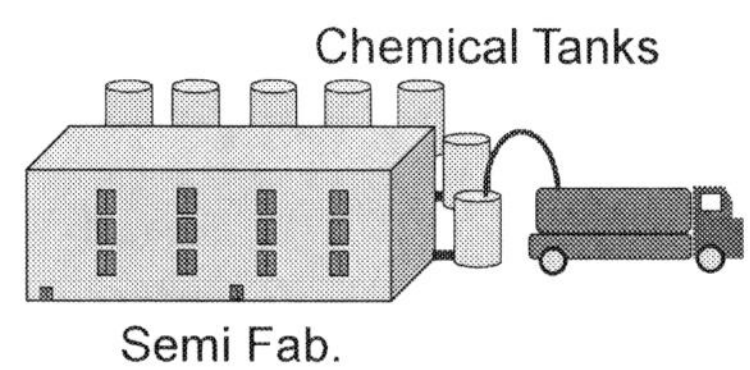

Compatible with existing etchant?

Area selective pre-protection

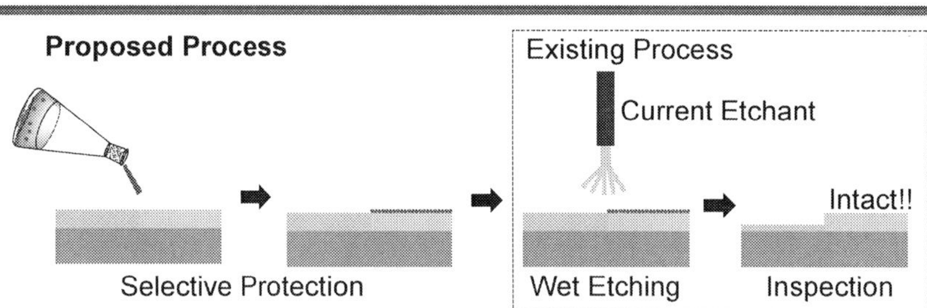

Breaking down into chemicals…

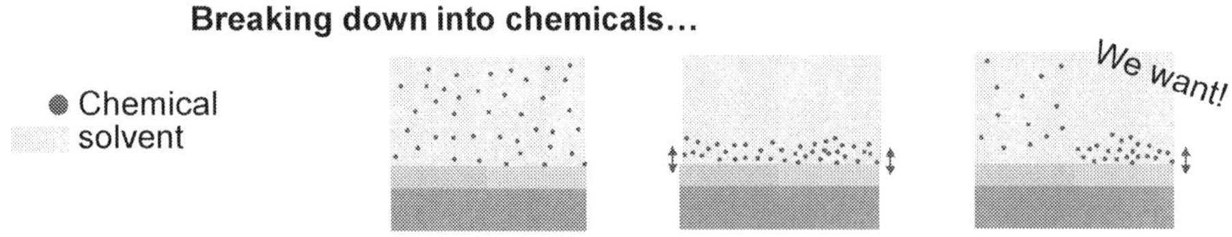

Affinity:	-	OK	**OK**
Selectivity:	-	NG	**OK**

Affinity measurements using QCM

Quartz Crystal Microbalance(QCM) is an excellent tool to screen chemicals having affinity.

[Experiments]

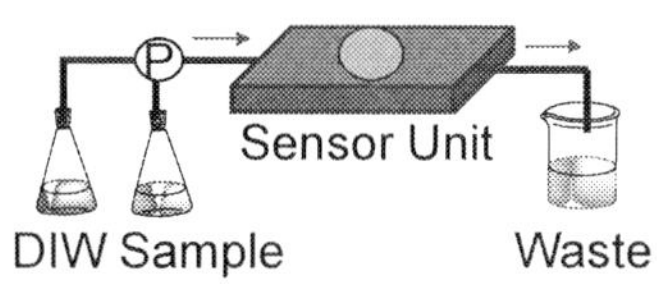

Sensor: SiO_2 or Si_3N_4 on Au electrode
Sample: Aqueous Polymer in DIW
Conc.: < 1.0 wt%
Protocol: DIW -> polymer aq. -> DIW

[Results of affinity]

Aqueous Polymer	SiO_2	Si_3N_4
Polyethylene glycol (PEG)	-	-
Polyvinyl alcohol (PVA)	-	-
Polyglycerol (PGL)	-	-
Polyvinylpyrrolidone (PVP)	✓	✓
Polymer-A(Nanotrex DCL07)	✓	✓
Ethyl cellulose (EC)*	✓	✓
Hydroxypropyl cellulose(HPC)	✓	✓

* PGME solution

QCM Chart & Repetitive analysis

Repetitive QCM analysis: Both sensors were new one and washed after each experiment.

Sensor: SiO_2

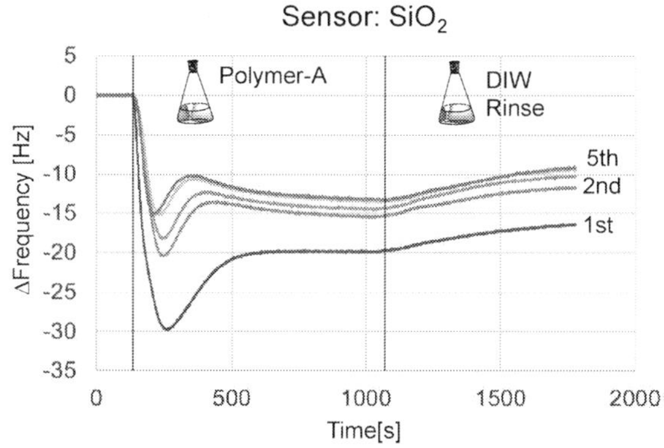

Seem to be removed from SiO_2 by washing.

Sensor: Si_3N_4

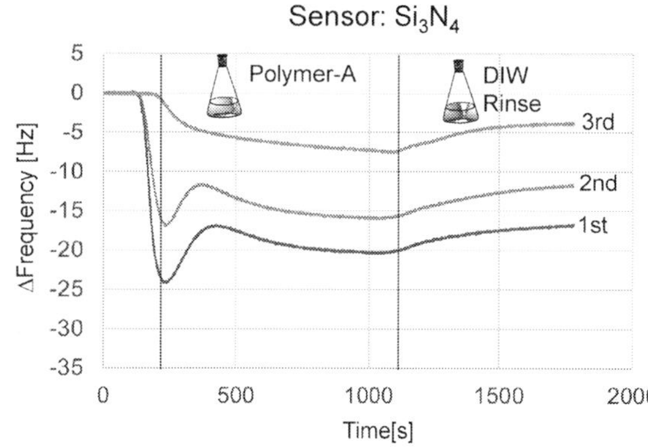

Polymer-A interacts with Si_3N_4 strongly.

Primitive investigation: Dipping

DAICEL Sustainable Value Together

[Etching Experiments]

Ref (non coat) ➡ ➡ ➡ BHF110 (5min)

Dip: Polymer Aq. (3min) ➡ DIW (3 min) ➡ N_2 Blow ➡ BHF110 (5min)

Substrates 1: LP-Si_3N_4[200nm]/Si
Substrates 1: Th-SiO_2[1.5um]/Si
Size: 2cm x 2cm coupon
Etchant: BHF110

Polymer A prevents the etching of nitrides from BHF.
But dipping has a problem in the view of uniformity.

[Results of Etching]

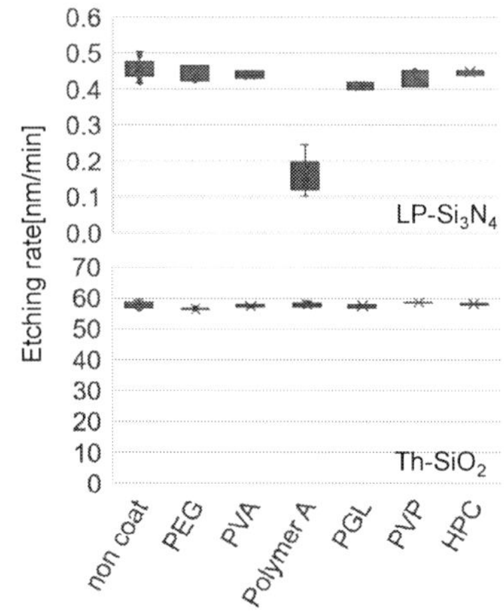

Results of etching

DAICEL Sustainable Value Together

Polymer-A dissolves in PGME. Polymer film(FT = 20nm) was prepared with spin-coat method.

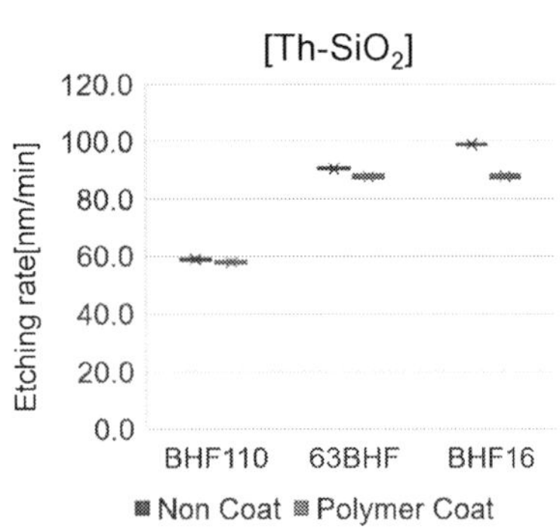

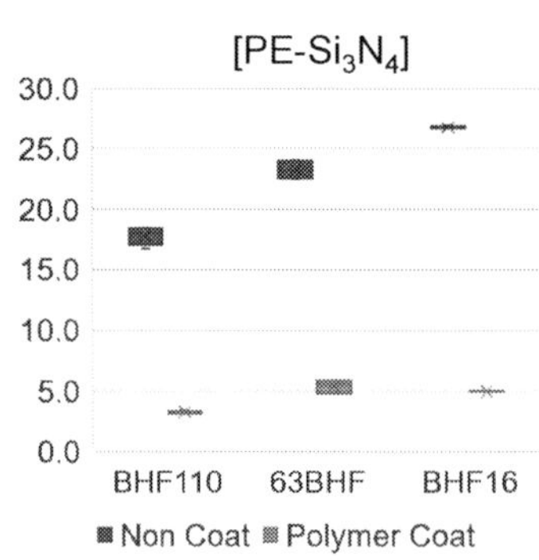

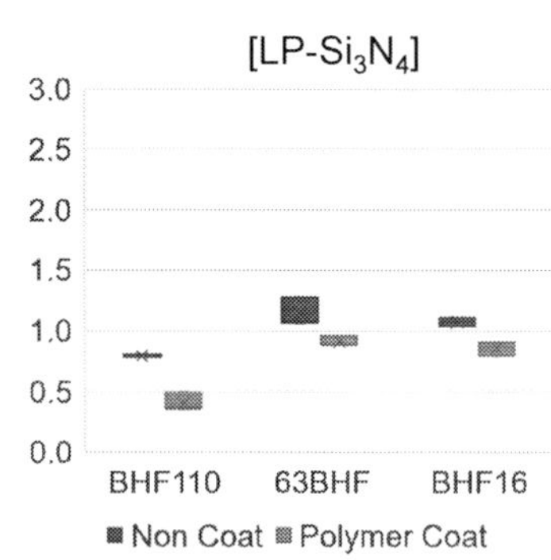

Polymer-A works with PE-Si_3N_4 especially.

Spin coat: 1500 rpm then 110 °C for 2 min
Substrates: Polymer-A [20nm]/SiO_2 or Si_3N_4/Si
Size: 2cm x 2cm coupon

Variation of the etching rate over time

Substrates: Polymer-A[20nm]/Th-SiO_2[1.5um]/Si
Size: 2cm x 2cm coupon
Etchant: BHF110

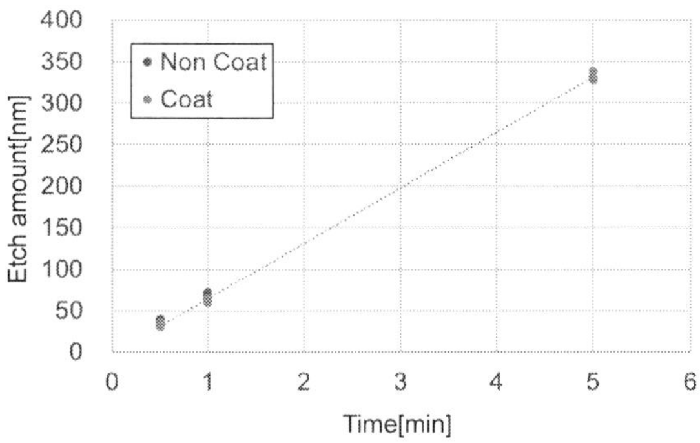

Overlapped perfectly!!

Substrates: Polymer-A[20nm]/PE-Si_3N_4[300nm]/Si
Size: 2cm x 2cm coupon
Etchant: BHF110

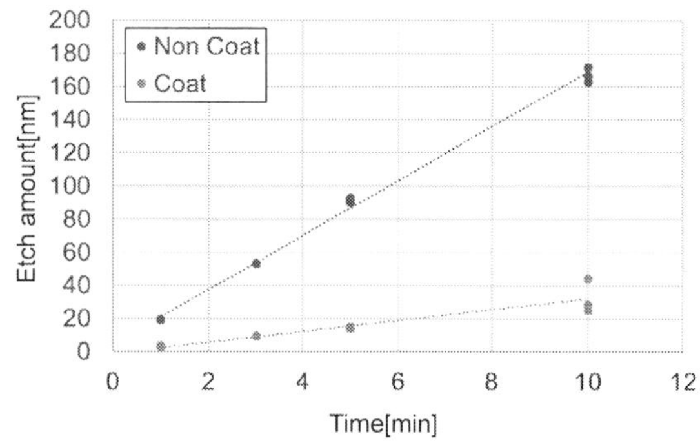

Etching rates are constant for over 5min.

2022/10/17 SPCC2022 9

Removing polymer film before etching

[Removing Experiments]

Ref	➡	➡	BHF110 (5min)
DIW	➡	DIW (x min) ➡	BHF110 (5min)
TMAH	TMAH (0.5min) ➡	DIW (0.5min) ➡	BHF110 (5min)

Substrates: Polymer-A[20nm]/PE-Si_3N_4[300nm]/Si
Size: 2cm x 2cm coupon

[Results]

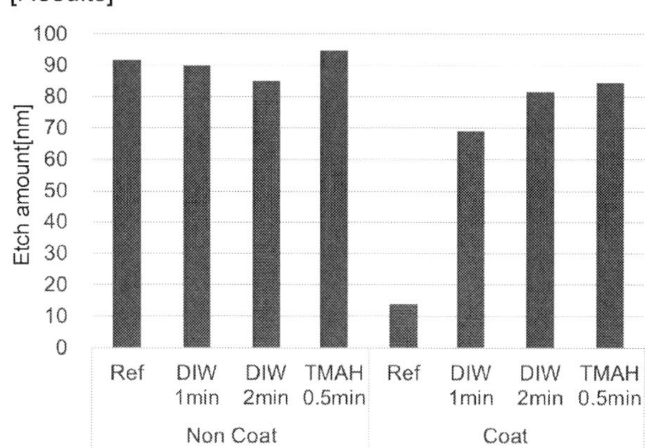

Polymer film can be easily removed with DIW or 2.38% TMAH. ERs are almost recovered.

2022/10/17 SPCC2022 10

Re-adsorption from BHF?

DAICEL
Sustainable Value Together

Etching rates are constant. Why? One scenario is that the dissolved polymer re-attaches to the SiN.

[Rinse Experiments]

Ref		➡		➡	BHF110 (5min)
3+2min	BHF110 (3min)	➡	DIW (10 sec)	➡	BHF110* (2min) * Fresh BHF
4+1min	BHF110 (4min)	➡	DIW (10 sec)	➡	BHF110* (1min) * Fresh BHF

Substrates: Polymer-A[20nm]/PE-Si_3N_4[300nm]/Si
Size: 2cm x 2cm coupon

[Results]

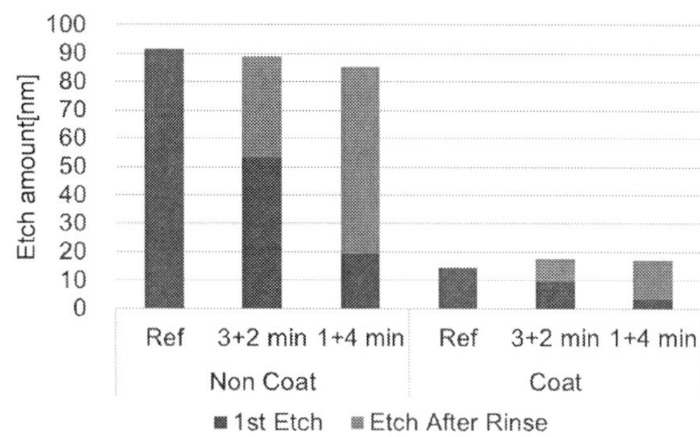

Re-adsorption from etchant is denied. The polymer-A seems to cling on the substrate in BHF solution.

Polymer removal at the middle

DAICEL
Sustainable Value Together

We examined if we could remove polymer coat during etching in situ.

[Removing Experiments]

Ref		➡		➡		➡	BHF110 (5min)
DIW	BHF110 (3min)	➡		➡	DIW (1min)	➡	BHF110 (2min)
TMAH/ DIW	BHF110 (3min)	➡	TMAH (0.5min)	➡	DIW (0.5min)	➡	BHF110 (2min)

Substrates: Polymer-A[20nm]/PE-Si_3N_4[300nm]/Si
Size: 2cm x 2cm coupon

[Results]

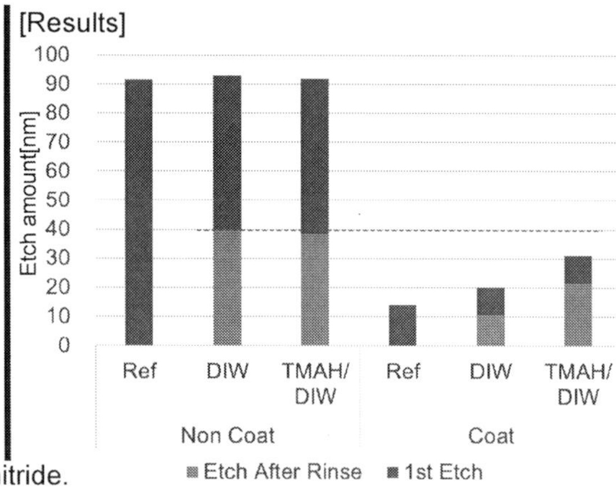

The polymer-A clings quite strongly to the silicon nitride.

Further exposure to TMAH

DAICEL Sustainable Value Together

Prolong a process time to estimate how strong the polymer clings to nitride film.

[Removing Experiments]

Ref ➡ ➡ ➡ BHF110 (5min)

TMAH/DIW BHF110 (3min) ➡ TMAH (x min) ➡ DIW (0.5min) ➡ BHF110 (2min)

Substrates: Polymer-A[20nm]/PE-Si_3N_4[300nm]/Si
Size: 2cm x 2cm coupon

[Results]

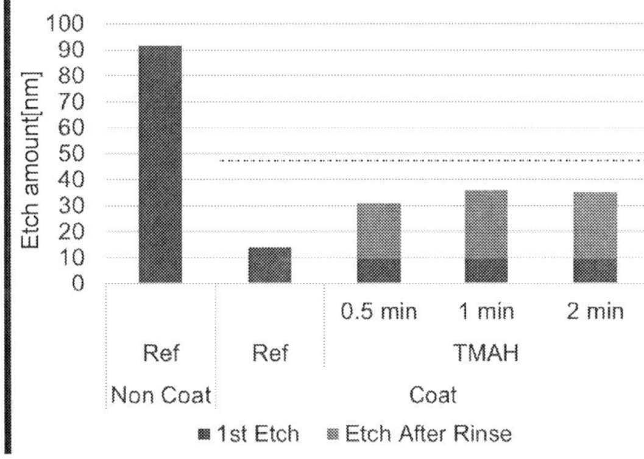

So far, we are not able to remove polymer-A layer.

Proposed Mechanism

DAICEL Sustainable Value Together

[Initial State]

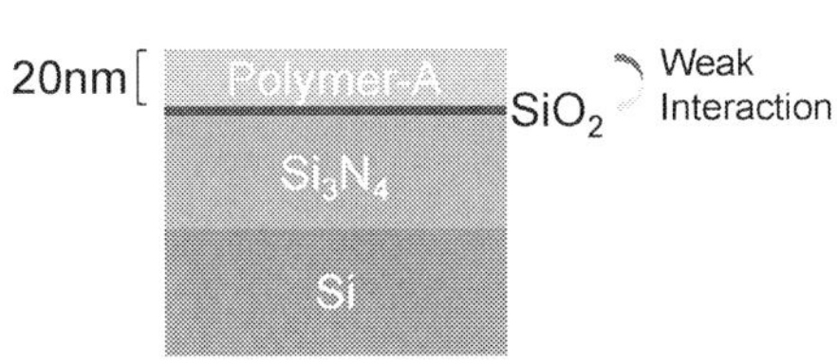

Polymer layer was removed easily.
This may be because there are natural oxide layer.

[Etching in situ]

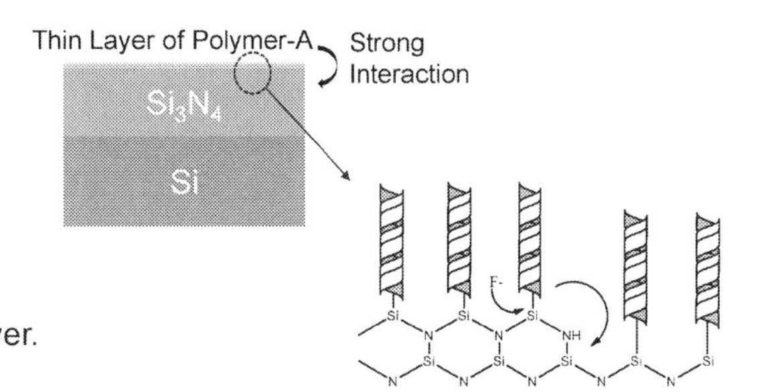

Polymer might re-attach to nitride layer immediately.
It looks like a sticky cobbler's pegs!!

Summary

Polymer-A (Nanotrex DCL07) has following functions.

1. Strong adsorption property to silicon nitrides
2. Retain the etching rate of silicon oxide by BHF
3. Suppress the etching rate of silicon nitride by BHF
4. Partially removed by basic condition

Further Study:

1. Etching Study: Other etchants, Other deposition species, Removing condition
2. Mechanism Study: Detection of polymer thin film during etching in situ.

Contacts

Kenji Mochida

Daicel corporation
Tokyo, Japan
E-mail:mochida.kenji@jp.daicel.com
Mobile: +81-70-7812-2622
Tel: +81-3-6711-8260

TEL
TOKYO ELECTRON

Highly Selective Dry Etching Process for the Removal of SiGe Layers for the Enablement of Stacked Nanosheet Gate-All-Around Transistor Architectures

SPCC, October 17th, 2022

I. V. Otto IV[1], S. Kal[1], C. Durfee[2], S. Pancharatnam[2], M. Flaugh[1], J. Frougier[2], A. Greene[2], N.Takahashi[1], N. Loubet[2], A. Mosden[1], N. Felix[2], P. Biolsi[1]

[1]TEL Technology Center, America, LLC, 255 Fuller Rd., Albany, NY 12203, US
[2]IBM Research, 257 Fuller Road, Albany, NY 12203, US
Email: ivo.otto@us.tel.com

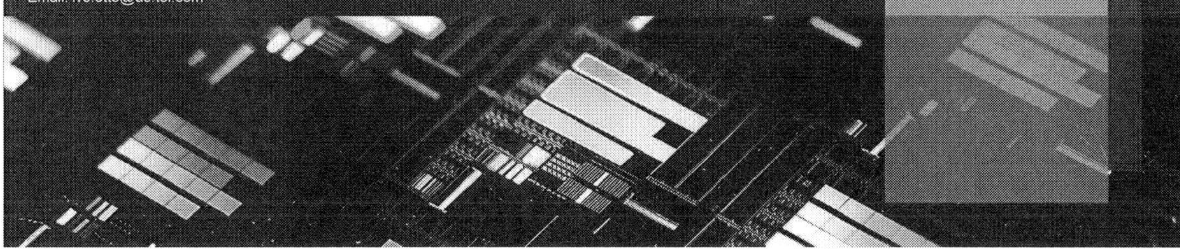

Movement to Nanosheet Gate-All-Around (GAA-NS)

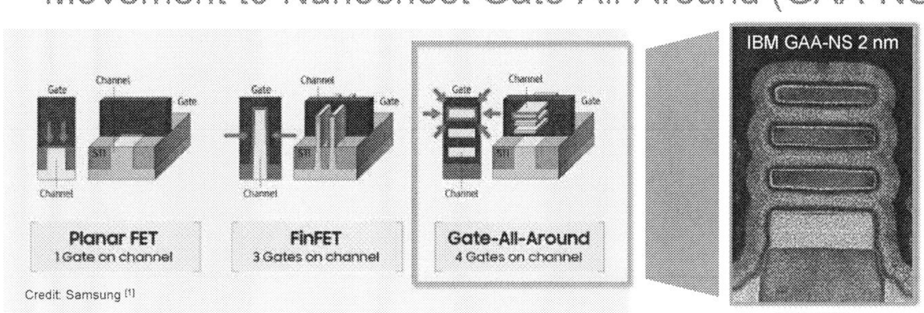

- **Industry is headed to GAA-NS for future nodes past 3 nm**

GAA Advantages

- **Total gate control by complete channel coverage →** reduces leakage and power consumption
- **Continuous active channel widths →** enable by non-quantized active footprint
- **Overall smaller device footprint by vertical stack design →** higher performance density
- **Channel dimensions and pitch defined by epitaxially-grown films →** better channel dimensional control

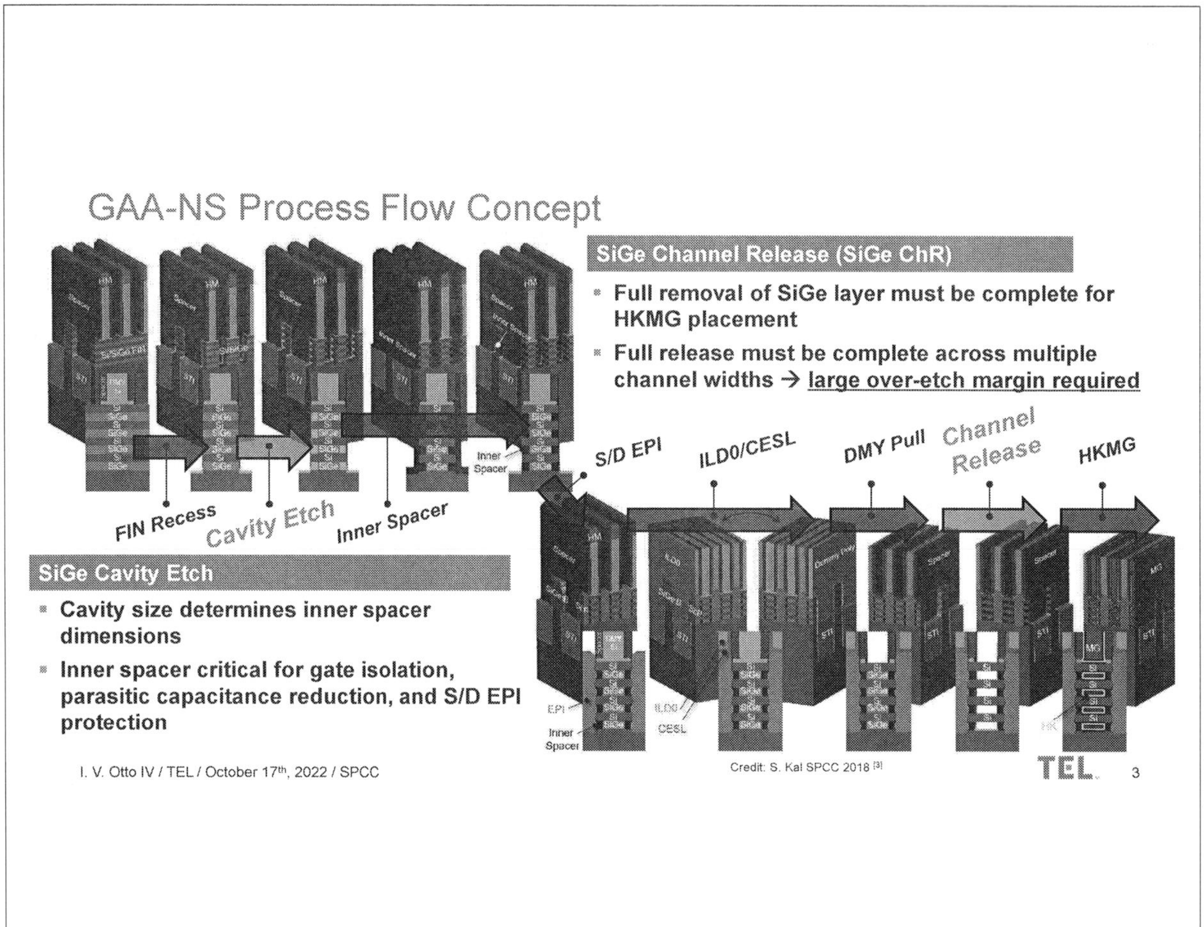
GAA-NS Process Flow Concept
SiGe Channel Release (SiGe ChR)
Full removal of SiGe layer must be complete for HKMG placement
Full release must be complete across multiple channel widths → large over-etch margin required
FIN Recess
Cavity Etch
Inner Spacer
S/D EPI
ILD0/CESL
DMY Pull
Channel Release
HKMG
SiGe Cavity Etch
Cavity size determines inner spacer dimensions
Inner spacer critical for gate isolation, parasitic capacitance reduction, and S/D EPI protection
I. V. Otto IV / TEL / October 17th, 2022 / SPCC
Credit: S. Kal SPCC 2018 [3]
TEL
3

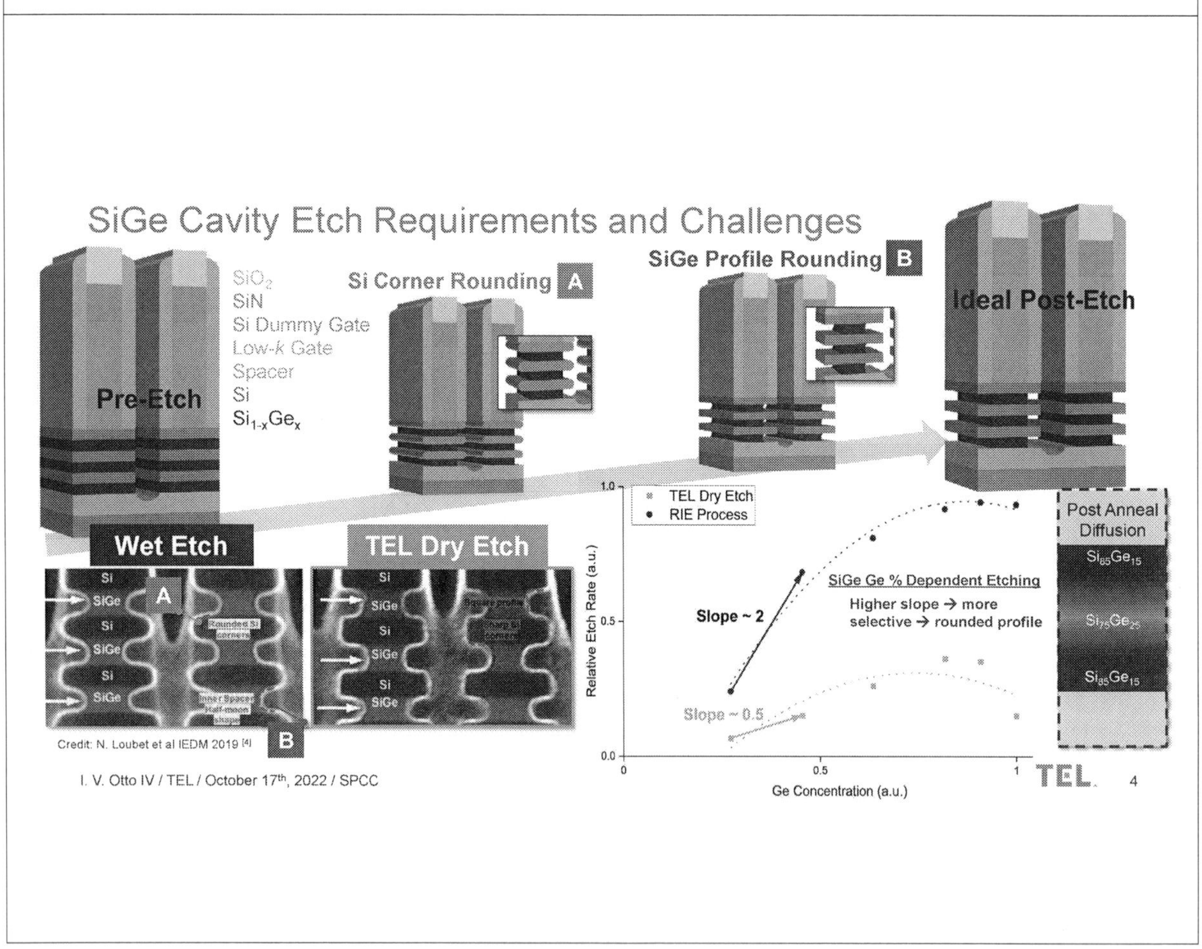
SiGe Cavity Etch Requirements and Challenges
SiO2
SiN
Si Dummy Gate
Low-k Gate
Spacer
Si
Si1-xGex
Pre-Etch
Si Corner Rounding A
SiGe Profile Rounding B
Ideal Post-Etch
Wet Etch
TEL Dry Etch
Credit: N. Loubet et al IEDM 2019 [4]
TEL Dry Etch
RIE Process
SiGe Ge % Dependent Etching
Higher slope → more selective → rounded profile
Slope ~ 2
Slope ~ 0.5
Relative Etch Rate (a.u.)
Ge Concentration (a.u.)
Post Anneal Diffusion
Si85Ge15
Si75Ge25
Si85Ge15
I. V. Otto IV / TEL / October 17th, 2022 / SPCC
TEL
4

SiGe Channel Release Requirements and Challenges

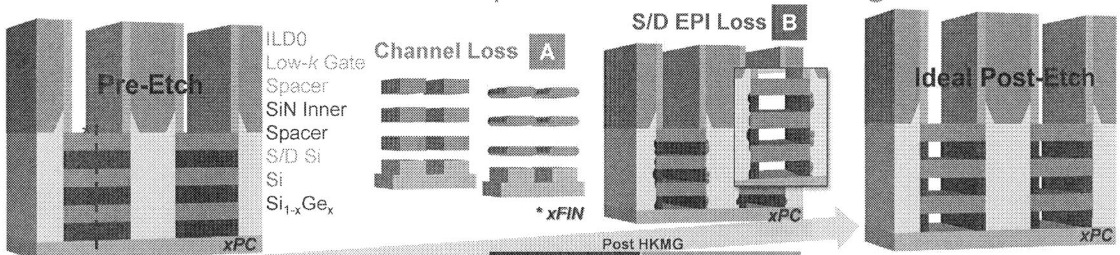

S/D EPI damage occurs if process penetrates inner spacer

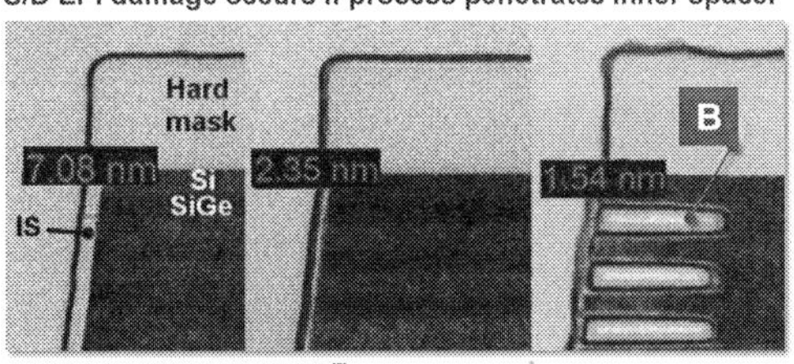

Credit. C. Durfee et al ECS 2021 [5]

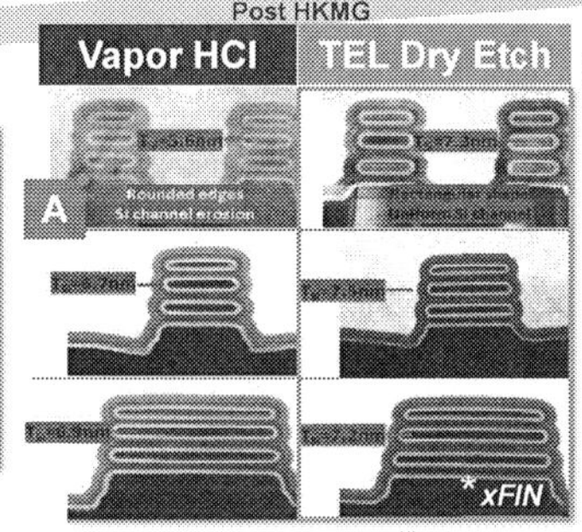

Credit: N. Loubet et al IEDM 2019 [4]

SiGe ChR Impact

- T_{Si} = channel thickness → preservation of Si need for optimal channel conductance
- Channel composition important to maintain → require removal of all SiGe and trace Ge
- S/D EPI integrity needs to be maintained

SiGe Channel Release S/D EPI Loss Expanded

Inner Spacer Impact

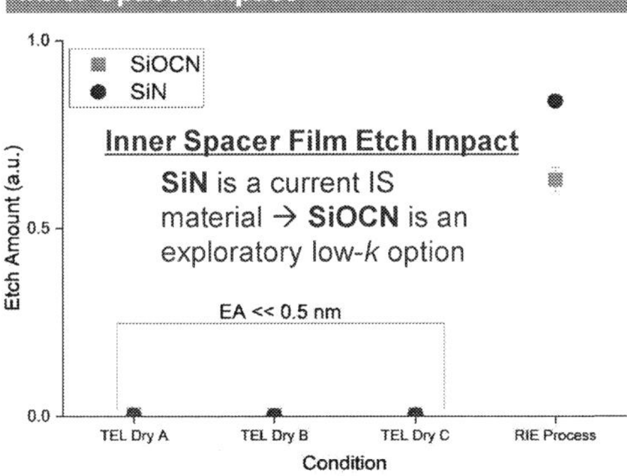

Inner Spacer Film Etch Impact

SiN is a current IS material → **SiOCN** is an exploratory low-*k* option

TEL dry processes have **high selectivity to SiN and SiOCN** (processes ~50 % OE)

Variable Channel Width Over-Etch nFET/pFET

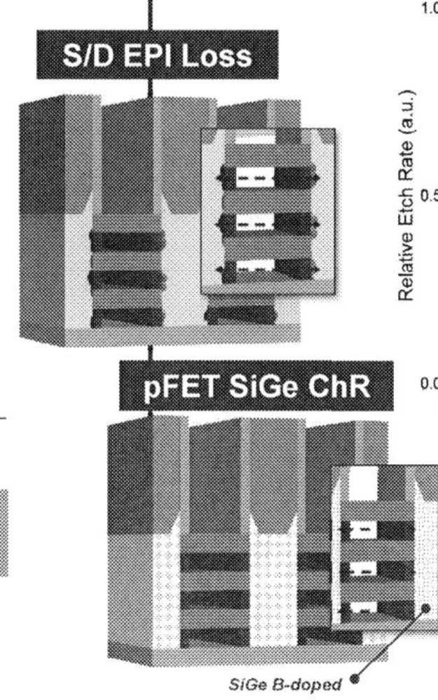

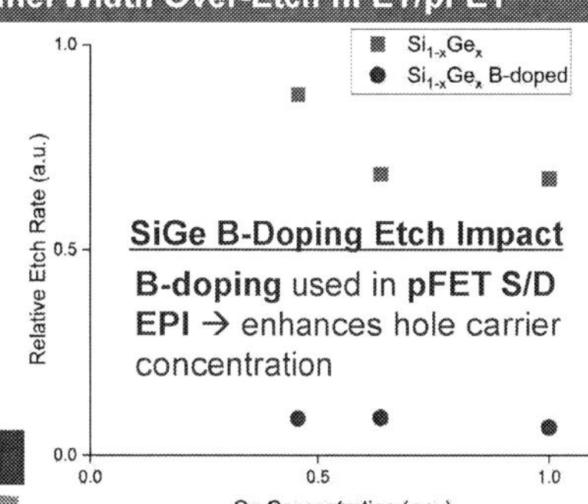

SiGe B-Doping Etch Impact

B-doping used in **pFET S/D EPI** → enhances hole carrier concentration

TEL dry processes can be tuned to have **>10:1** $Si_{0.75}Ge_{0.25}$:$Si_{0.75}Ge_{0.25}B$ **selectivity** → **extends pFET SiGe ChR OE margin**

SiGe Etch Device Impact

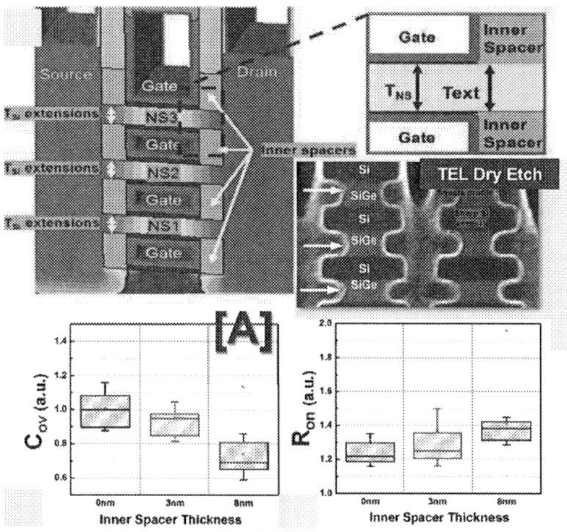

Credit: N. Loubet et al IEDM 2019 [4]

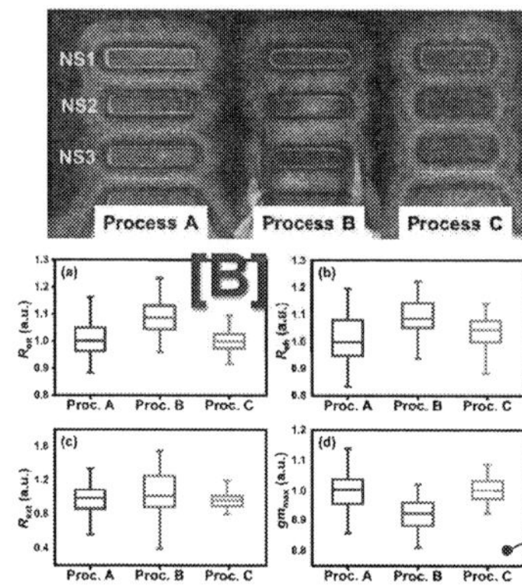

Credit: C. Durfee et al ECS 2021 [5]

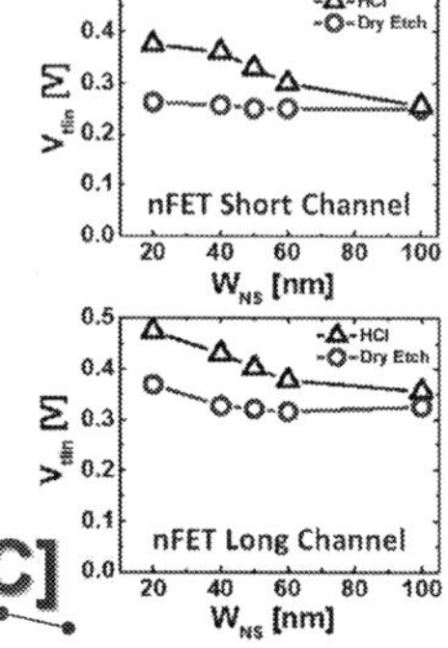

Credit: N. Loubet et al IEDM 2019 [4]

- **[A]: SiGe cavity etch directly determine IS thickness and shape → implications for on resistance (R_{on}) and overlap capacitance (C_{ov})**
- **[B]: Si channel profile impacts resistance from channel extension (R_{ext}) through channel (R_{ch}) to R_{on} overall**
- **[C]: Si channel thinning and profile affects transconductance (gm_{max}) and linear threshold voltage (V_{tlin})**

SiGe Etch Future Outlook → Past GAA

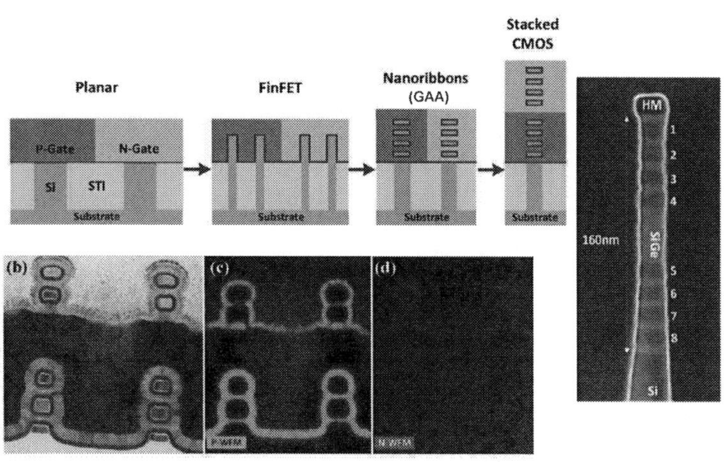

Credit: C.-Y. Huang et al IEDM 2020 [6]

- Stacked CMOS consolidates features into a further vertically integrated footprint
- Si/SiGe superlattice will need to undergo layer thickness and Ge % modification for stacked integration → stress engineering of superlattice
- **TEL dry process high selectivity and over-etch margin through tuning offers possible solution to integration challenges**
- **Dry nature of TEL process offers lower loading and more resistance to larger AR**

Summary and Conclusions

- GAA integration is the standard for movement to 2-3 nm past FinFET
- SiGe etch processes like **SiGe cavity etch** and **SiGe channel release** play key roles in device function and tuning
- The TEL dry processes showcased offer **robust process performance** with some **advantages over wet and RIE processes**
- These SiGe etches will only transfer to future architectures like stacked CMOS and may offer **resistance to new challenges introduced by the larger aspect ratio and new Si/SiGe superlattice**

References

- [1] "Samsung Electronics' Leadership in Advanced Foundry Technology Showcased with Latest Silicon Innovations and Ecosystem Platform," *Samsung Global Newsroom*, 15-May-2019. [Online]. Available: https://news.samsung.com/global/samsung-electronics-leadership-in-advanced-foundry-technology-showcased-with-latest-silicon-innovations-and-ecosystem-platform
- [2] J. Frougier and D. Guo, "Introducing the world's first 2 nm node chip," IBM Research Blog, 06-May-2021. [Online]. Available: https://research.ibm.com/blog/2-nm-chip
- [3] S. Kal et al., "Selective isotropic etching of Group IV semiconductors to enable gate all around device architectures," SPCC, p. 17, 2018.
- [4] N. Loubet et al., "A Novel Dry Selective Etch of SiGe for the Enablement of High Performance Logic Stacked Gate-All-Around NanoSheet Devices," in 2019 IEEE International Electron Devices Meeting (IEDM), San Francisco, CA, USA, Dec. 2019, p. 11.4.1-11.4.4. doi: 10.1109/IEDM19573.2019.8993615.
- [5] C. Durfee et al., "Highly Selective SiGe Dry Etch Process for the Enablement of Stacked Nanosheet Gate-All-Around Transistors," ECS Trans., vol. 104, no. 4, pp. 217–227, Oct. 2021, doi: 10.1149/10404.0217ecst.
- [6] C.-Y. Huang et al., "3-D Self-aligned Stacked NMOS-on-PMOS Nanoribbon Transistors for Continued Moore's Law Scaling," in 2020 IEEE International Electron Devices Meeting (IEDM), San Francisco, CA, USA, Dec. 2020, p. 20.6.1-20.6.4. doi: 10.1109/IEDM13553.2020.9372066.

TEL™

TOKYO ELECTRON

TEL
TOKYO ELECTRON

Development of UV-assisted Electrochemical Etching

SPCC 2022

Rintaro Higuchi, Koji Kagawa, Mitsunori Nakamori, Itaru Kanno
Process Technology Dept., Tokyo Electron Kyushu Ltd.
1-1 Fukuhara, Koshi, Kumamoto 861-1116, Japan
(e-mail) rintaro.higuchi@tel.com (phone) +81-96-349-5746

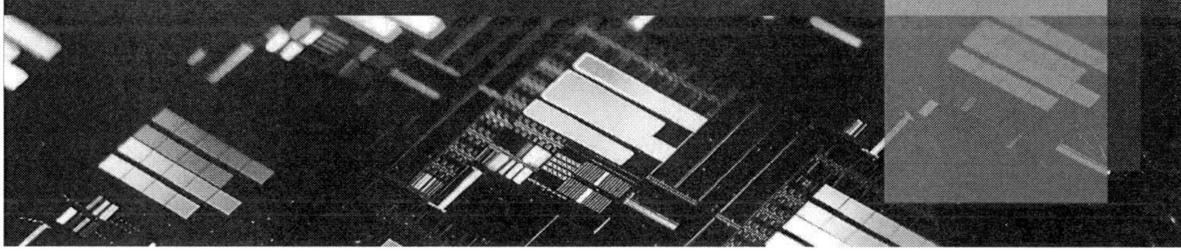

Electrochemical Etching (ECE)

- ECE: wet etching based on electrochemical oxidation of target films

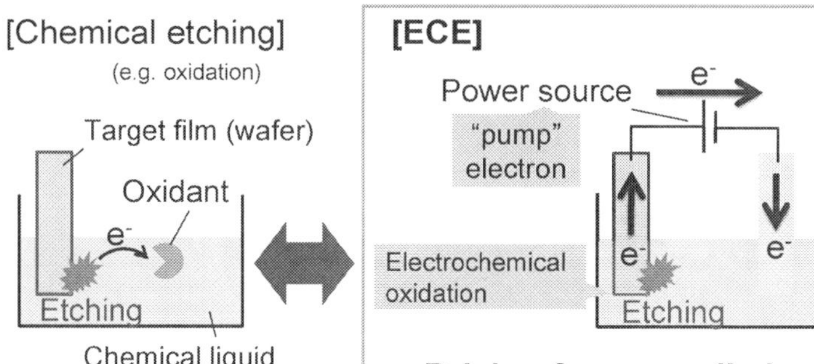

- **Driving force: applied voltage**
- **Common chemicals applicable**

Prior art of ECE

Removal of Ru bevel film using HCl + brush has been reported.*

*H. Aoki *et al.*, Japanese Journal of Applied Physics, **48**, 04C019(2009).

Target Materials

Material	Use	Current etching process
Ru	Interconnect	Special chemicals
Amorphous carbon (a-C)	Hard mask	Plasma etching (bevel)

Table: Chemicals for Ru-etching

Chemical	Etching result
SPM ($H_2SO_4+H_2O_2$)	No etching
Conc. HF	No etching
Conc. BHF	No etching
SC-2 ($HCl+H_2O_2$)	No etching
$Ce(NH_4)_2(NO_3)_6$	Etching
H_5IO_6	Etching

Strong oxidizer / Conc. acids
No etching

Special chemicals
High cost / metal-containing

Direct / Indirect ECE

[Direct]
Electrode-wafer: **direct contact**

[Indirect]
Electrode-wafer: **contact through liquid**

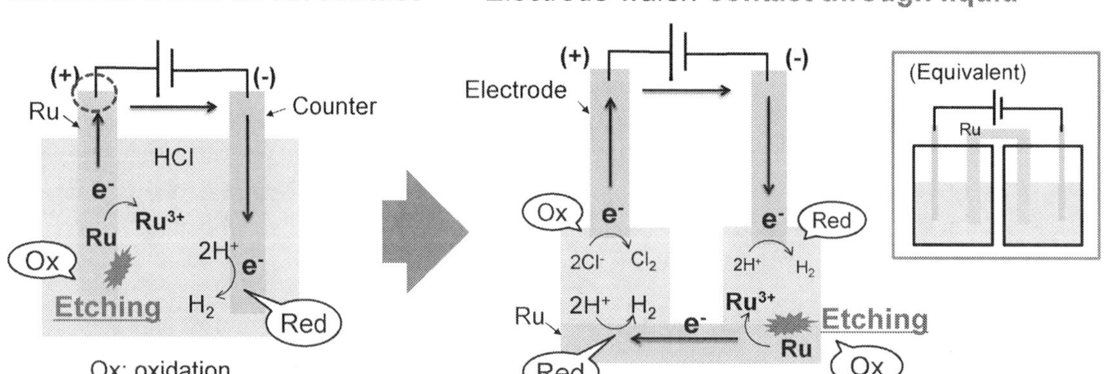

Ox: oxidation
Red: reduction

Ru Removal by Indirect ECE

Sample:
CVD-Ru (35 nm) / TiN (2 nm) / SiO_2 / Si

[Experimental]

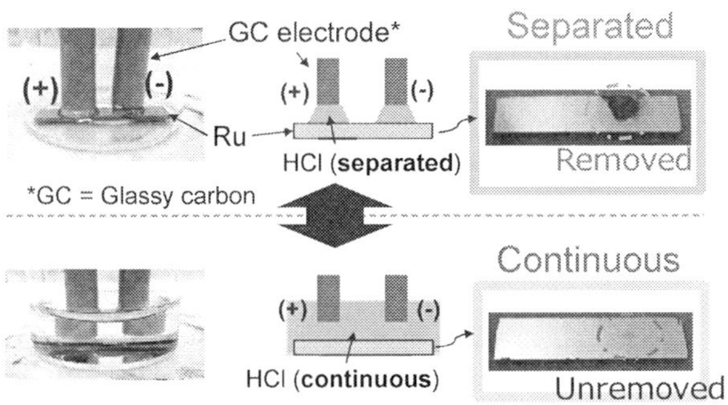

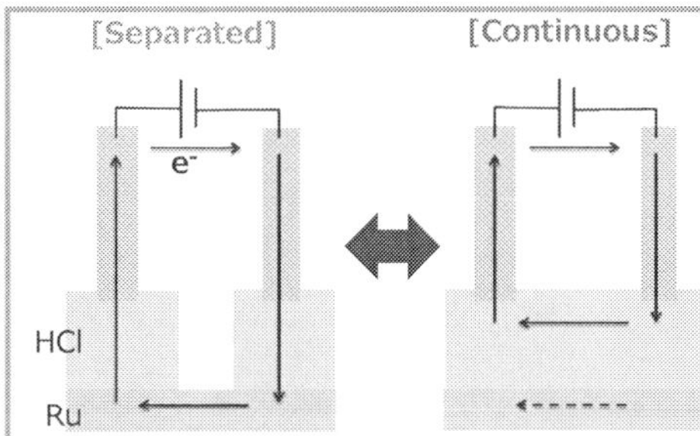

Separating the solution is necessary for efficient ECE.

Chemical	Voltage (V)	Process time (s)	Temp.
1 wt% HCl	5	300	R.T.

- **Confirmed Ru removal by indirect ECE**

Ru Removal by Electrode-built-in Nozzle

[Experimental]

Sample:
CVD-Ru (35 nm) / TiN (2 nm) / SiO_2 / Si

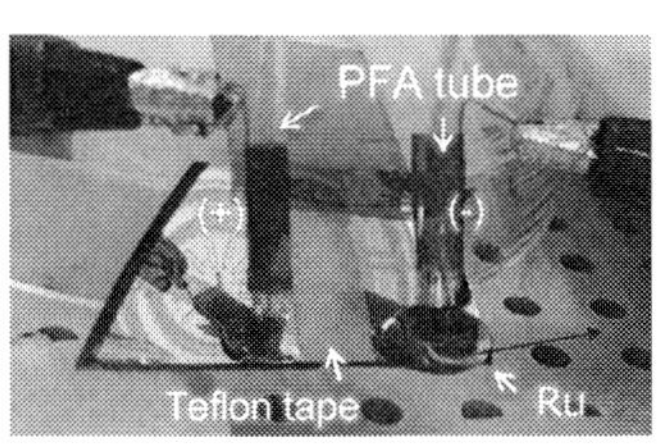

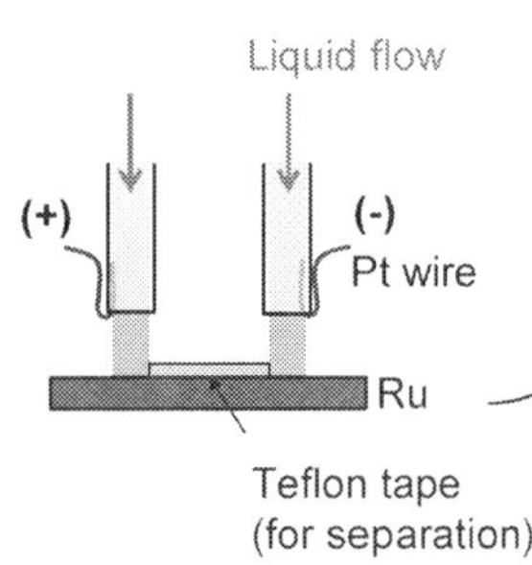

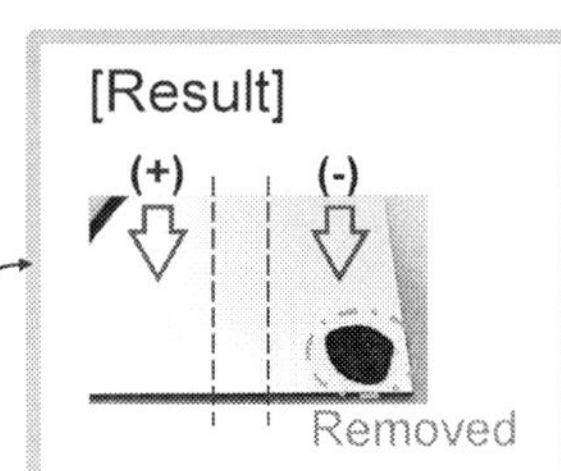

Chemical	Voltage (V)	Process time (s)	Temp.
1 wt% HCl	10	40	R.T.

- **Ru was removed by ECE with liquid flow**

Application for a-C Removal

[Resistance of a-C and Ru film]

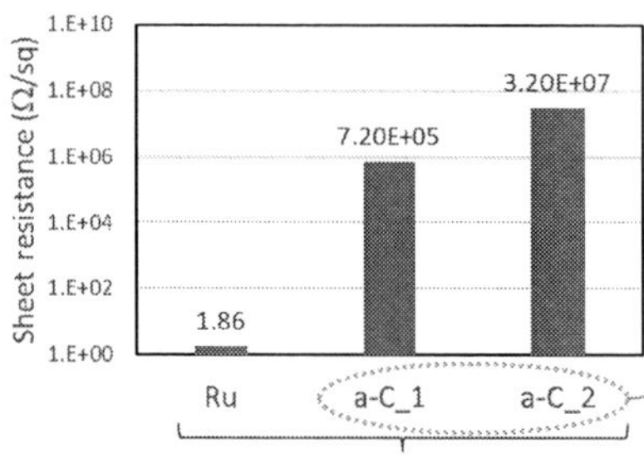

Samples used in this study

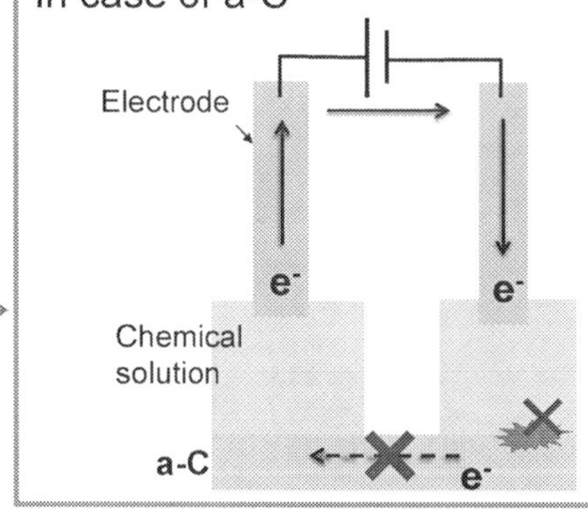

- The resistivity of a-C is much higher than Ru.
- Challenging/Impossible to apply ECE!

➡ **UV-assisted ECE**

a-C Removal by ECE with Photoexcitation

- Target: a-C, ~10^5 Ω/sq

Sample: a-C (400 nm) / Si

[Experimental]

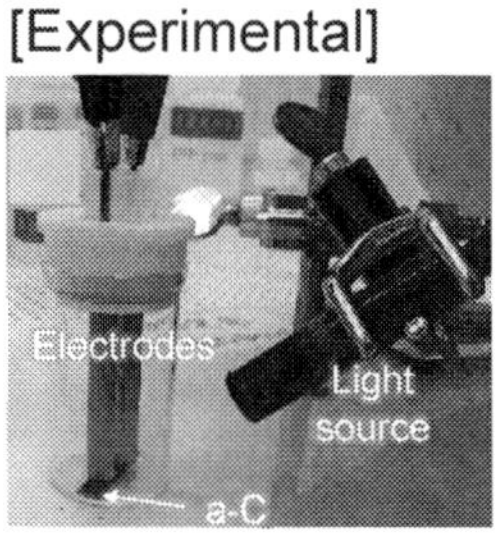

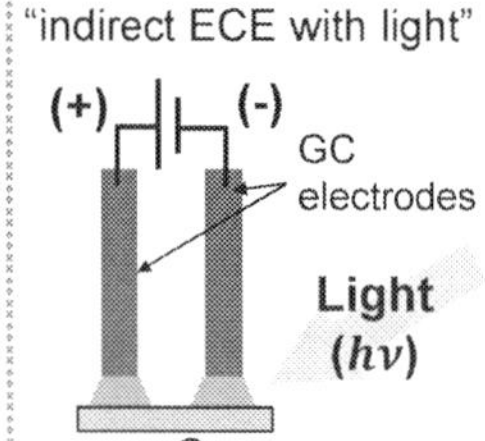

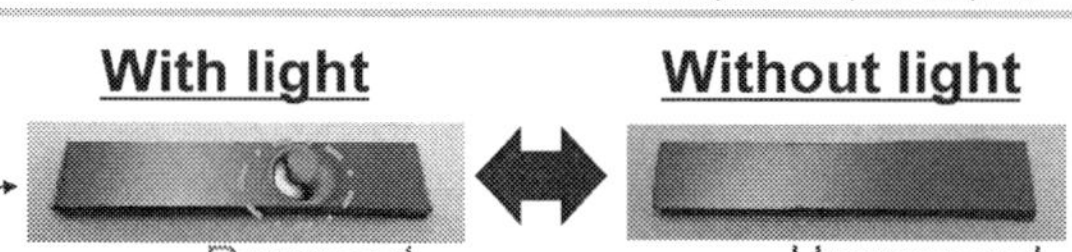

Light	Chemical	Voltage (V)	Process time (min)
UV 365 nm	1 wt% TMAH	10	20

*TMAH = Tetramethylammonium hydroxide

Conc.TMAH condition

Removed (within 5 min)

Light	Chemical	Voltage (V)	Process time (min)
UV 365 nm	25 wt% TMAH	10	5

- **a-C film was removed by ECE with photoexcitation**

Photoelectrochemical etching

*All experiments were done at R.T.

Highly Resistive a-C Removal by ECE with Photoexcitation

- a-C resistivity varies with sp2/sp3 bond ratio (graphite/diamond-like)
- Target: highly resistive a-C, ~10^7 Ω/sq

[Experimental]

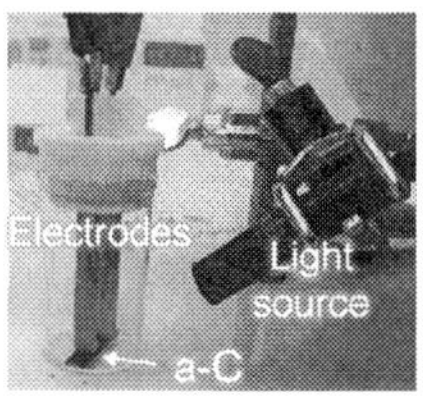

Sample: a-C (150 nm) / SiN / Si

Process time (min)	0 (initial)	1	3
Photo	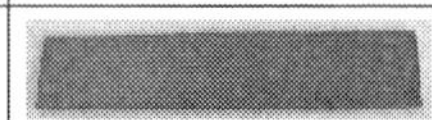	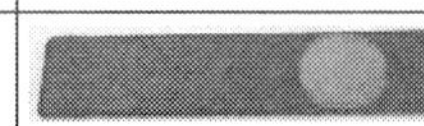	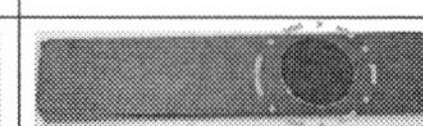
SEM (X-section)	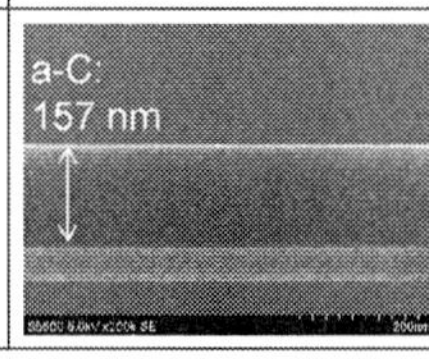	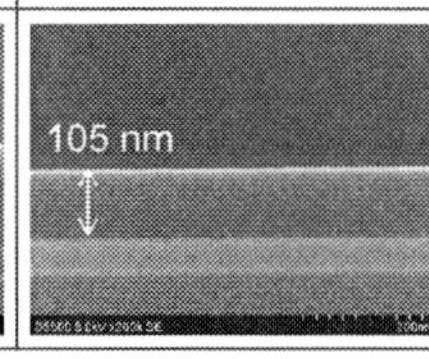	

- **a-C film was also removed by ECE**

Light	Chemical	Voltage (V)	Temp.
UV 365 nm	25 wt% TMAH	60	R.T.

Mechanism: ECE with Photoexcitation

- Why does photoexcitation enhance ECE of a-C? ⇒ **Band structure**

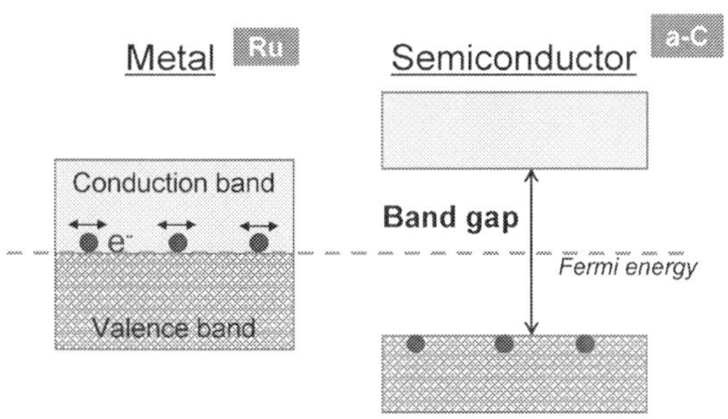

Band gap blocks current
⇒ No oxidation
= No etching

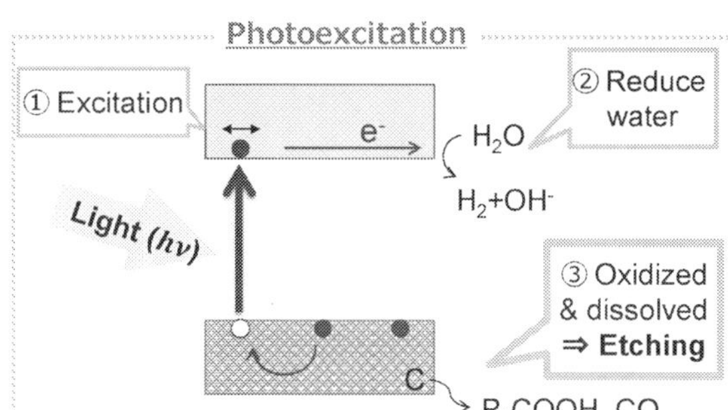

Role of light:
- Excite electron (higher energy)
- Generate electrical current

Enhance ECE of a-C

Summary

- Ru and a-C films were removed by ECE using common chemicals.
- Applying external energy on ECE can dramatically enhance the etching of a-C films.

- Challenges:
  - Implementation of ECE complicates the wet tool (electrodes, light source, liquid separation, ...etc.)
  - Removal of higher resistive a-C

Appendix

Current Path

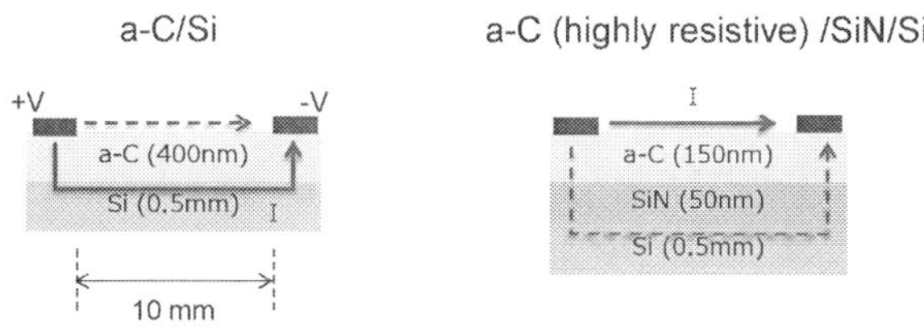

I: Main current path

- a-C/Si: current passes through underlayer (Si substrate).
- a-C (highly resistive) /SiN/Si: current passes through a-C because resistance of SiN in thickness direction is higher than a-C in plane.

TEL™
TOKYO ELECTRON

THE SURFACE PREPARATION AND CLEANING CONFERENCE (SPCC)

SPCC 2022 | Wild Horse Pass, Chandler, AZ, USA | October 17-18, 2022

Characterization of impurities from incoming PVA brush for sub 10 nm post CMP cleaning process

October 17, 2022

Kwang-Min Han[1], Suprakash Samanta[2], Jerome Peter[2], and Jin-Goo Park[2,*]

[1]Department of Bio-Nano Technology and [2]Department of Materials Science and Chemical Engineering, Hanyang University, Ansan, 15588, Republic of Korea

*jgpark@hanyang.ac.kr

The Engine of Korea

Outline

- Introduction and Motivation
- Experimental Materials and Procedure
- Experimental Results and Discussion
  - Optical Analysis for Extracted Impurities
  - LPC and UV-visible Analysis for Extracted Solution
  - ^{1}H NMR Analysis for Dissolved Solution
- Summary

Introduction and Motivation

Defect Issues after CMP Process

- **Chemical Mechanical Planarization (CMP)**

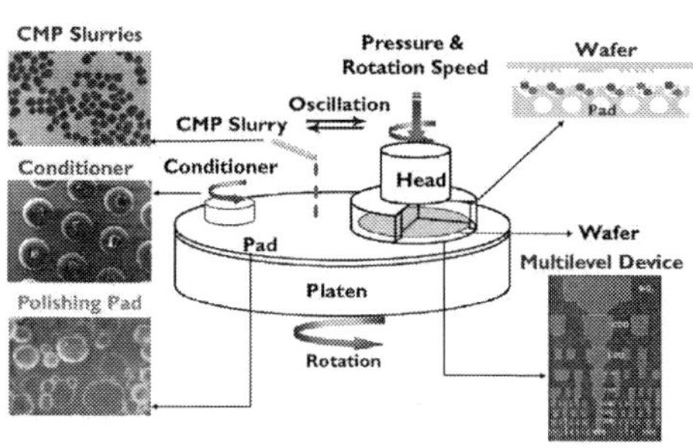

- **Common Defects after CMP Process**

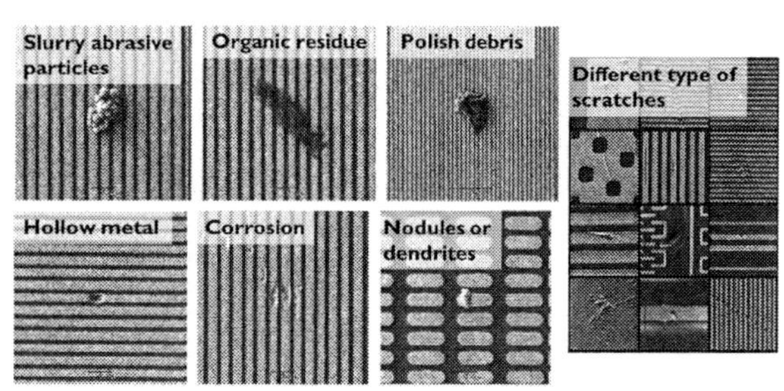

Ref. : Wei-Tsu Tseng et. al., ASMC, 2012 23rd Annual SEMI
Ref. : M. Krishnan et. al., Chem. Rev. 2010, 110, 178-204

- CMP is a well-known process to remove film materials and achieve highly planarized surface
- Various kinds of defects remain on the wafer surface after the CMP process
- These defects cause serious problems such as yield reduction and device failure

Post CMP Cleaning Process

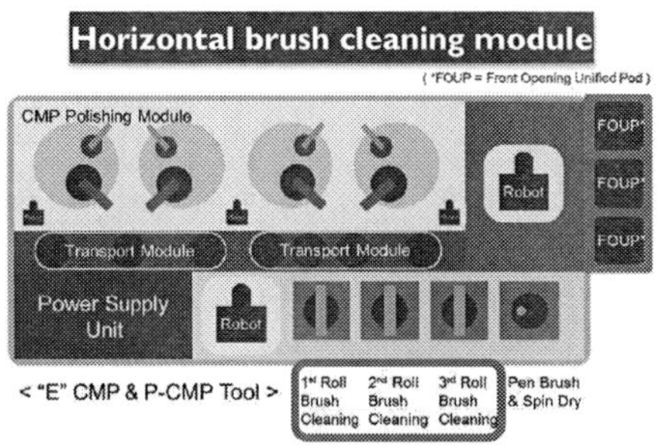

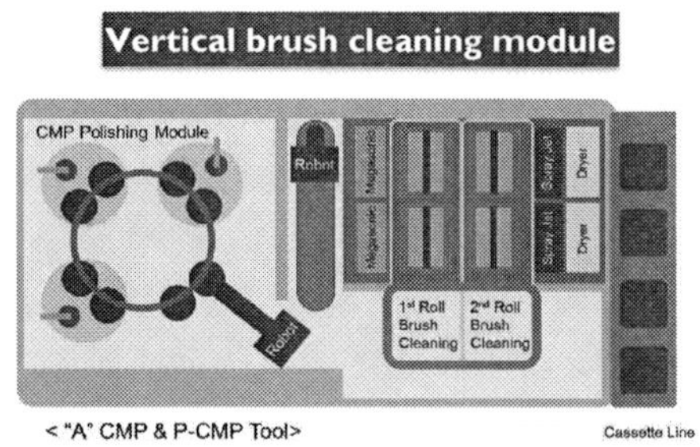

Ref. : J. H. Lee et al., SPCC 2018

- A post-CMP cleaning process is necessary to remove the defects after the CMP process
- Among the various post-CMP cleaning processes, brush cleaning is one of the most effective methods
- In the CMP module, a brush cleaning module is included in the equipment for post-CMP cleaning process

PVA Brush Cleaning Process

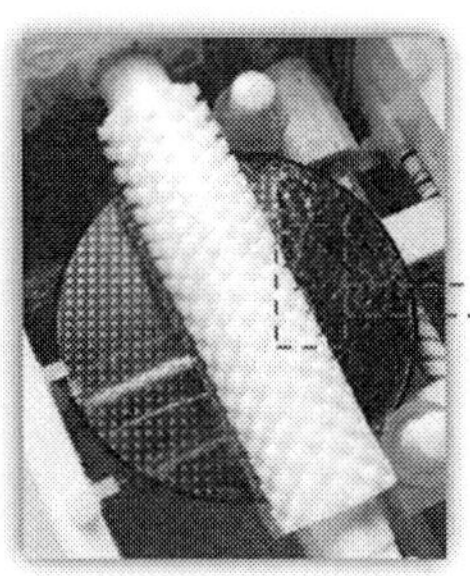

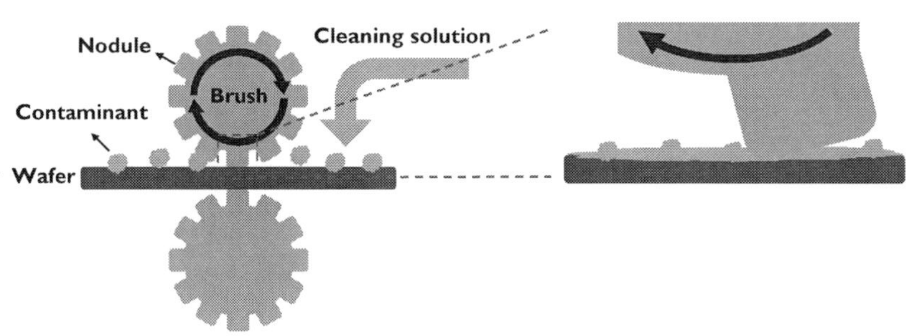

- **High cleaning efficiency** due to its physical force by direct contact between brush and wafer surface
- **Low cost of ownership (COO)**
- **Process flexibility with various solutions**

Defects from Incoming PVA Brush after Break-in Process

- **Defect requirements in break-in process**

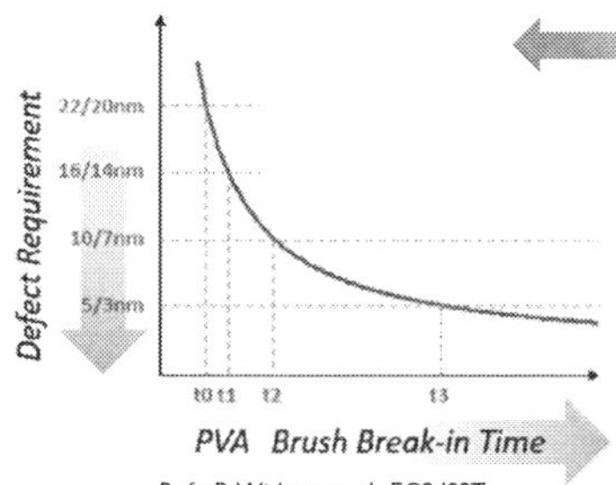

Ref. : B. Withers et al., ECS JSST, 8(12), P794-P798 (2019)

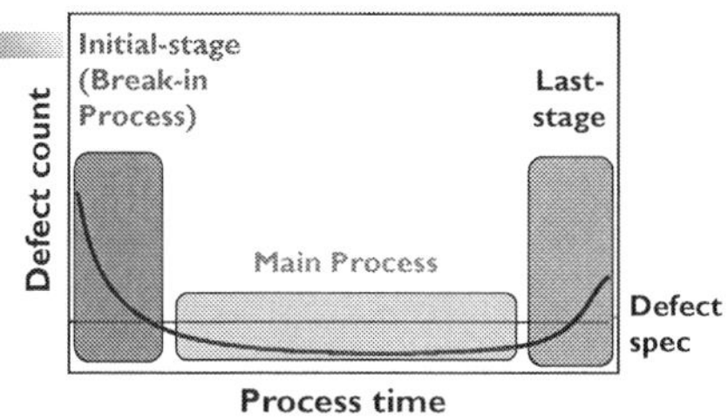

Ref. : J. H. Lee et al., SPCC 2018

- **Defects after break-in process**

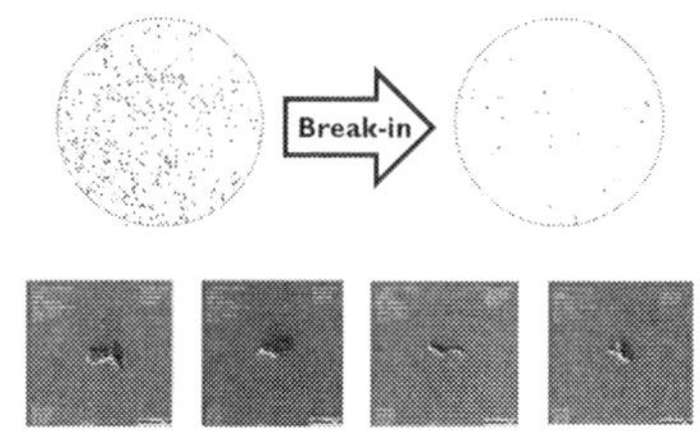

Ref. : H.J. Kim et al., J. Korean Soc. Tribol. Lubr. Eng., 31, 239-244 (2015)

- Since there are many impurities in the incoming PVA brush, break-in process is performed in the initial stage
- As the technology node is advanced, the defect requirements become more strict in the break-in process
- **However, after the break-in process, unknown impurities still exist on the wafer surface**

Common Impurities from Incoming PVA Brush

- **Schematic of wafer contamination after brush scrubbing process**

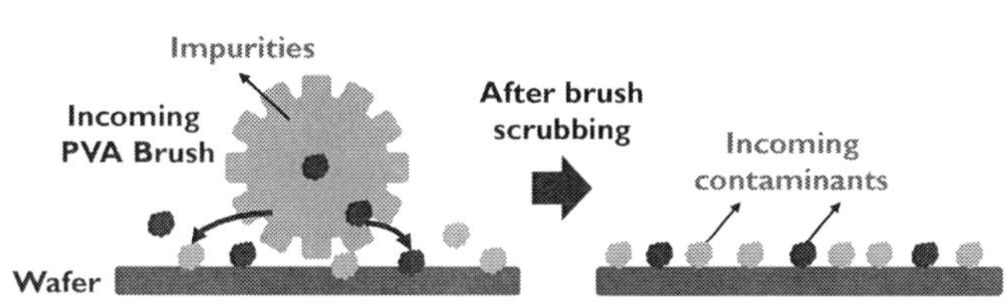

- **Common impurities from PVA brush**

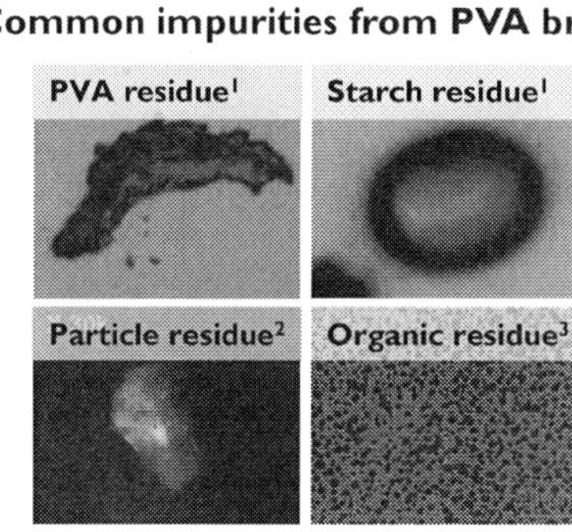

Ref. 1 : B. Withers et al., ECS JSST, 8(12), P794-P798 (2019)
Ref. 2 : J.H. Lee et al., Polymer Testing, 77, 105921 (2019)
Ref. 3 : J.H. Lee et al., Polymer Testing, 90, 106669 (2020)

- Impurities inside the PVA brush can be extracted and adsorbed on the wafer surface during brush scrubbing
- Some researchers reported that the impurities are PVA, starch, particle, and organic residues
- **However, the root causes of the impurities from PVA brush have not been clearly identified yet**

Typical Formulation Process for Making PVA Brush

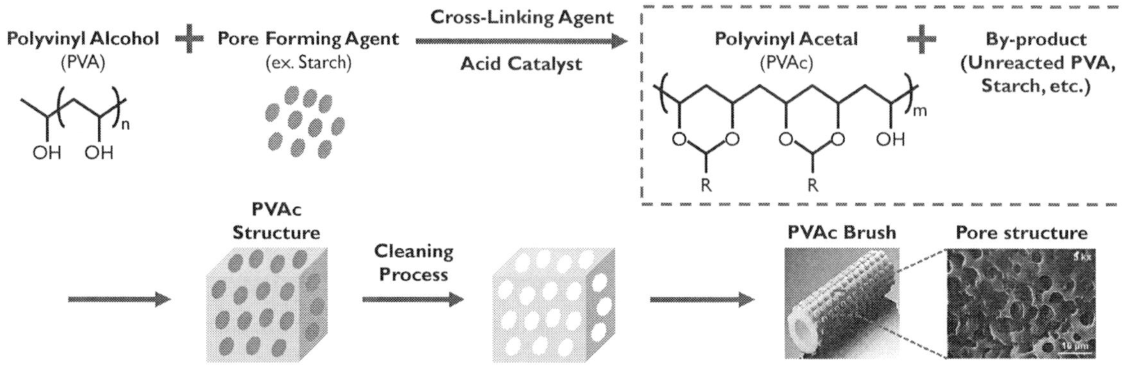

- To identify the root causes of the impurities, the formulation process for making PVA brush was investigated
- The PVAc is formulated by the acetalization reaction between PVA and cross-linking agent
- After the cleaning process, the by-product and pore forming agent are removed from the PVAc brush
- **The development of characterization methods was necessary to identify the by-products**

Experimental Materials and Procedure

Experimental Materials

Brush scrubbing

- **Commercial PVA brush**
  (300 mm)

- **Bare-Si wafer**
  (300 mm)

Drop deposition

- **Extracted solution**
  from PVA brush

- ***SC1-cleaned Bare-Si coupon wafer**
  (20 x 20 mm²)

*SC1 cleaning condition
- $NH_4OH : H_2O_2 :$ DIW = 1:2:50
- Temp. and Time : 70 °C, 10 min

UV-visible analysis

- **Extracted solution**
  from PVA brush

- **Indicator solution**
  used to identify the amount of **starch**

^{1}H NMR analysis

- **Dissolved solution**
  from PVA brush

- **Organosulfur solvent**
  used to extract the **unreacted PVA** from PVA brush

- **Internal standard solution**
  used to quantify the amount of **unreacted PVA**

Experimental Procedure for Impurity Extraction by Brush Scrubbing

As-received Brush

- Roll inner rinse with DI Water for 30 min

As-received wafer

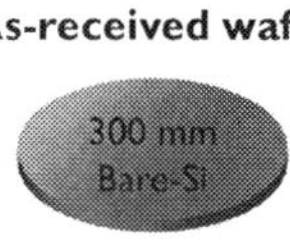

Surface scan before scrubbing

Optical Surface Analyzer
(Candela CS10, KLA-TENCOR, USA)

Scrubbing test with EBARA scrubber

300 mm Brush scrubber
(Special-made, EBARA, Japan)

Surface scan after scrubbing

Analysis of particle number

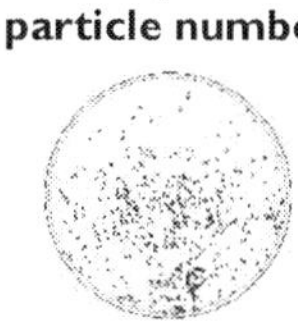

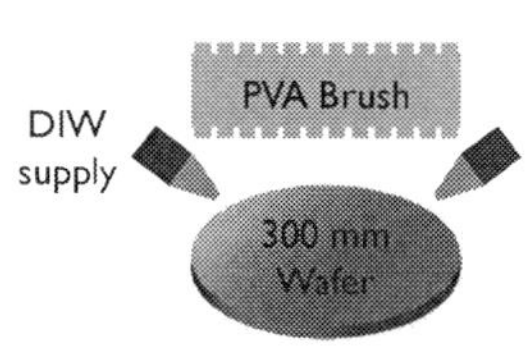

Brush	Commercial brush
Solution	DI Water
Wafer	300 mm Bare-Si

Scrubbing process condition
- Brush rotation : 100 rpm
- Wafer rotation : 100 rpm
- Gap distance : -1.5 mm
- Flow rate : 500 mL/min
- Cumulative time : 1, 10, 30, 60 min

Experimental Procedure for Impurity Analysis

Extracted solution from incoming PVA brush → Concentrate the solution using **rotary evaporator** →
- **Liquid particle count analysis** → **Liquid Particle Sizer** (Accusizer 780AD, PSS, USA)
- Drop deposition on wafer for **impurity shape analysis** → **Optical Microscope** (LV-100D, Nikon, Japan)
- Mixing with indicator solution for **starch content analysis** → **UV-visible spectroscopy** (Lambda 365, Perkin Elmer, USA)

Rotary Evaporator
(R-100, BUCHI, Switzerland)

Liquid Particle Sizer
(Accusizer 780AD, PSS, USA)

Optical Microscope
(LV-100D, Nikon, Japan)

UV-visible spectroscopy
(Lambda 365, Perkin Elmer, USA)

Dissolved solution from dried PVA brush by solvent → Concentrate the solution using **rotary evaporator** → Mixing with internal standard solution for **unreacted PVA content analysis** → **^{1}H NMR spectroscopy** (AVANCE III 400, Bruker, USA)

^{1}H NMR spectroscopy
(AVANCE III 400, Bruker, USA)

Experimental Results and Discussion

Observation of Wafer Contamination during Break-in Process

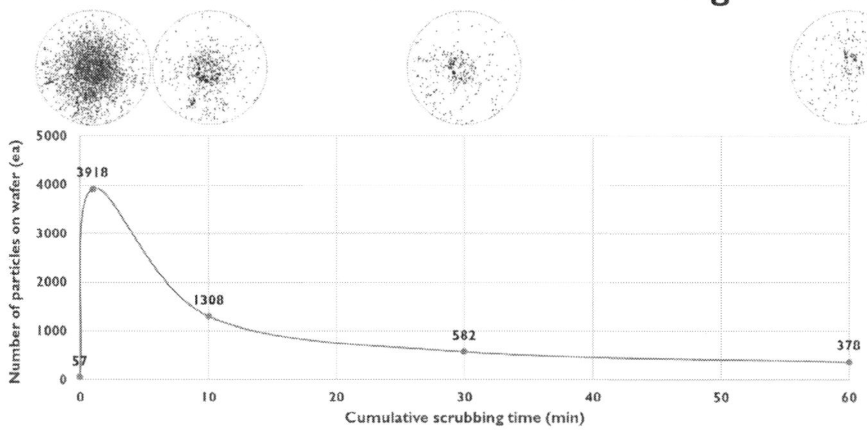

Scrubbing Condition
Brush rotation : 100 rpm
Wafer rotation : 100 rpm
Gap distance : -1.5 mm
Flow rate : 500 mL/min

- In the initial break-in process, many particles were contaminated on the wafer surface
- As the scrubbing time increased, the number of particles on the wafer decreased
- It was necessary to find out what particles were contaminated on the wafer surface during brush scrubbing

Observation of Impurities on Wafer Surface after Drop Deposition

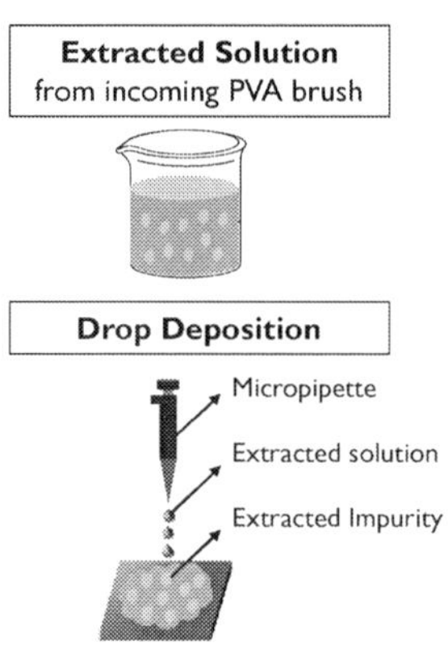

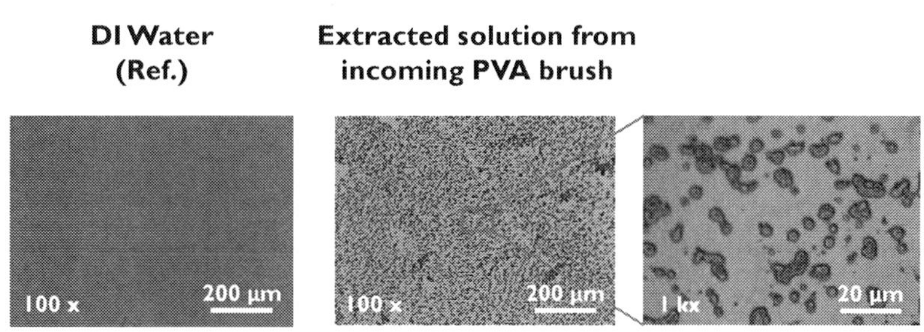

- To investigate the impurity shape in the extracted solution, drop deposition method was performed
- After the drop deposition with DI water as a reference, there was no wafer contamination
- After the drop deposition with the extracted solution, many impurities were observed on the wafer surface

Number of Particles in DI Water and Extracted Solution from Brush

DI Water (Ref.)

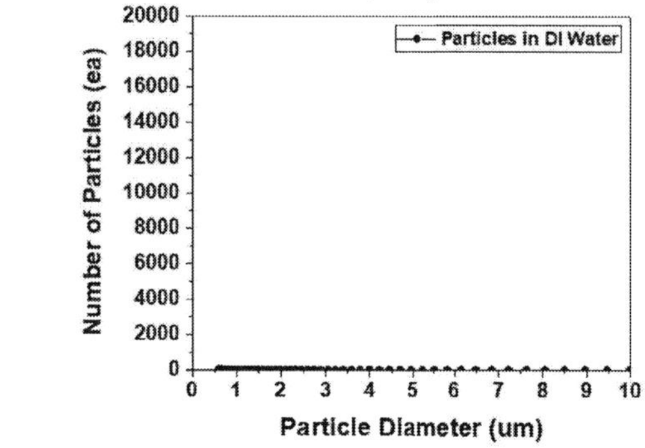

Extracted solution from incoming PVA brush

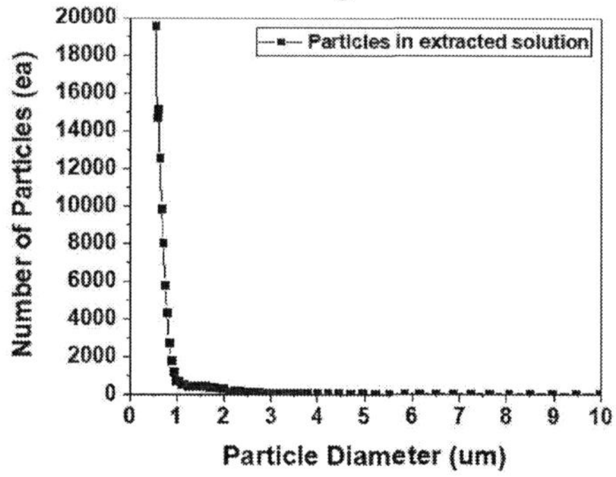

- To know the number of particles in the extracted solution, LPC was analyzed using Accusizer
- Compared to the DI water, the number of particles in the extracted solution was measured to be very high
- It was necessary to identify the components of the particles in the extracted solution

Quantitative Analysis of Starch Content using UV-visible Spectra

- **UV-visible spectra of indicator solution by pure starch concentration**
- **Absorbance values of starch-indicator peak as a function of starch concentration**

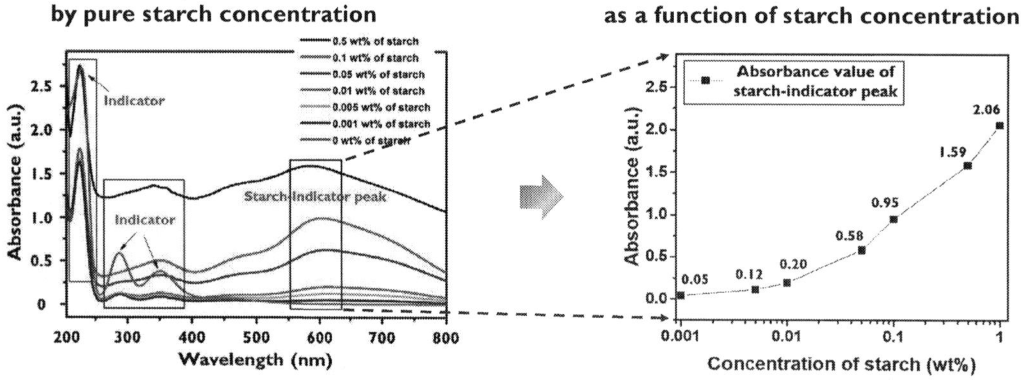

- To identify the starch amount quantitatively, UV-visible analysis was performed using indicator solution
- The intensity of absorbance peak increased with increasing the starch concentration
- The absorbance value at the starch-indicator peak increased as a function of starch concentration

UV-visible Spectra of Extracted Solution with Indicator Solution

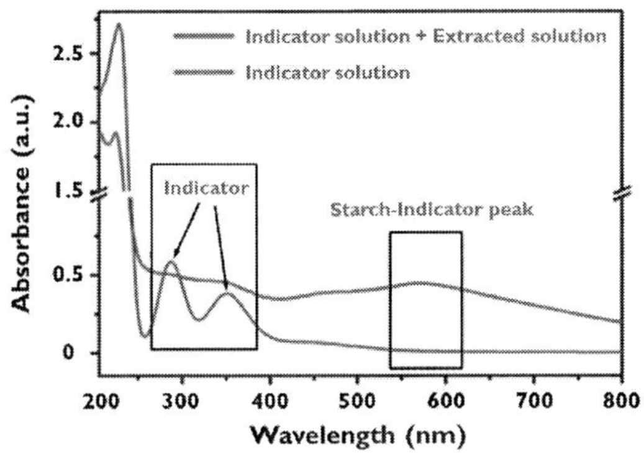

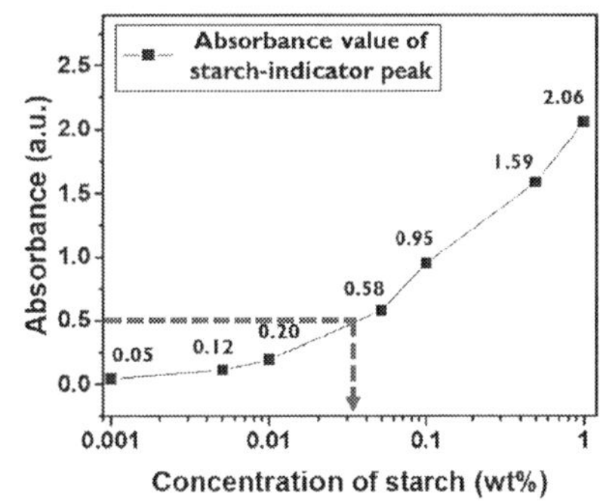

- When the indicator solution was measured, there was no signal at the starch-indicator peak
- When the extracted solution was measured with indicator, the starch-indicator peak was observed
- Based on the quantitative analysis by pure starch, the starch amount in the extracted solution was estimated

UV-visible Spectra of Pure PVA Solution with Indicator Solution

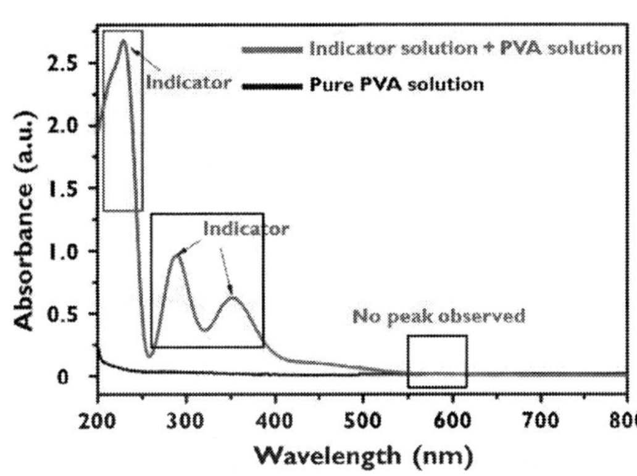

- When the pure PVA solution was measured, there was no signal at the whole wavelength range
- When the pure PVA solution was measured with indicator, the starch-indicator peak was not observed
- It was confirmed that only starch was detected using UV-visible spectroscopy with indicator solution

^1H NMR Spectra of Pure PVA Powder with Internal Standard Solution

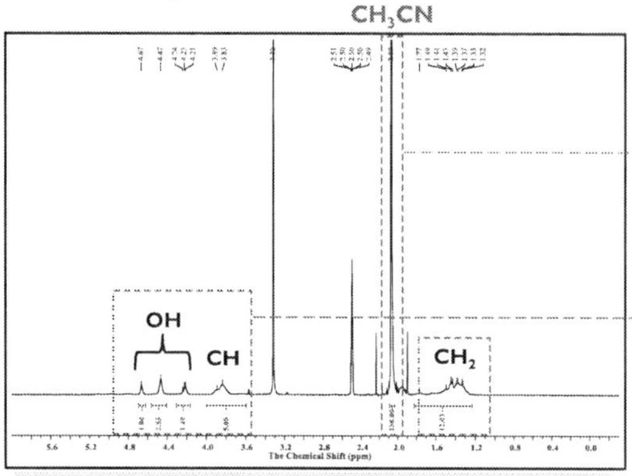

Internal standard solution:
Acetonitrile (CH_3CN) = 138 H (25 μL)

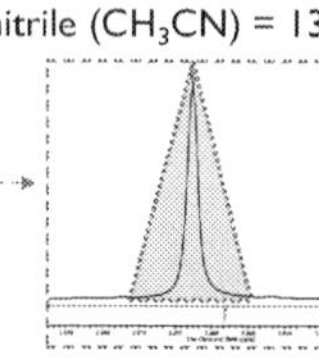

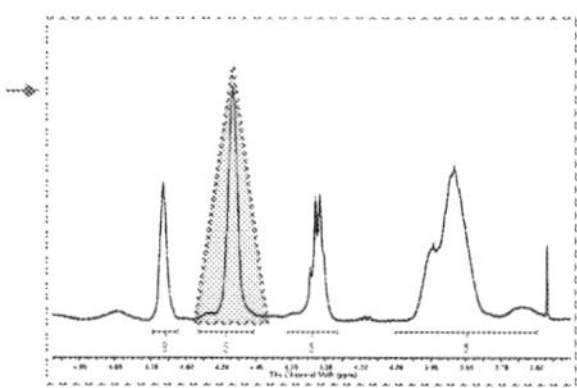

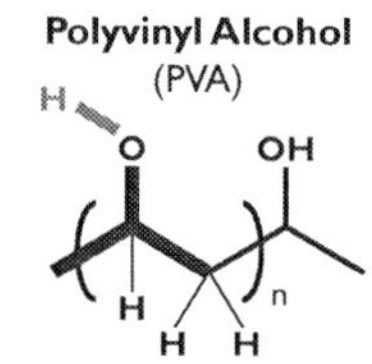

138 H of CH_3CN : 2.5 H of PVA (3 mg in 1 mL)

- To identify the amount of PVA component quantitatively, ^1H NMR analysis was performed
- In the measured ^1H NMR spectra, the signal at 4.5 ppm is the proton peak of OH group from pure PVA
- Through the relative ratio of the peak area to the internal standard, the amount of OH proton was calculated

^1H NMR Spectra of Dissolved Solution from Incoming PVA Brush

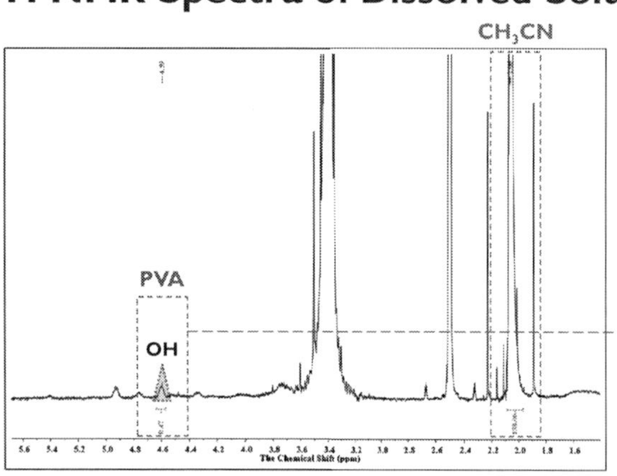

Pure PVA 3 mg in 1 mL 138 : 2.5 (CH_3CN : PVA)

Unknown PVA in 1 mL 138 : 0.47 (CH_3CN : Unknown PVA)

$$\frac{3}{2.5} * 0.47 = 0.56\ mg\ of\ \boldsymbol{unreacted\ PVA\ residues}\ from\ 1\ g\ of\ PVA\ brush\ in\ 1\ mL\ of\ dissolved\ solution$$

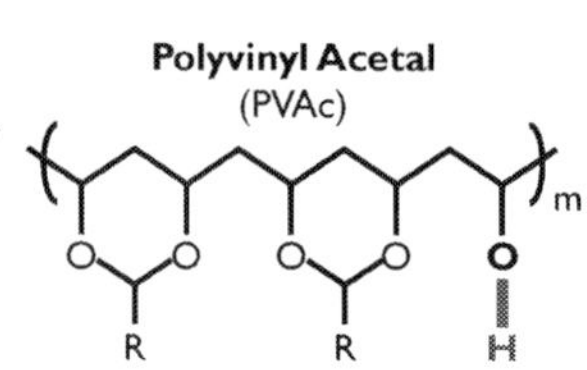

- The proton peak of OH group appeared at around 4.5 ppm in the measured ^1H NMR spectra
- The proton peak is the unreacted PVA in the formulated PVAc brush structure
- The amount of unreacted PVA in the PVAc brush was calculated by relative comparison with pure PVA

Summary

- The wafer contamination by brush in the initial break-in process was observed by **optical surface analyzer**
- The morphology of impurities from the extracted solution was observed by **optical microscope**
- The **starch** content in the extracted solution was quantitatively identified by **UV-visible spectroscopy**
- The amount of **unreacted PVA** in the brush was quantitatively identified by ^{1}**H NMR spectroscopy**
- The **starch residues** and **unreacted PVA** could be a defect source during brush scrubbing process

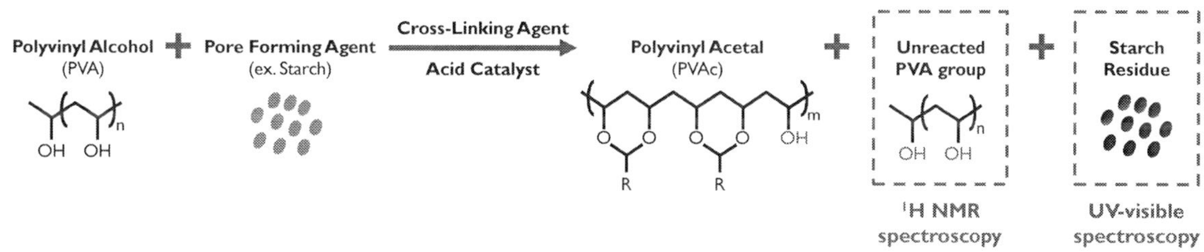

HANYANG
UNIVERSITY

한양대학교 ERICA 캠퍼스

Akrion Technologies
Diffusing Chemistry into High Aspect-Ratio Microstructures through Vacuum Technology

Ismail Kashkoush, Steven McKinley, Darian Waugh, Tyler Webber and Dennis Nemeth

Email: ikashkoush@akriontech.com Phone: +1(610) 530-3379

SPCC 2022, Chandler AZ Oct 17-18

Outline

- Introduction
  - Problem Statement
  - Technical Background
- Experimental Setup
  - Vacuum Prime/Dry Process Description
  - Experiment A – Prime vs No-Primed Etch Comparison
  - Experiment B – Vacuum Prime and Dry Characterization
- Results & Discussion
- Conclusions

Introduction

- In IC and MEMS production, manufacturers incorporate high aspect ratio microstructures into silicon wafers for various applications
  - Examples include pressure sensors, gyroscopes, gas flow sensors and 3D integrated circuits.
- These microstructures present challenges when attempting to process them in batches through a wet bench
- When these microstructures are submerged in chemical baths, air pockets form within the structures, preventing the chemical from reaching the bottom of the vias and leaving them partially unprocessed

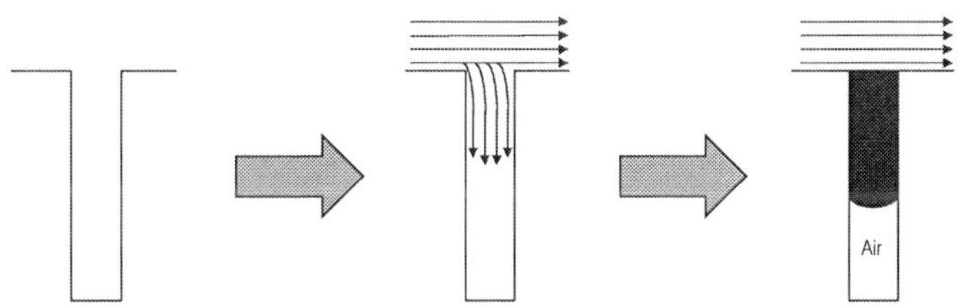

Introduction

- One way to potentially circumvent this issue is to prevent the air pockets from forming in the first place using a vacuum. Air evacuated from microstructures is replaced with priming fluid.
- When primed wafers are immersed in chemical solutions, there is a concentration gradient between the bath and the priming fluid
- Fick's First Law of Diffusion: Solute will move from a region of high concentration to one of low concentration across a concentration gradient
  - $J = -D\frac{d\varphi}{dx}$
  - Chemical would move from the bath into the primed microstructures in a process tank and vice-versa in a rinse tank

Introduction

- Vacuum could also dry microstructures filled with priming fluid.
  - Exposing liquid to low pressure environment induces evaporation at lower temperatures
- Clausius Clapeyron Equation
  - $\ln P_{sat} = -\left(\frac{\Delta H_{vap}}{RT}\right) + C$
  - Vacuum reduces the saturation pressure; minimal external energy must be applied for the liquid residing in the vias to evaporate
- Langmuir Evaporation Equation
  - $\frac{dM}{dt} = \left(P_{sat} - P_p\right) * \sqrt{\left(\frac{m}{2\pi RT}\right)}$
  - The vacuum evacuating the vapor from the system will keep the partial pressure low, thus allowing for a constant and rapid evaporation rate

Experimental Setup

- Wafers are placed and sealed in a stainless-steel chamber
- Vacuum activates and evacuates the air from the chamber until the pressure matches the low pressure setpoint. Chamber repressurizes after this phase in a drying process.
- Chamber is brought to priming pressure. DI water would be introduced into the chamber, filling to the point of completely submerging the wafers.
- After being held at the priming pressure for a set amount of time, the chamber would be repressurized with nitrogen then unsealed.

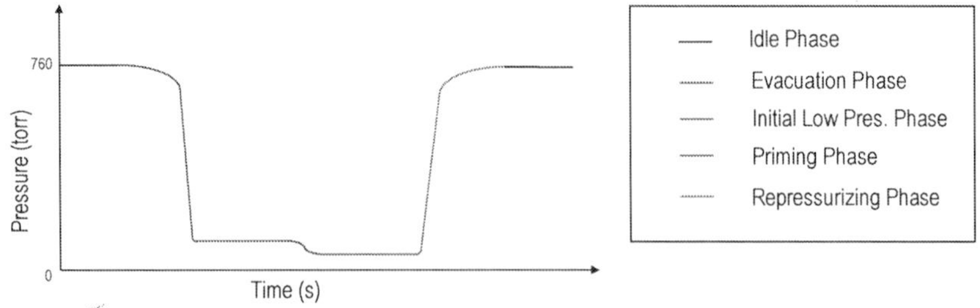

Experimental Setup (A) – Prime vs Non-Prime Etch Comparison Tests

- Goal: Determining effectiveness of priming process in providing improved pathway for diffusing chemicals
- Used silicon wafers with features of a ~50:1 aspect ratio coated with 1-micron layer of thermal oxide
  - One set would be primed in the vacuum prime process while the other remained untreated to serve as the control
- Wafers would be processed in a 100:1 HF bath for a set amount of time and then be analyzed in a scanning electron microscope
- Wafers would be considered fully processed if the entire layer of oxide in the microstructures is etched

Experimental Setup (B) – Vacuum Priming/Drying Characterization Tests

- Goal: Determining the ideal process conditions to prime/dry any high aspect-ratio microstructures
- Drummond Micropipettes were used to simulate the high aspect-ratio microstructures
  - Inner Diameter = 99 μm, length = 32 mm, Aspect Ratio = ~320:1
  - One end of the pipettes was sealed with a butane torch and mounted onto bare silicon wafers at different orientations with an adhesive
- For priming tests, system is held at initial low pressure for 1 minute and then for three minutes at the priming pressure
- For drying tests, system is held at setpoint pressure for 10 or 20 minutes
- Results determined by optical microscope

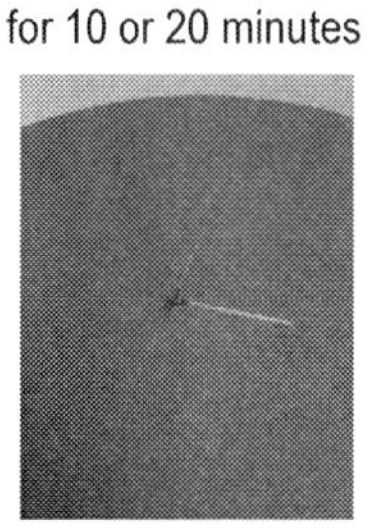

Experiment A Test Results

- Wafers with primed microstructures showed complete etching of the oxide layer
- Non-primed wafers showed only partial etching of the oxide layer
- Complete etching was achieved in primed wafers within a process time as low as 20 minutes in 100:1 HF
- Conclusion:
  - Chemical is more likely to permeate through the entirety of the vias when they are first primed with DI water.
  - Chemical diffuses into the priming fluid at a fast enough rate to fully etch the oxide layer in a practical amount of time.

After 1 hour Etch in 100:1 HF, Via A.R. = 50:1

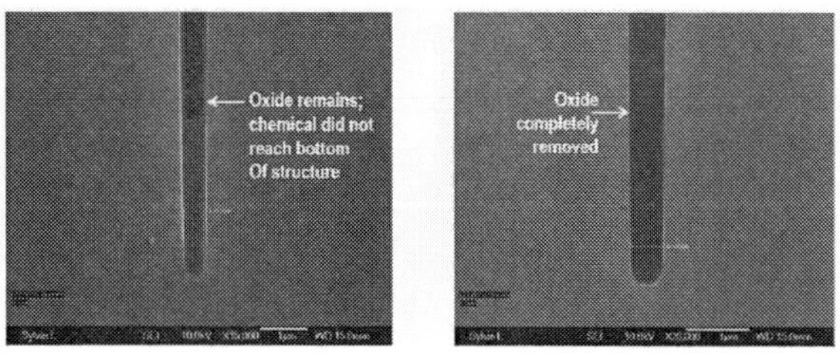

Non-Primed Wafer (Left) vs Primed Wafer (Right)

After 20 minute Etch in 100:1 HF, Via A.R. = 50:1

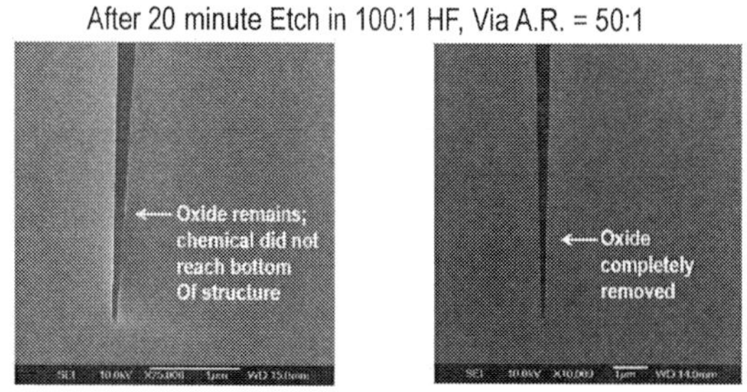

Non-Primed Wafer (Left) vs Primed Wafer (Right)

Experiment B Vacuum Prime Results

Run Details	Results	Pictures
Control Evac Pressure = 760 torr Prime Pressure = 760 torr	• Water would only fill pipette up to 250 um from open end at best • Priming failed	
Evac Pressure = 7.6 – 20 torr Prime Pressure = 7.0 – 7.6 torr	• Pipettes were filled with priming fluid with no air pockets • Priming successful	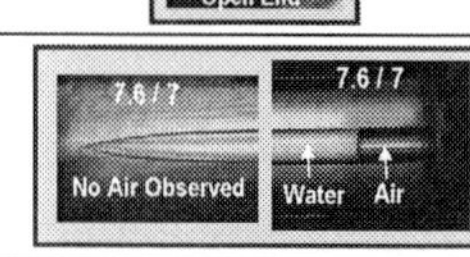
Evac Pressure = 10 – 20 torr Prime Pressure = 10 – 20 torr	• Pipettes had air pockets at the bottom of the closed end • Priming failed	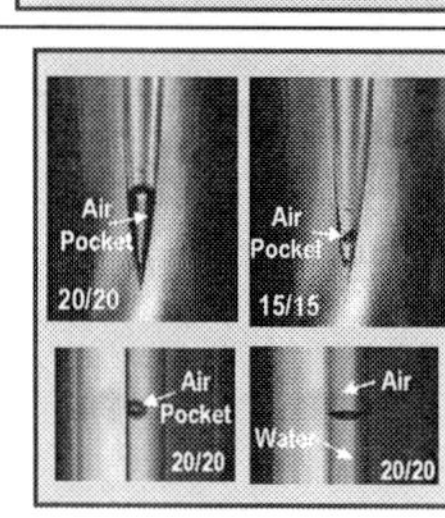

Experiment B Vacuum Prime Field Validation

- Another series of priming tests was conducted at higher pressures for 10:1 aspect ratio vias
  - Vias were coated in a 1-micron layer of oxide, which would be etched in a BOE process for 35 minutes after priming
- All tests resulted in a complete etching of the oxide layer in the wafer vias according to SEM results, thus proving that the vias were successfully primed at the higher pressure setpoints
- Conclusions: For lower aspect-ratio structures, it is possible for higher pressures to be used for vacuum priming in the circumstances that low pressures are not a viable option

Vacuum Prime Via Wafer Priming w/35 min BOE Process				
Pressure (Torr)	Wafer Type	# of Wafers	Priming Successful?	SiO2 Etched?
60	Via	1	Yes	Yes
80	Via	1	Yes	Yes
80	12 Via, 19 Bare Si	31	Yes	Yes

Experiment B Vacuum Dry Results

Hot N2 High Flow (SCFH)	Evac P. (torr)	Vac. Time (minute)	Pipette Orient.	Pre	Post	Remark
No	7.6	10	12	fully filled	dried to 16mm from open-end	Consistently dried to 16mm - 160:1 A.R.
			3	fully filled	dried to 16mm from open-end	
			6	fully filled	dried to 16mm from open-end	
No	7.6	10	12	fully filled	dried to 16mm from open-end	
			3	fully filled	dried to 16mm from open-end	
			6	fully filled	dried to 16mm from open-end	
No	7.6	10	12	fully filled	dried to 16mm from open-end	
			3	fully filled	dried to 16mm from open-end	
			6	small gas pocket at closed-end	dried to 16mm from open-end	
No	7.6	Rerun 10 more	12	dried to 16mm from open-end	dried to 25mm from open-end	Consistently dried to 25mm - 250:1 A.R. if vac. time doubled
			3	dried to 16mm from open-end	dried to 25mm from open-end	
			6	dried to 16mm from open-end	dried to 25mm from open-end	
No	7.6	20	12	fully filled	dried to 25mm from open-end	
			3	fully filled	dried to 25mm from open-end	
			6	fully filled	dried to 25mm from open-end	
			9	fully filled	dried to 25mm from open-end	
5	200	10	12	fully filled	dried to 1.5mm from open-end	Not enough driving force to make it work
			3	fully filled	dried to 1.5mm from open-end	
			6	fully filled	dried to 1.5mm from open-end	
			9	fully filled	dried to 1.5mm from open-end	

Experiment B Vacuum Dry Results

- After 10 minutes total of drying at 7.6 torr, pipettes that were filled completely dried up to 16 mm from the open end
- Pipettes that were dried a total of 20 minutes at 7.6 torr consistently dried up to 25 mm from the open end
- Pipettes dried at 200 torr with a 5 scfm flow of hot nitrogen only dried up to 1.5 mm from the open end
- Conclusions:
  - The Vacuum Dry process is shown to be capable of drying out 160:1 aspect-ratio microstructures within a practical process time (~10 minutes). Adding more processing time can increase the range of aspect ratios that can be completely dried
  - Hot nitrogen may be able to assist in drying out these structures, but only if it can be added while the pressure is maintained at a setpoint of ~7.6 torr.

Conclusions

- Results show that vacuum priming proven to be an effective method for processing wafers with high aspect-ratio microstructures
  - Chemicals can reach into the full length of the microstructures by diffusing through the priming fluid
  - The most suitable conditions for priming would be at a pressure of 7.6 torr, but it is also possible for complete priming of structures to occur at higher pressures
- Vacuum drying is a viable means to dry out the primed microstructures at the end of the process
- Further Research:
  - Determining the minimum required process time for diffusing microstructures of varying aspect ratios
  - Finding the maximum pressure at which complete priming of various microstructures can be achieved

Thank You

For Your Attention

AKrion

Meta

Wet Cleans and Surface Preparation for Augmented Reality (AR) Device Fabrication: Challenges and Novel Technology Developments.

Dennis Oriero
Waveguides Display & Optics, Meta Reality Labs
dennisao@fb.com
415-238-9208
Surface Preparation and Cleaning Conference, Phoenix, AZ - October 2022

Meta

- Introduction
- Waveguide and uLED Nanofabrication Overview
- Wets Cleans Fabrication Challenges
- Novel Technologies
- Questions

Augmented Reality (AR)
Technology designed to enhance or augment your reality
Next wave of computing platforms
AR devices provide truly immersive AR experience
Meta
FLIGHT ALERT
NY → SEA
Airways 351
3.15pm
Gate 9
2.45 pm
NY Airport

Meta
AR Glasses/Smart Glasses
All-day wearable, fashionable AR Glasses to transform how we live and work in the Metaverse*
Mark Zuckerberg, Connect 2021 –
"Our hope is that within the next decade the metaverse will reach a billion people, host $100's of billions of dollars of digital commerce and support jobs for millions of creators and developers."

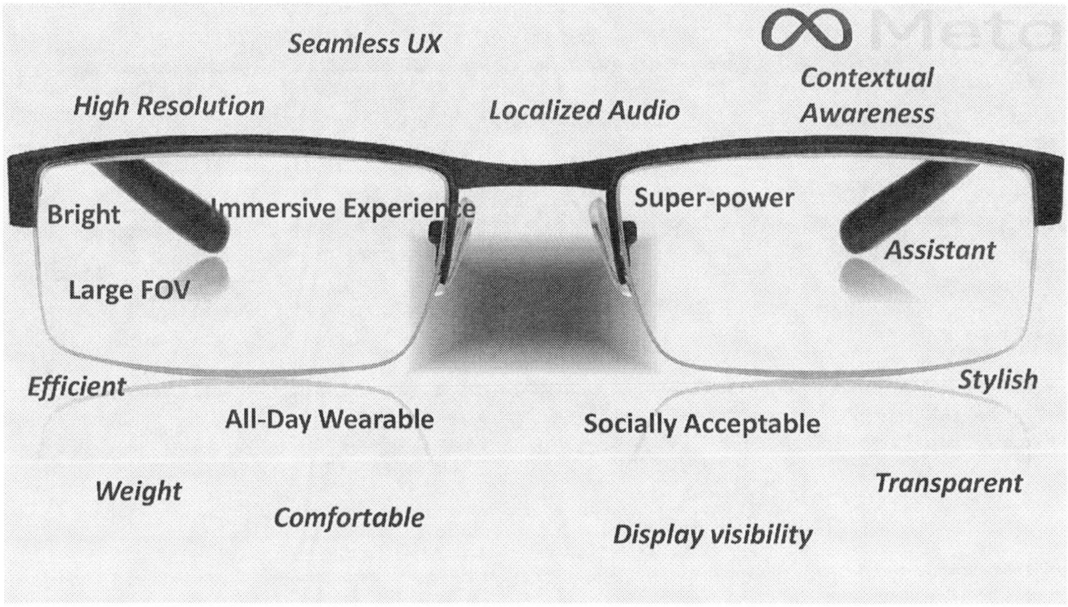
Meta
Seamless UX
High Resolution
Localized Audio
Contextual
Awareness
Bright
Immersive Experience
Super-power
Assistant
Large FOV
Efficient
Stylish
All-Day Wearable
Socially Acceptable
Weight
Transparent
Comfortable
Display visibility

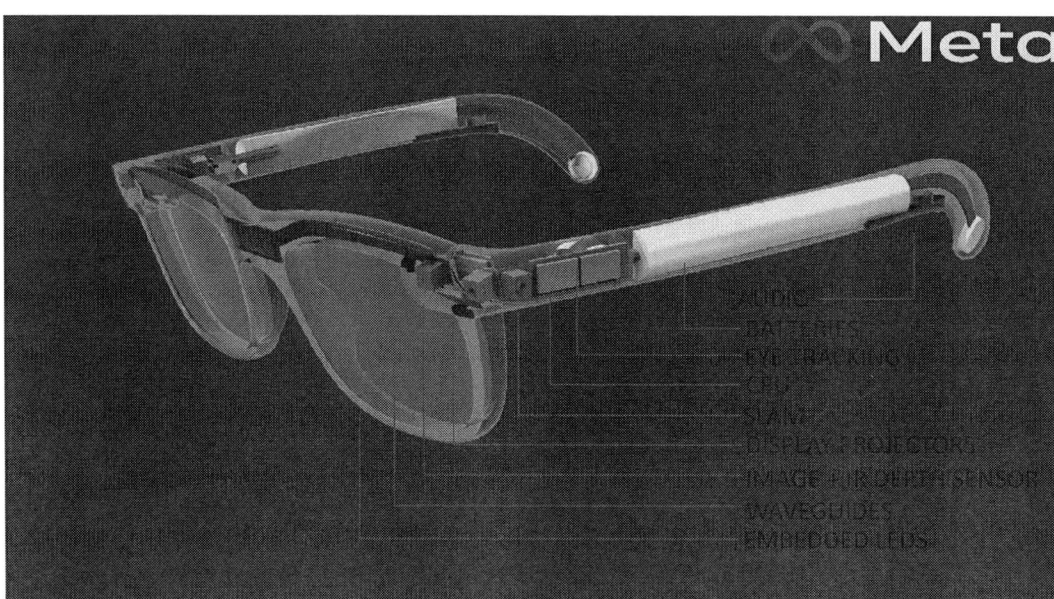
Meta
AUDIO
BATTERIES
EYE TRACKING
CPU
SLAM
DISPLAY PROJECTORS
IMAGE + IR DEPTH SENSOR
WAVEGUIDES
EMBEDDED LEDS

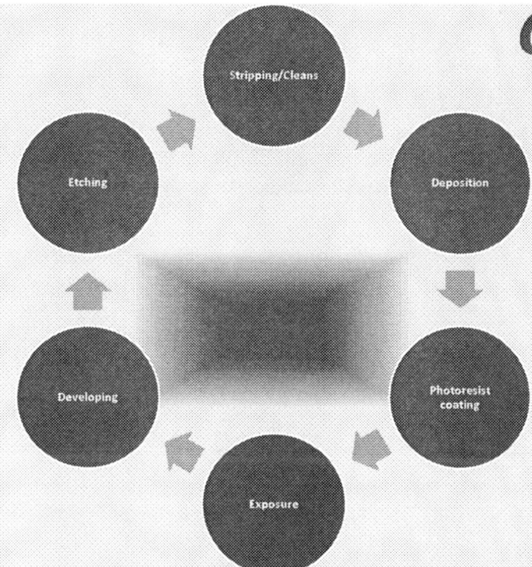

Typical Semiconductor Process Flow

Waveguide and uLED Fabrication Borrow Semiconductor Unit Fabrication Steps

Waveguide

- Geometrical structures designed to confine, guide and direct the propagation of electromagnetic energy
- Principle of Total Internal Reflection (TIR)
- Waveguide gratings
- Borrow semiconductor fabrication process

uLEDs

- Light emitting diodes in sub-micron range
- High resolution displays, high switching rates
- Color controlled by epitaxy band gaps
- Efficiency challenges in extracting theoretical light limits

Meta

Display Technology	LCD	OLED	Micro-LED
Luminous mode	Backlight module	Self-luminous	Self-luminous
Luminous efficiency	Low	Medium	High
Brightness (cd/sqm)	3000	1000	10,000
Contrast	5000:1	10,000:1	1,000,000:1
Life (hours)	60 K	20–30 K	80–100 K
Color rendering	75% NTSC	124% NTSC	140% NTSC
Response time	Millisecond level	Microsecond level	Nanosecond level
Energy consumption	High	About 60–85% of LCD	About 30–40% of LCD
Pixels per inch (PPI)	800	500	>2000

NTSC—National Television Standards Committee.

10.3390/nano10122482

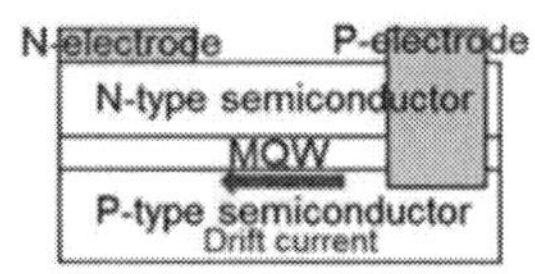

P-contact is made through a hole in the n-type semiconductor, MQW and landing on p-type semiconductor. N-contact is made directly on the n-type semiconductor. Light is extracted in the opposite end

Micro Light Emitting Diode: Fabrication and Devices : Micro-LED Technology, Series in Display Science and Technology, J-H. Ahn and J.H. Kim

Meta

Wets Cleans Fabrication Challenges: Waveguides and uLED Display

- Chemistry Compatibility and Wet Etch Selectivity
- Metrology for Cleans Effectiveness Validation
- Wet Cleans Processing Tool/Equipment

Chemistry Compatibility and Wet Etch Selectivity

- Waveguide
  - Compatible chemistries for unique substrates surface prep, bonding process etc. (High Refractive Index (RI), optical transparent substrates).
  - Aspect ratio limiting cleans and etch
  - Dry etch residue/polymer cleans
    - Selectivity for residue removal from unique grating features/structures
- MicroLED
  - Always have tertiary compounds and require chemistries that are selective to different combinations of Epi's used
  - Substrate removal (critical)
    - Selective to phosphide
    - Chemistry stability (spiking, secondary reactions,
    - Onboard conc/comp monitoring
  - Metal corrosion (galvanic/photo)
  - Dry etch residues/polymers
    - B-doped residue removal

Metrology Challenges

- Waveguide
  - Cleans effectiveness validation of high RI optical transparent substrates
  - Residue removal/cleans effectiveness validation of high RI optical transparent substrates
- MicroLED
  - How to filter signals from quantum wells
  - Optical EP detection, but not robust
  - Onboard fluorescence detection
- Concentration/composition onboard monitoring (tertiary acid mixtures)

Wet Cleans Processing Tool/Equipment

- Waveguide
  - Unique substrates geometry
    - Transparent substrates
    - Shape and size
    - Low plastic deformation capacity
- MicroLED
  - Advanced capabilities on 6"/8" wafers (prefer SWC)
  - Wafer sensing on transparent wafers
  - High BOW handling (>500um)
  - Backside/bevel processing
  - Onboard lamp capability for photo-induced reactions (6"/8")

Meta

Novel Technologies: Waveguides and uLED Display

Meta

- Cryogenic Cleans
- Photoinduced Fluorination

Questions

Thank you

uLED Display Team

- Rajesh Balachandran
- Michaela Wentz

18

MACOM™

Partners from RF to Light

Sustainable Solvent Metal Lift-Off for Compound Semiconductor Fabrication with Improved Manufacturability

Pradeep Waduge[a], Khody Javaherchi[a], Joel A. Bahena[b], Mikhail Doble[b], Phillip Tyler[b], Lynne Michaelson[c], Douglas Holmes[c]

[a]Macom Technology Solutions (Pradeep.Waduge@macom.com), [b]Veeco Instruments, [c]Technic Inc.

TECHNIC

Veeco

MAKING A MATERIAL DIFFERENCE

MACOM

Background

- Specifically in compound semiconductor processing, for sensitive substrates and metals, wet PR removal generally requires the use of a dipolar aprotic solvent and historically NMP has been broadly adopted.
- Bottom anti-reflective coatings (BARC's) are commonly coated in between the substrate and photoresist to minimize interference effects incident and reflected light.
- The BARC requires a secondary cleaning step, commonly a dry etch as photoresist strip chemistries (e.g. NMP) generally do not remove it.

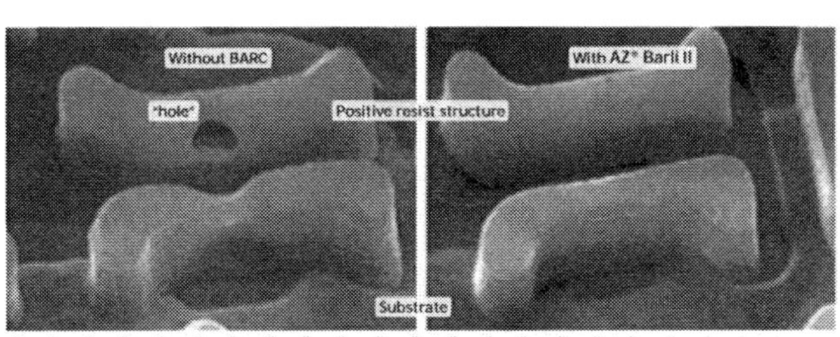

BARC helps to:

I. Reduce interference related artefacts such as periodic groove structure on the resist sidewalls.
II. Minimize unwanted exposure and subsequent development of nominally unexposed areas.

https://www.microchemicals.com/technical_information/anti_reflective_coating_photoresist

2

Objective

- Explore a safer and more environmentally-friendly solvent that can concurrently remove both photoresist and BARC, with no adverse surface effects.

Partially lifted metal disk at the MESA

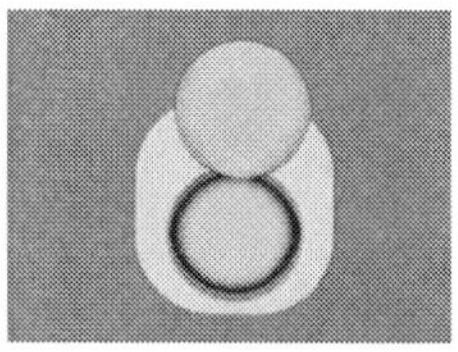

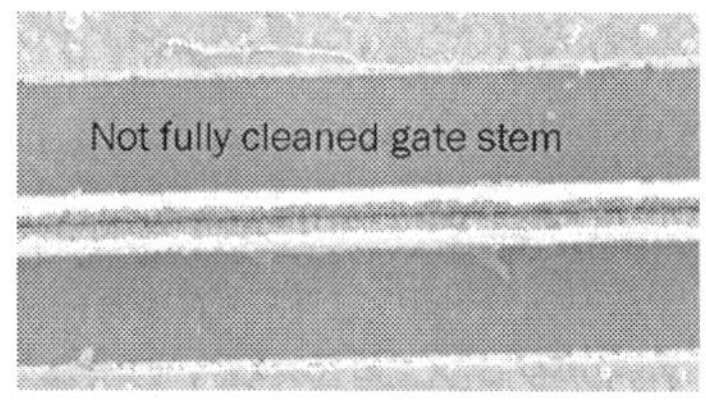

GaAs corrosion

Health data for NMP and potential solvent substitutes

Chemistry	LC50 (mg/ m³ 4 hr)	Skin permeability (mg/m²/hr)	Understanding of reprotoxicity
NMP	5100	171	Category 1B*
DMF	4700	98	Category 1B*
DMAc	1240	107	Category 1B*
DMSO	40,250,000	176	No evidence
Sulfolane	12,000	0.2	Category 1B*

*Category 1B: Can damage fertility or the unborn child

3

Results: Summary of Beaker Level Experiments with Various Resist Types

#	Resist Type	MLO-07	MicroD2	Cyrene
1	Lift off resist w/ bake	Dissolved immediately	Dissolved immediately	Dissolved slowly
2	Novolak	Dissolved immediately	Dissolved immediately	Dissolved slowly
3	BARC – no bake	Dissolved Immediately	Not removed	Not removed
4	BARC – hard bake	Dissolved Immediately	Not removed	Not removed
5	Spin on Dielectric – not cured	Dissolved immediately	Dissolved immediately	Dissolved immediately

Technistrip® MLO-7 demonstrated very promising results, where it successfully removed both hard baked photoresist and BARC without inducing any damage to the substrate surface.

Comparison of GaAs surface post resist strip

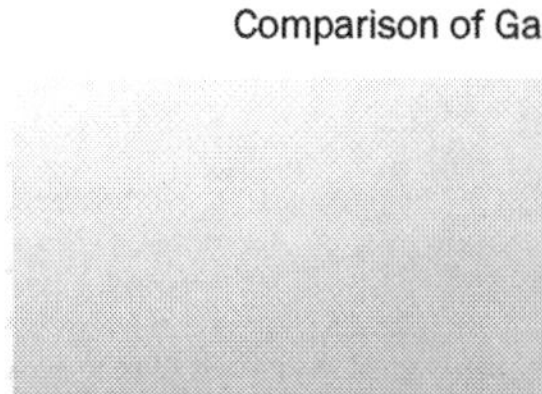

Surface of GaAs post Technistrip® MLO-7

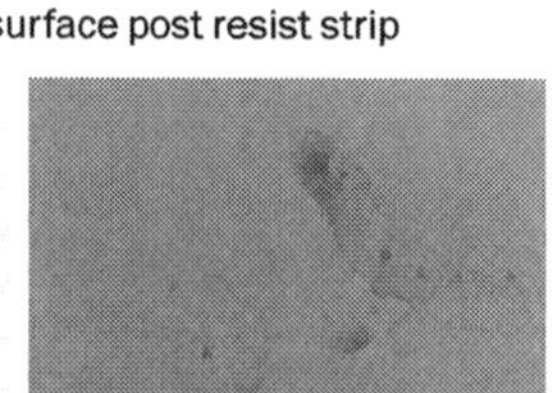

Surface of GaAs post Cyrene®

4

MACOM

Hygroscopicity of Photo Strip Chemistry

- It is well-known that common solvents employed in photoresist strip processes such as metal liftoff ("MLO") tend to be hygroscopic, and will pick up ambient H_2O if conditions allow
- Such elevated H_2O levels could potentially corrode/etch the semiconductor substrate, leading to optically rejected devices due to excessive surface roughness
- To assess this corrosion risk, TechniStrip® MLO-7 was compared with NMP for water absorption, solvent evaporation, metal corrosion and surface roughness (haze), as shown in the following slides

5

MACOM

Results: Hygroscopicity, Metal Corrosion and Evaporation

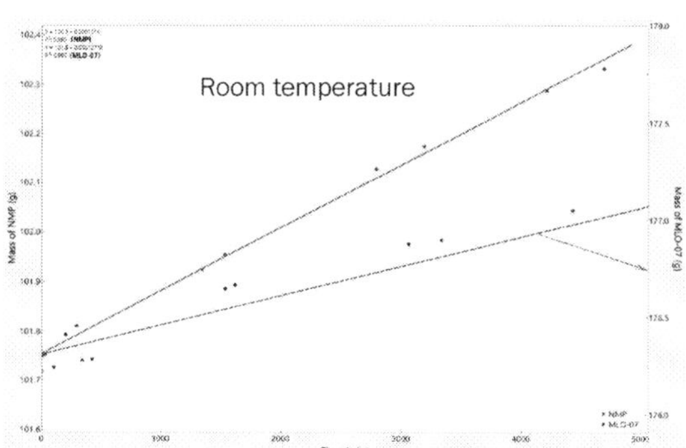

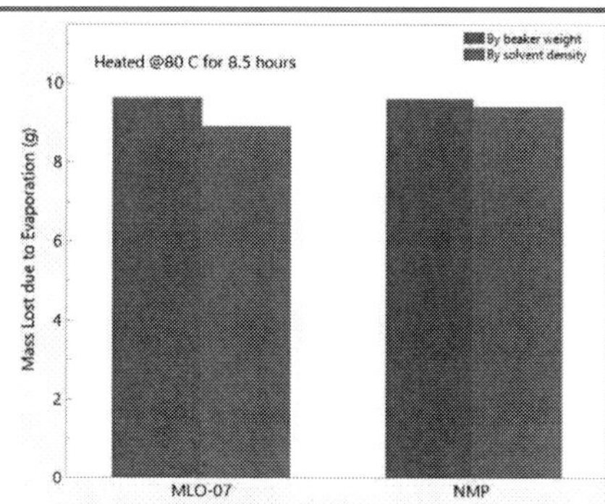

Water absorption rate of Technistrip® MLO-7 = 6E-3 g/hr (@room temp)

Water absorption rate of NMP = 6E-3 g/hr (@room temp)

Evaporation rate of Technistrip® MLO-7 = 1.13 g/hr

Evaporation rate of NMP = 1.12 g/hr

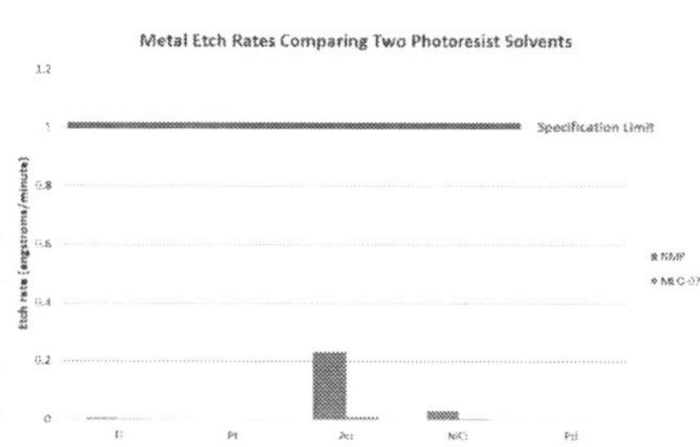

MACOM

Results: Surface Roughness and Surface Charge Induction

	% Water Content				15 min Phosphoric exposure
	0	1	3	5	
NMP	0	0	0	0	MT1 Haze Grading
	0	0	0	0	MT2 Haze Grading
MLO-07	1*	0	0	0	MT1 Haze Grading
	0	0	0	0	MT2 Haze Grading

- *Random particle on surface resulted in higher haze grading
- Solvent Temp: 75-80 C
- Solvent Exposure Time: 8 min

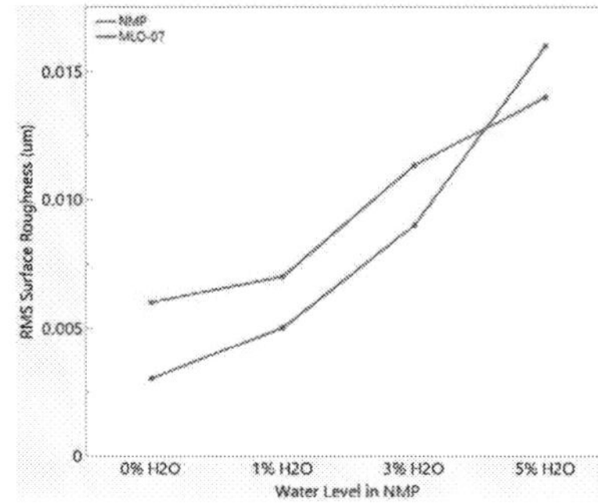

Hysteresis CV Curves

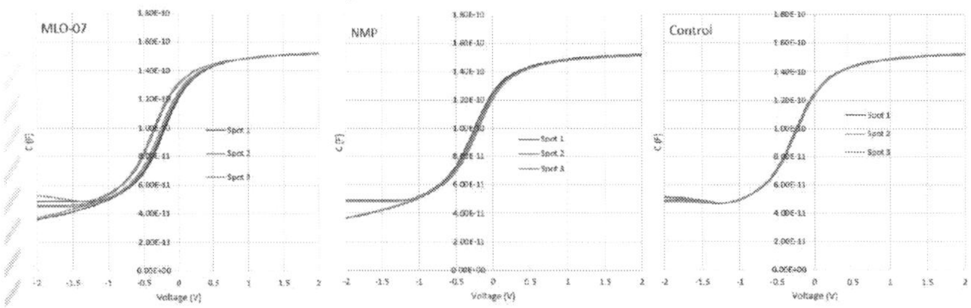

No significant surface damage via trapped charge induction

7

MACOM

Results: Technistrip® MLO-7 on Veeco tool compared to NMP

Technistrip® MLO-7 was compared with an NMP process utilizing a Veeco WaferStorm® tool with ImmJET™ Technology for various MLO processes that Macom employs on various product types

Metal liftoff (MLO) using NMP and Technistrip® MLO-7

A

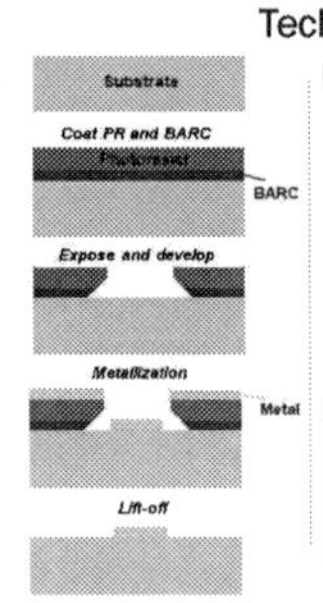

B

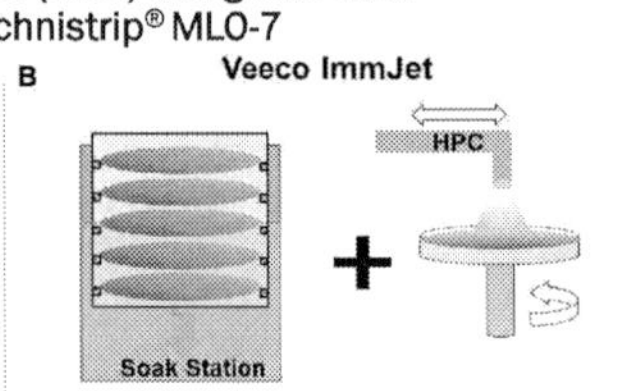

C

Chemistry	Soak (min)	HPC Spray (min)	Temperature (°C)
NMP	8	1	80
MLO-07	8	1	75
MLO-07	5	1	75

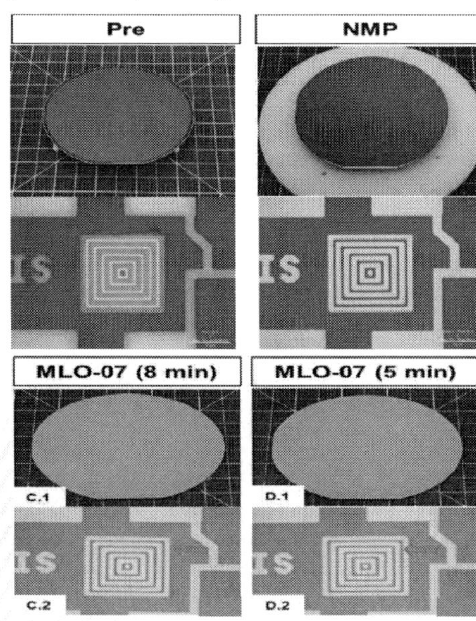

- MLO-07 removed both photoresist and BARC in less time than NMP removed just the photoresist

8

Results: Mesa Metal Disk Liftoff

Metal liftoff (MLO) using NMP

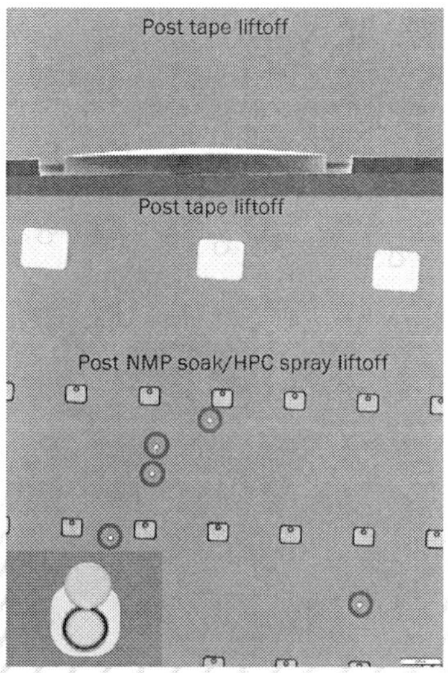

Metal liftoff (MLO) using Technistrip® MLO-7

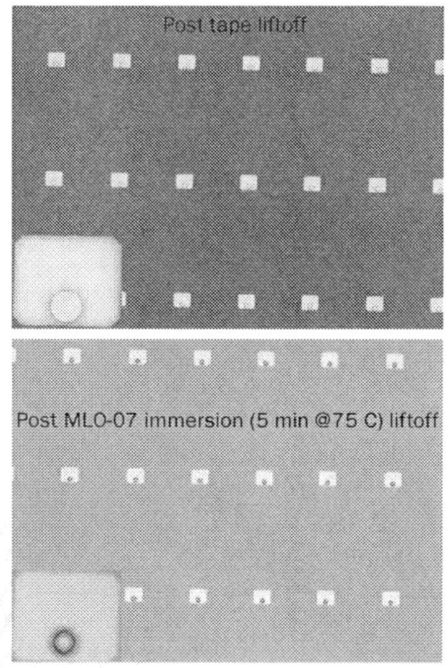

- MLO-07 removed both photoresist and BARC in less time than NMP removed just the photoresist with zero redeposited and/or partially lifted disks

Summary

- Replacing NMP with a single dipolar aprotic solvent that is environmentally safer and is comparable in performance or better than NMP is challenging.

- However, preliminary experiments and evaluations performed suggest that Technistrip® MLO-7 is a promising candidate to replace NMP (photoresist stripper) and ACT412/ST22 (BARC strippers) in MLO processes.

- This new chemistry qualification will ultimately ensure the integrity of various wet cleans processes that we use in the Macom Lowell fab while improving the device yield and cycle time with potential OPEX and CAPEX savings.

Acknowledgement

We want to thank Macom Lowell fab operation team for the support for running some tests for us.

We also want to thank Macom IAT Si transistor process integration team for helping on CV measurements.

11

TEL
TOKYO ELECTRON

Ru Post Etch Residue Removal by Wet Cleans

October 18, 2022

Sangita Kumari, Shan Hu, Nicholas Joy, Kai-Hung Yu
TEL Technology Center, America, LLC

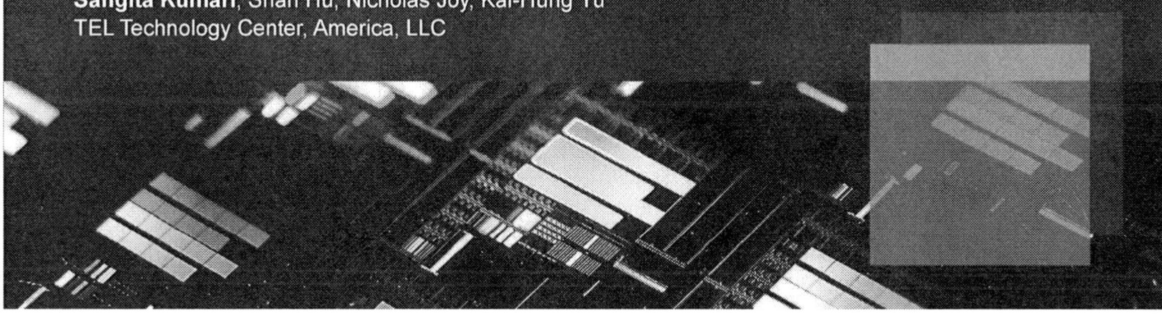

Outline

- Motivation
- Challenges
- Materials and Methods
- Characterization
- Results and Discussion
- Summary

Motivation

Ru is the metal of interest for advanced BEOL metallization

Advantages of using Ru for BEOL metallization.

- Low bulk resistivity
- High melting point
- No liner/barrier needed
- No electromigration issue
- Compatible with dielectrics and other semiconductor processes

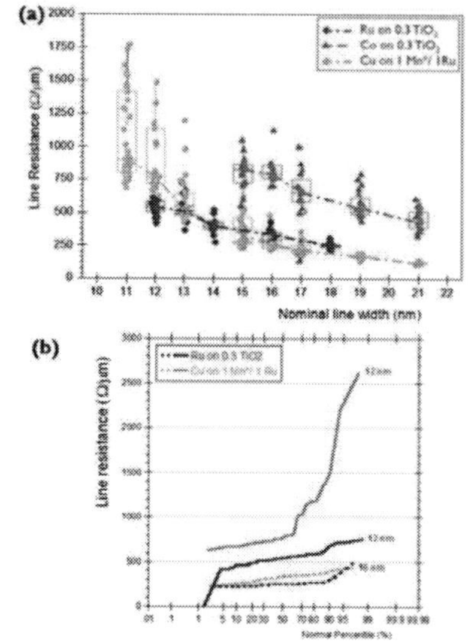

Source: Marleen H. van der veen, et.al./April 30, 2021/ IMEC

Challenges

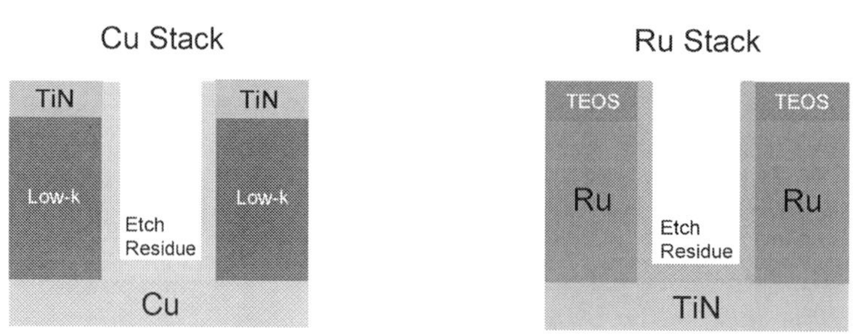

Source: TEL

- Check conventional chemicals for residue removal
- Understand residue removal mechanism

Materials and Methods

- Blanket Ru, CVD
- Conventional Etch
- Conventional and Proprietary Wet Cleans
- XPS Analysis
- Four-Point Probe

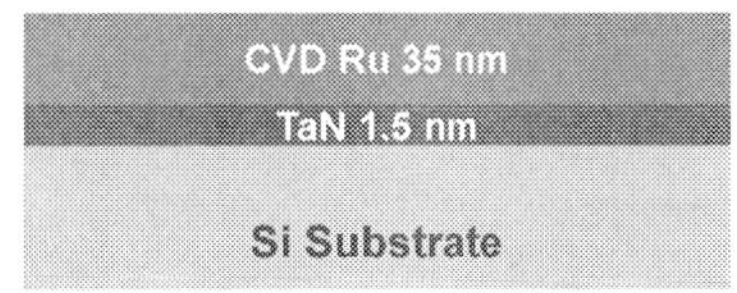

Source: TEL

Wet Clean Chemicals Tested

1. DHF(1:100 & 1:1000), Hot SC1
2. Chem1 (Ru Metal Etch)
3. Chem2, Chem3, Chem4 (TiN HM post RIE clean)
4. Chem5 (Ru Metal Etch)

Materials and Methods

- Process Flow

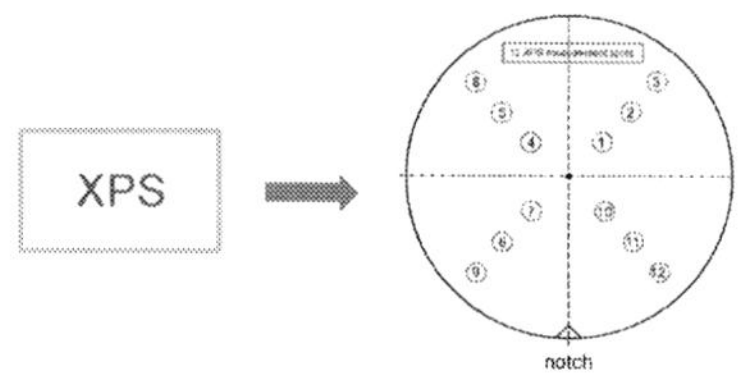

Source: TEL

Results and Discussion - HF

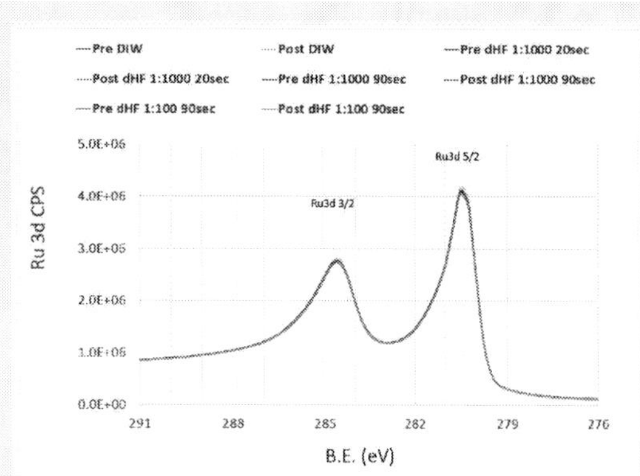

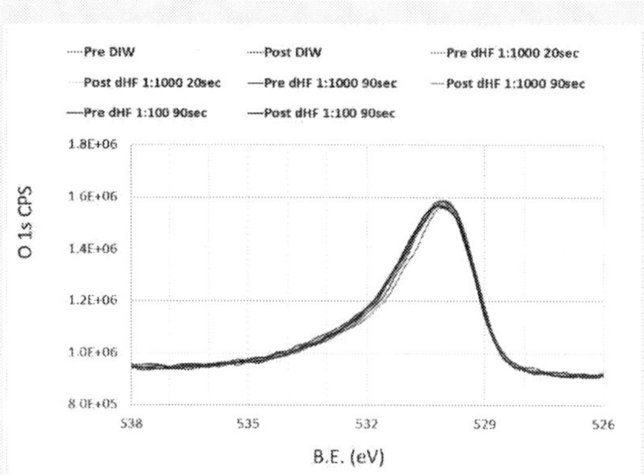

Source: TEL

- No change in Ru and Oxygen signal using dilute or concentrated HF

Results and Discussion - HF

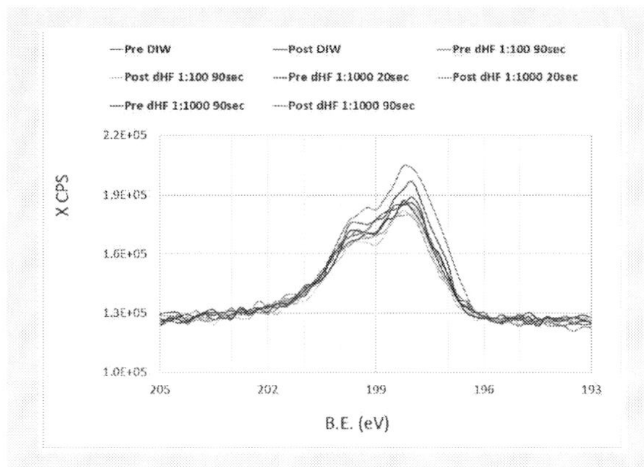

Source: TEL

- No change in element X using dilute or concentrated HF

Results and Discussion - Chem1

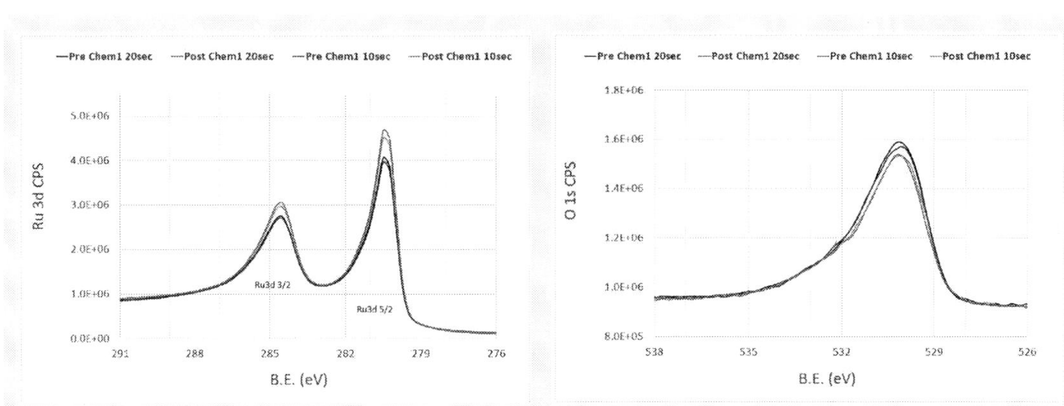

Source: TEL

- Ru peak highest for 20 sec Chem1
- Oxygen peak low post Chem1

Results and Discussion - DHF and Chem1

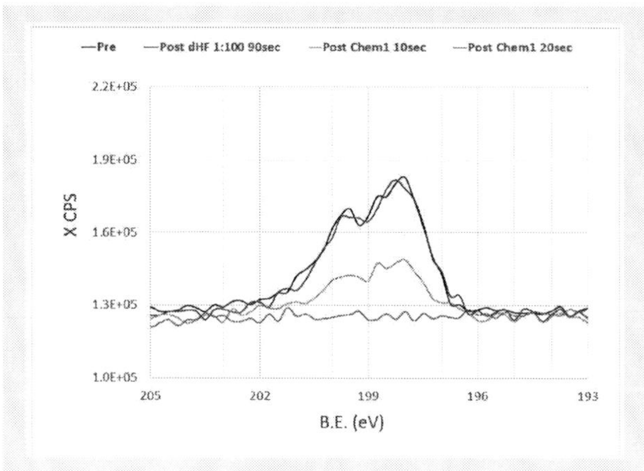

Source: TEL

- DHF and Chem1 compared here
- X is a major etch component representing residue
- 90 sec of DHF shows no residue removal
- 10 sec of Chem1 shows partial residue removal
- 20 sec of Chem1 shows full residue removal
- More wet cleans data in next page

Results and Discussion

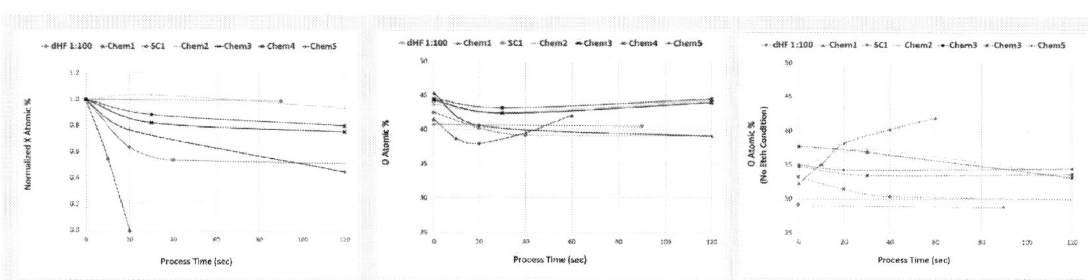

Source: TEL

- DHF, Chem2, Chem3, Chem4 show no residue removal
- SC1 and Chem5 show partial residue removal
- 20 sec of Chem1 shows complete residue removal
- Chem1 removes etch oxidized Ru surface and in the process also oxidizes the Ru surface
- Ru Etch rates for Chem1, Chem5 and SC1 in next page

Results and Discussion

Wet cleans	Ru ER
SC1	0
Chem1/ Etched	1
Chem1/ Non-Etched	0
Chem5	0

- Sheet resistance data used for thickness check
- No Ru Etch observed for SC1 or Chem5
- Chem1 ER = 1.xx for etch exposed Ru
- Chem1 does not etch non-etched Ru surface / Blanket Ru
- Chem1 etches the "Etch-induced" oxidized Ru surface and in the process the residues are removed

Results and Discussion

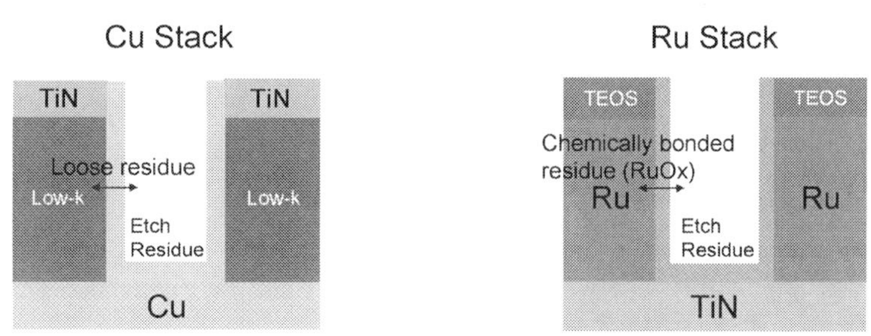

Source: TEL

- Post low-k Etch residues can be removed using DHF and SC1 in addition to proprietary chemicals
- However, post Ru etch residue cannot be removed by conventional wet cleans. Ru needs to be oxidized first for Chem1 to remove the first layer of "chemically bonded" residue

Summary

1) Conventional wet cleans DHF and SC1 do not remove Ru post etch residue
2) Chem1 oxidizes Ru surface
3) 20 sec Chem1 process shows complete Ru residue removal
4) Chem1 etches Ru @ 1.xx
5) Wet removal mechanism by Chem1 involves oxidized Ru removal

Thank You!

TEL™

TOKYO ELECTRON

The Electronics business of Merck KGaA, Darmstadt, Germany operates as EMD Electronics in the U.S. and Canada.

Development of Wet Etchants for Filling Material Removal to Enable 3D NAND Process

Jhih Kuei Ge[1]†, Yi Chia Lee[1] and Aiping Wu[2]
[1]Merck, 2F, No.25, Lane 62, Chung Ho Street, Chupei City, Hsinchu County 30267, Taiwan
[2]EMD Electronics, 8555 South River Parkway, Tempe, AZ85284, USA

† Corresponding author: ck.ge@merckgroup.com
Phone: (886)978587956
Address: 2F, No.25, Lane 62, Chung Ho Street, Chupei City, Hsinchu County 30267, Taiwan

EMD Electronics

1

Introduction

Wet Etchant for Exhuming Filing Material

Vertical Channel (VC) Hole Filling Materials Removal

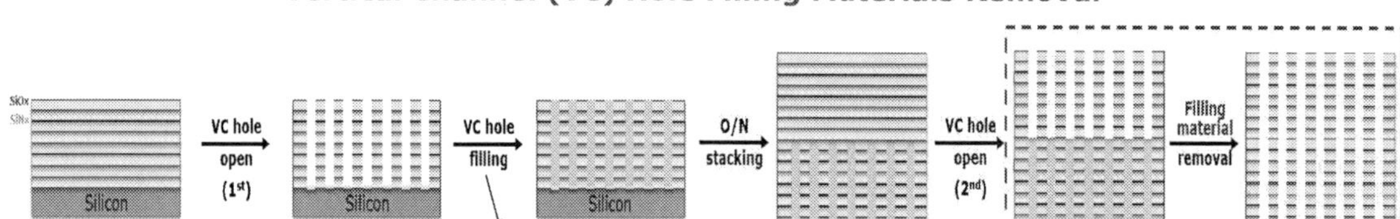

Filling Materials:
- Poly Si
- W/TiN

❑ Goals:
- Complete removal of filling material from HAR channel
- No negative impact to the channel

❑ Technical Targets:
- High etch rate for filling materials
- High etch selectivity between filling material and SiNx or SiOx

2

01 Poly Si Exhume

3

Poly Si Exhume
Mechanisms

✓ **Anisotropic etching of silicon in aqueous alkaline media**

$$Si + 2OH^- + H_2O \rightarrow SiO_2(OH)_2^{2-} + 2H_2$$

✓ **Isotropic etching of silicon with HF/HNO_3**

(1) Formation of NO2 from nitric acid: $4\ HNO_3 \rightarrow 4\ NO_2 + 2\ H_2O + O_2$

(2) Oxidation of silicon by NO2: $2\ NO_2 + Si \rightarrow SiO_2 + 2\ NO$

(3) Etching of SiO2: $SiO_2 + 6\ HF \rightarrow H_2SiF_6 + 2\ H_2O$

Overalll reaction: $4\ HNO_3 + 2\ Si + 12\ HF \rightarrow 4\ NO + 6\ H_2O + O_2 + 2\ H_2SiF_6$

➢ **Our design concept:**

Components	Functions
Alkaline source	Main etchant for poly Si etch
Additive	Minimize SiN and oxide etch
DIW/solvent	Adjust selectivity and enhance poly residue cleaning

4

Poly Si Exhume
Effect of Alkaline Source

Chemical	Aqueous Ammonia	Example 1	Example 2
Alkaline source	NH_4OH	**QAH1**	QAH2
Temperature (^oC)	60	**60**	60
Si Etch Rate (Å/min)	159	**330**	148
TEOS Etch Rate (Å/min)	0.6	**0.9**	0.7
Si/TEOS Etch Selectivity	265	**367**	211

- Quaternary ammonium hydroxide (QAH1) demonstrated much higher Si etch rate (ER) attributed to its high basicity. Although there was a slight increase on oxide ER, it showed the best Si/oxide selectivity.

5

Poly Si Exhume
Additive Effects

Chemical	Example 1	Etchant A	Example 3
QAH1	+	**+**	+
Additive	-	**I1**	I2
Temperature (^oC)	60	**60**	60
Si Etch Rate (Å/min)	330	**309**	308
TEOS Etch Rate (Å/min)	0.9	**0.2**	0.7
Si/TEOS Etch Selectivity	367	**1545**	440

- Oxide etch rate can be suppressed by adding additives, and lower oxide ER can be achieved by introducing additive I1
- I1 has a stronger affinity to oxide surface than I2, resulting in better performance

6

Poly Si Exhume
Temperature Effects

Chemical	Etchant A		Example 4
QAH1	+		+
I1	+		++
Temperature (^oC)	60	75	**75**
Si Etch Rate (Å/min)	309	720	**647**
TEOS Etch Rate (Å/min)	0.2	0.7	**0.5**
Si/TEOS Etch Selectivity	1545	1029	**1294**

- Si etch rate can be improved by raising process temperature, but the Si to oxide selectivity is reduced
- Increasing of additive I1 can improve Si/TEOS selectivity

7

Poly Si Exhume
Solvent Ratio Effects

Chemical	Example 4	Etchant B	Example 5
QAH1	+	+	+
I1	++	++	++
Solvent/Water Ratio	-	**R1**	R2
Temperature (^oC)	75	**75**	75
Si Etch Rate (Å/min)	649	**657**	694
TEOS Etch Rate (Å/min)	0.5	**0.3**	0.01
Si/TEOS Etch Selectivity	1294	**2190**	69400
Poly residue cleaning	Not Good	**Good**	Not Good

- Oxide ER was reduced by adding solvent and reducing water content, while Si/oxide selectivity was increased
- Si residue was observed on structured wafer after processing where solvent/water ratio was above a certain threshold

8

Poly Si Exhume
Further Optimization

Chemical	Aqueous TMAH	Etchant D
Alkaline source	$(CH_3)_4NOH$	**$(CH_3)_4NOH$**
Additive	-	**I1**
Solvent/Water Ratio	-	**R1**
Temperature (^{O}C)	65	**75**
Si Etch Rate (Å/min)	1747	**2350**
Thermal Oxide Etch Rate (Å/min)	0.4	**0.2**
Si/Th Oxide Etch Selectivity	4368	**11750**
SiNx Etch Rate (Å/min)	0.7	**0.4**
Si/SiNx Etch Selectivity	2496	**5875**

- Higher Si etch rate can be achieved using TMAH
- Additive and proper solvent water ratio can improve Si/oxide, Si/SiNx etch selectivity
- Etchant D performance exceeds conventional TMAH aqueous solution

9

Poly Si Exhume
Performance

	Etchant B	Etchant D
Structured wafers	1xx layers	3xx layer
Process condition	75°C/90min	75°C/90min
SiOx and SiNx compatibility	No damage	No damage
Poly Si and residue	Fully removed	Fully removed

- Etchant B and D demonstrated complete removal of poly Si and residue on structure wafer
- There was no obvious damage on SiOx and SiNx layers

10

O2 W/TiN Exhume

11

W/TiN Exhume
Mechanisms

- **Mechanisms for W, TiN/Ti removal**

W removal	TiN/Ti removal
$2H_2O_2 + W \rightarrow WO_2 + 2H_2O$	$H_2O_2 + OH^- \rightarrow HO_2^- + H_2O$
$H_2O_2 + OH^- \rightarrow HO_2^- + H_2O$	$Ti + HO_2^- + H_2O \rightarrow TiO^{2+} + 4OH^-$
$WO_2 + 2HO_2^- \rightarrow WO_4^{2-} + H_2O$	$TiN + HO_2^- + 4H_2O \rightarrow TiO^{2+} + 4OH^- + NH_4OH$

- **Issues with conventional SC-1**

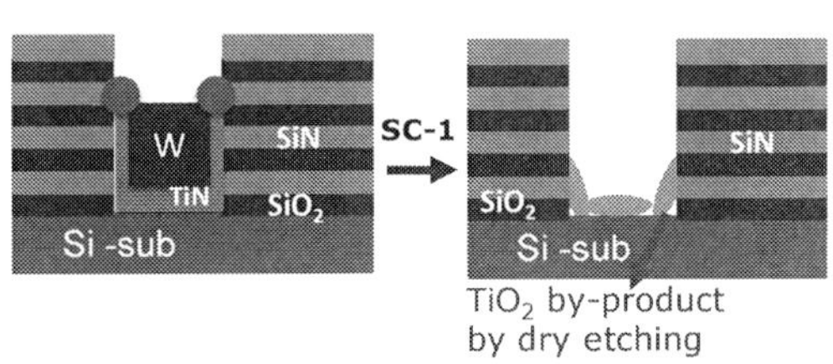

> **Our solution: incorporate a chelating agent in SC-1 to enhance cleaning of TiO_2 residue**

12

W/TiN Exhume
Matrix Adjustment and Additive Effect

Adjusting SC-1 matrix (SC-1 → Example 6) Adding chelating agent (Example 6 → Etchant C)

Formulations	SC-1	Example 6	Etchant C
Temp	80°C	80°C	80°C
TiO_2 Etch Rate (Å/min)	**4**	**19**	**25**
TiN Etch Rate (Å/min)	>500	>1000	>1000
W Etch Rate (Å/min)	>2000	>2700	>2700
SiOx Etch Rate (Å/min)	3	2	1
SiN Etch Rate (Å/min)	1	<1	<1

- TiO_2 etch rate can be increased by increasing the pH value and/or increasing the wt% of oxidant
- A carboxylic acid type chelator would further increase TiO_2 etch rate

13

W/TiN Exhume
Performance

Chemical		Etchant C		
Blanket wafer	Temperature	80°C	65°C	60°C
	W Etch Rate (Å/min)	>1000	>1000	>1000
	TiN Etch Rate (Å/min)	>2700	>2700	>2700
	TiO2 Etch Rate (Å/min)	**25**	**17**	**13**
	SiOx Etch Rate (Å/min)	1	<1	<1
	SiNx Etch Rate (Å/min)	<1	<1	<1
Patterned wafer	**Process condition**	**80°C/240s**	**65°C/200s**	**60°C/300s**
	TiN/W and TiO_2 residue	Fully removed	Fully removed	Fully removed

- Etchant C demonstrated adequate TiO_2 etch rate at lower temperature
- W/TiN exhume was achieved by Etchant C at various temperatures with minimal SiNx and SiOx loss

14

Summary

EMD has developed high selective wet etchants for vertical channel filling material exhume for 3D NAND application

✓ **For Poly Si exhume**

- With effective additive and proper solvent/water ratio adjustment, the alkaline wet etchant can fully remove poly Si filling material from HAR channel without negative impact on the channel

✓ **For W/TiN exhume**

- By adding a chelating agent to SC-1 matrix, the wet etchant can fully remove W/TiN filling material at lower process temperature

15

Acknowledgement

❖ SP&C lab technical service team for etch rate measurement and beaker tests

❖ Collaboration from customers on various projects

16

Thank you

SiGe selective etch for the formation of dielectric isolations in monolithic CFET

Pallavi Puttarame Gowda*, Yusuke Oniki, Ju-Geng Lai, and Efrain Altamirano Sanchez

imec, Kapeldreef 75, 3001 Leuven, Belgium

Pallavi.PuttarameGowda@imec.be (+32498719977)

Overview

SiGe selective etch for the formation of dielectric isolations in monolithic CFET

- Potential roadmap of logic device scaling towards CFET
- Bottom/middle dielectric isolations (BDI/MDIs)
- SiGe selective etch by commodity wet chemicals
  - Alkaline (APM) vs. acidic (FPM based) solutions
- Summary

imec

2

Potential roadmap of device scaling towards CFET

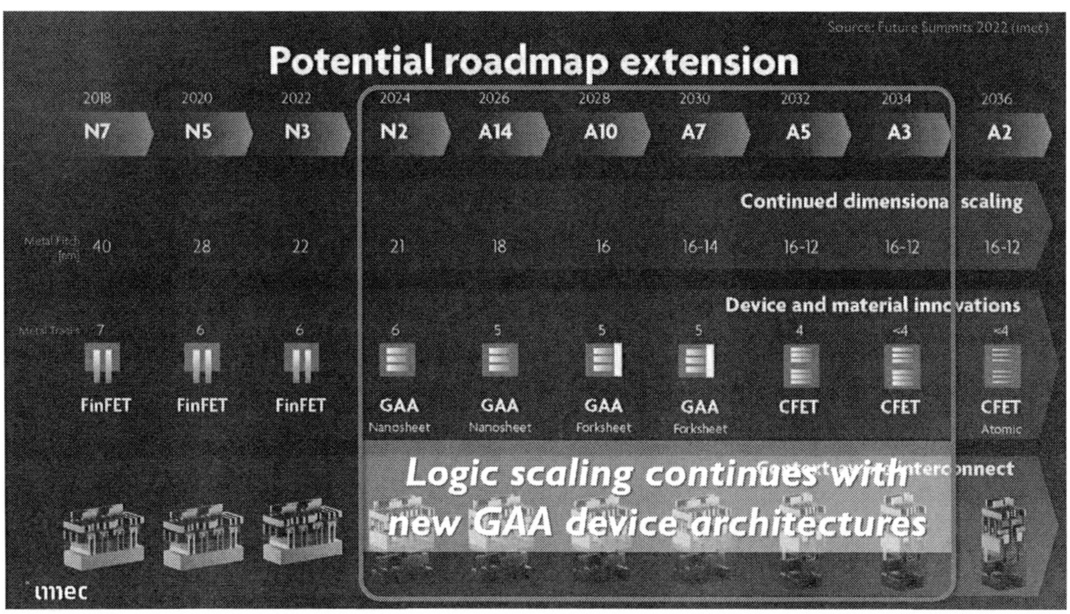

Logic scaling enabled through disruptive device innovations

Recent progress

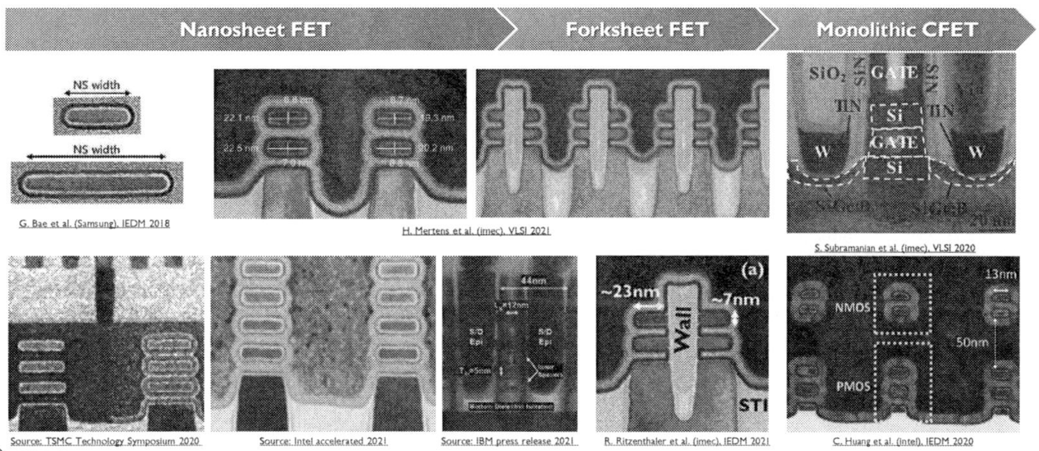

imec

Bottom/middle dielectric isolations (BDI/MDIs)

Parasitic channel leakage reduction

Ground plane doping

- Off-state leakage can be reduced by ground plane doping (ion implantation before the Si/SiGe superlattice epi)

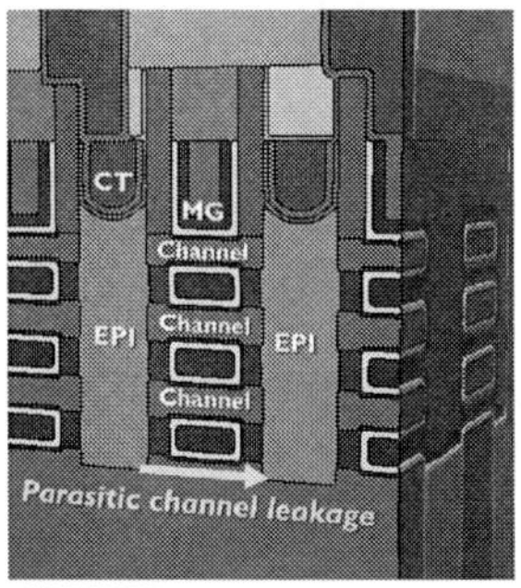

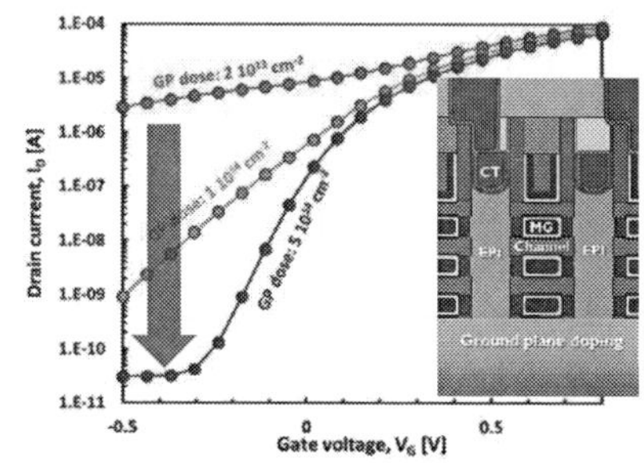

R. Ritzenthaler et al. (imec), ESSDERC 2017

imec

Parasitic channel leakage reduction

Ground plane doping

- Off-state leakage can be reduced by ground plane doping (ion implantation before the Si/SiGe superlattice epi)

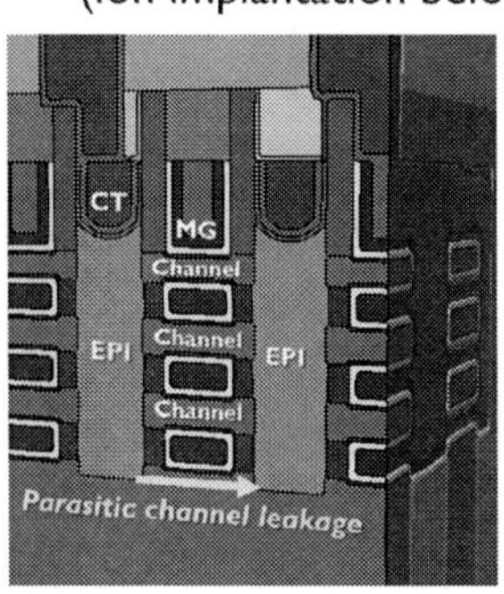

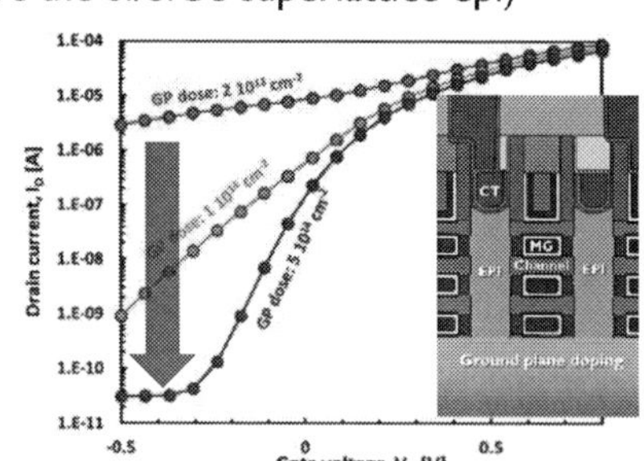

R. Ritzenthaler et al. (imec), ESSDERC 2017

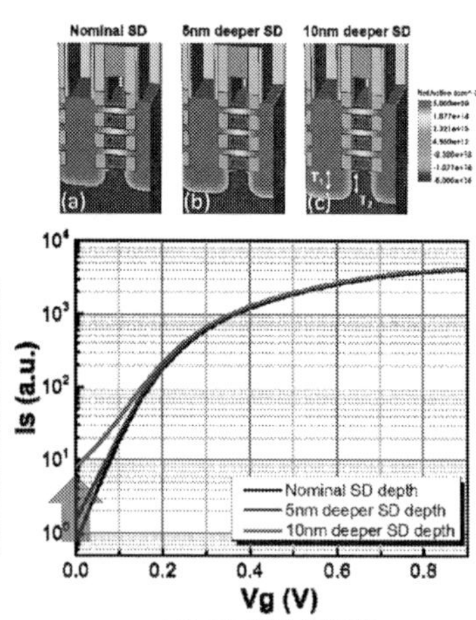

J. Zhang et al. (IBM), IEDM 2019

- Ioff increases with deeper SD recess and wider nanosheets
- → need for a robust solution to suppress the leakage

imec

Parasitic channel leakage reduction

Bottom and middle dielectric isolations (BDI/MDIs)

Nanosheet FET → **Forksheet FET**

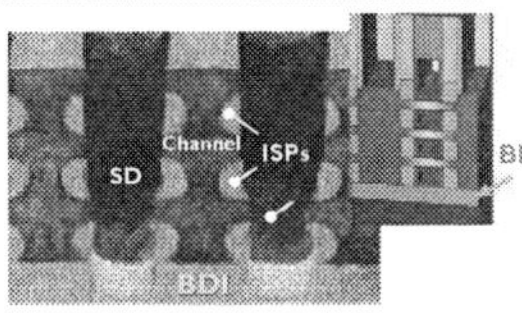

J. Zhang et al. (IBM), IEDM 2019

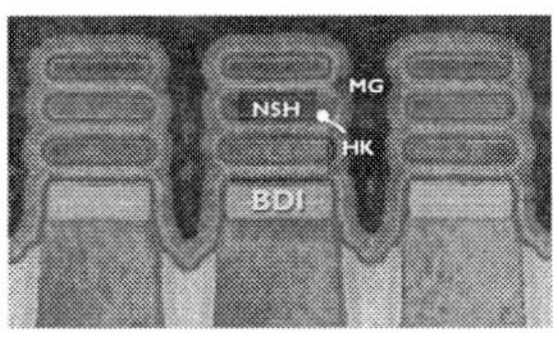

IBM press release

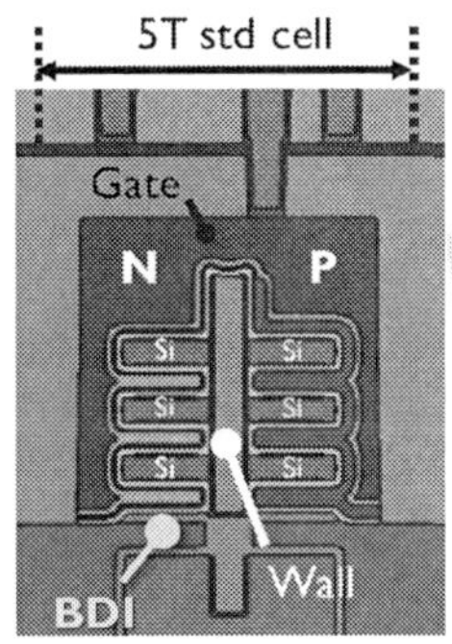

H. Mertens et al. (imec), VLSI 2021

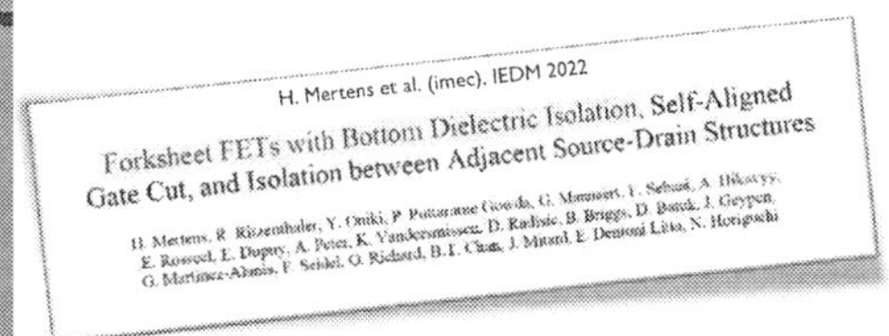

H. Mertens et al. (imec), IEDM 2022

Forksheet FETs with Bottom Dielectric Isolation, Self-Aligned Gate Cut, and Isolation between Adjacent Source-Drain Structures

imec

Parasitic channel leakage reduction

Bottom and middle dielectric isolations (BDI/MDIs)

Nanosheet FET → **Forksheet FET** → **Monolithic CFET**

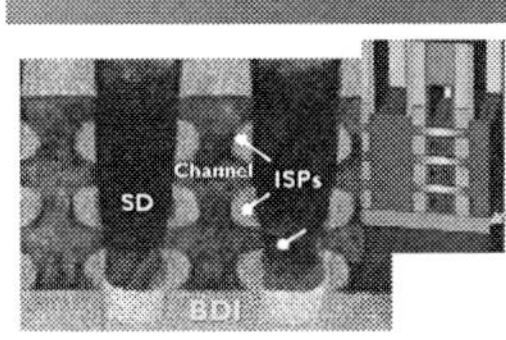

J. Zhang et al. (IBM), IEDM 2019

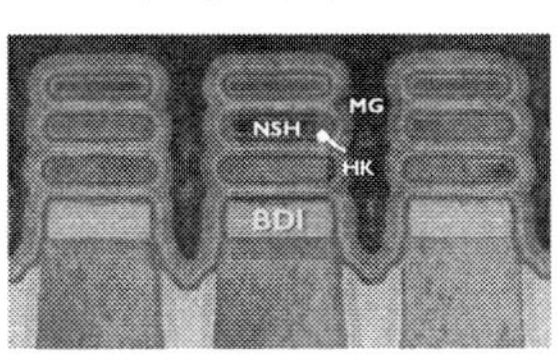

IBM press release

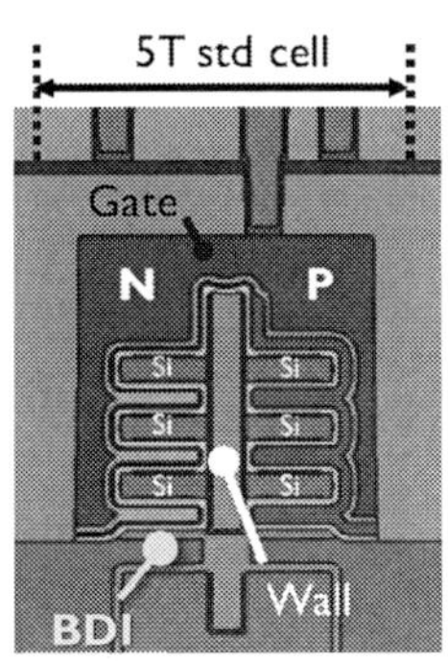

H. Mertens et al. (imec), VLSI 2021

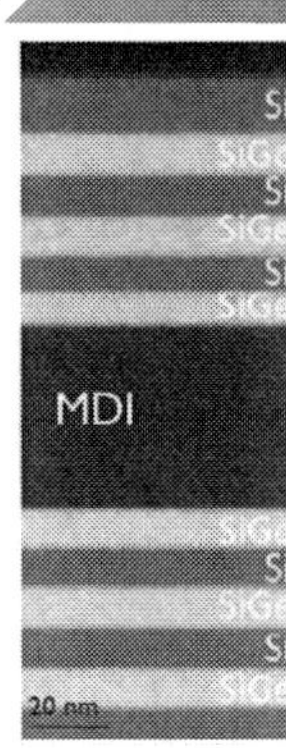

L. Van den hove (imec), SPIE 2022

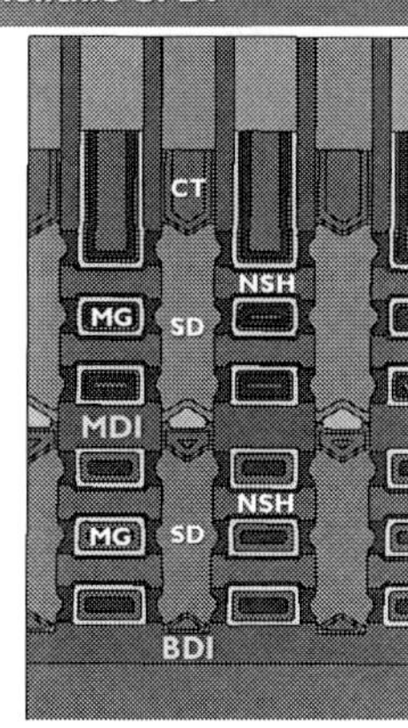

imec

Bottom/middle dielectric isolations (BDI/MDIs)

Methodology

- **Potential solution:** bottom/middle **SiGe layers w/ higher [Ge]** to be replaced by dielectric material(s)

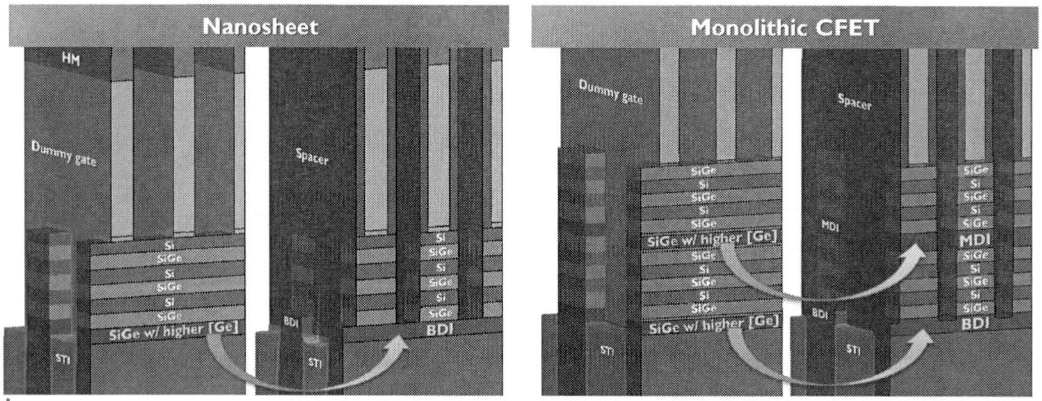

imec

BDI SiGe selective etch

Nanosheet

- **Potential solution:** bottom/middle **SiGe layers w/ higher [Ge]** to be replaced by dielectric material(s)

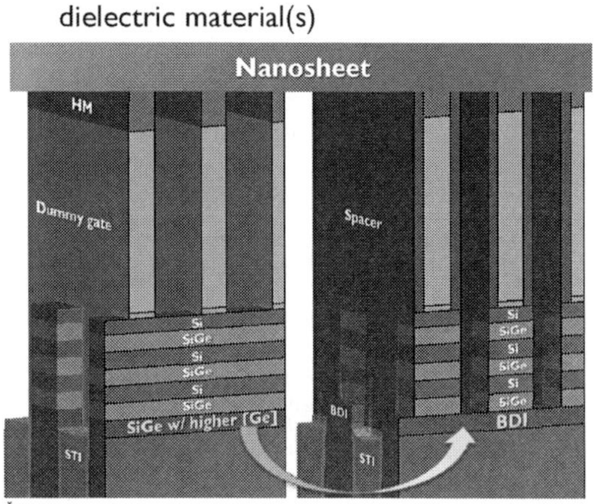

- BDI SiGe selective etch (APM): SiGe50% vs. SiGe20%, and dielectric fill demonstrated

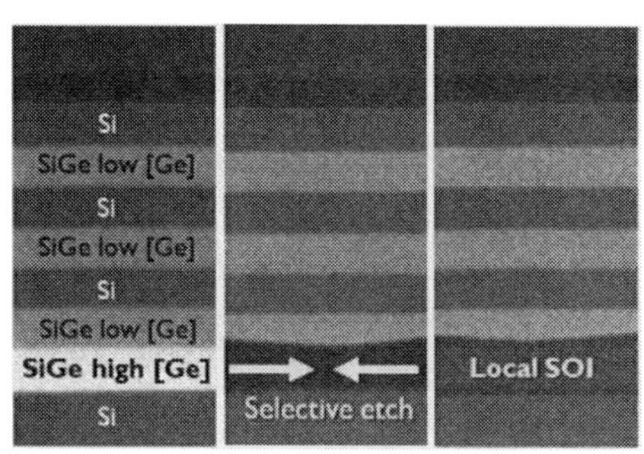

Y. Oniki et al. (imec), SPCC 2020

imec

Lower Ge% in SiGe layers needed for monolithic CFET

Need to find common process window of EPI and selective etch

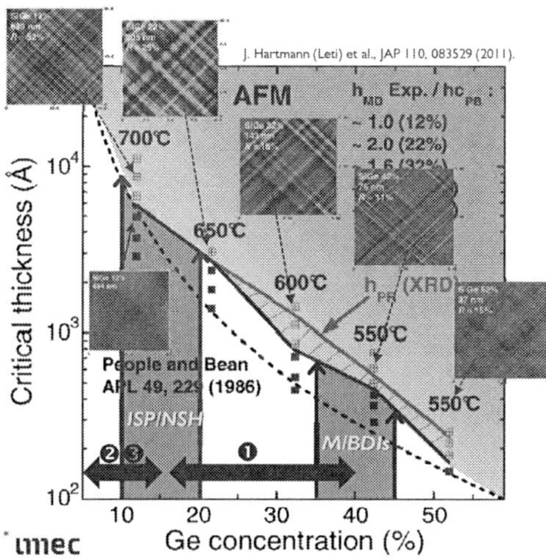

imec

mCFET Si/SiGe epi stack design requirements:

- Need for many Si/SiGe layers...
- Ge% reduction to avoid stress relaxation
- Need to guarantee sufficient etch contrast

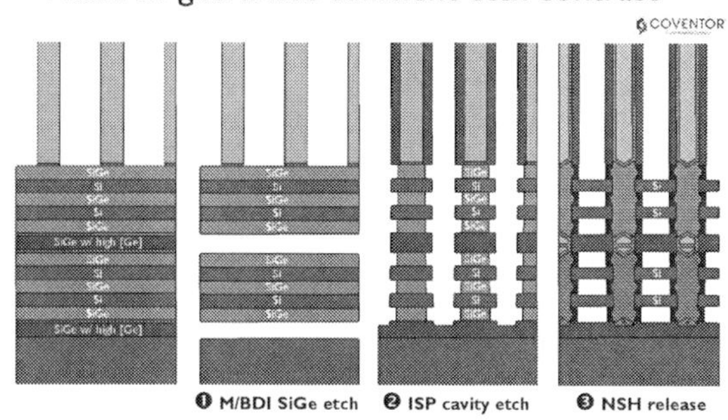

SiGe40% selective etch by APM

Selective etch SiGe40% vs. SiGe20%

APM (NH_4OH/H_2O_2/DIW)

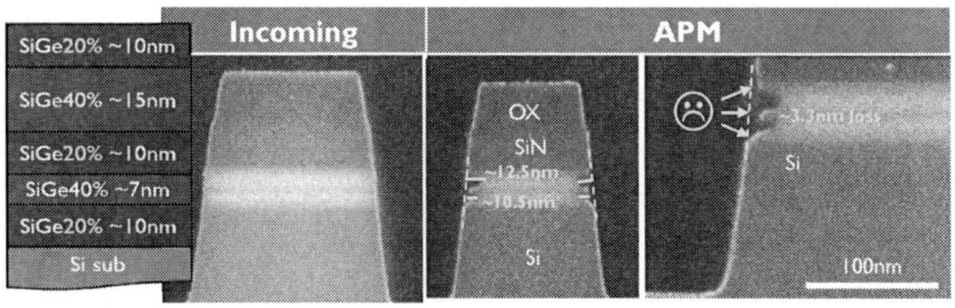

Selectivity SiGe40%:SiGe20% ~4:1

- SiGe40%/SiGe20% multilayer stack was etched by APM w/ HF pre clean
- Poor selectivity to SiGe20% seen

imec

SiGe40% selective etch by FPM based wet

Selective etch SiGe40% vs. SiGe20%

FPM ($HF/H_2O_2/DIW$) vs. FPM+HCl ($HF/HCl/H_2O_2/DIW$)

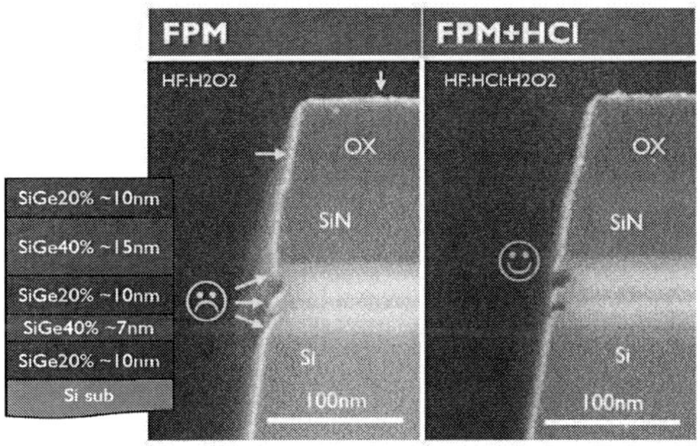

- SiGe40%/SiGe20% multilayer stack was etched by FPM and FPM with HCl w/ HF pre clean
- Selectivity to OX and SiGe20% improved with the addition of HCl (lower pH)

imec

Selective etch SiGe40% vs. SiGe20% by FPM+ ($HF/HCl/H_2O_2/DIW$)

Impact of **HF dilution**

- Higher HF conc, higher SiGe40% ER, but poorer selectivity to OX and SiGe20%
- Lower HF conc, controlled SiGe40% etch but no obvious impact on the selectivity to SiGe20%

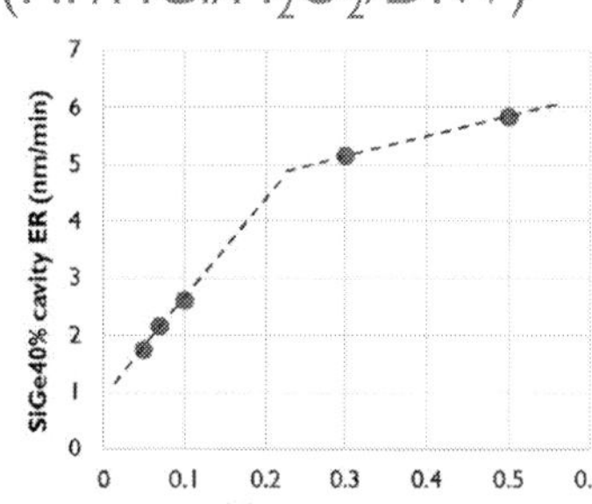

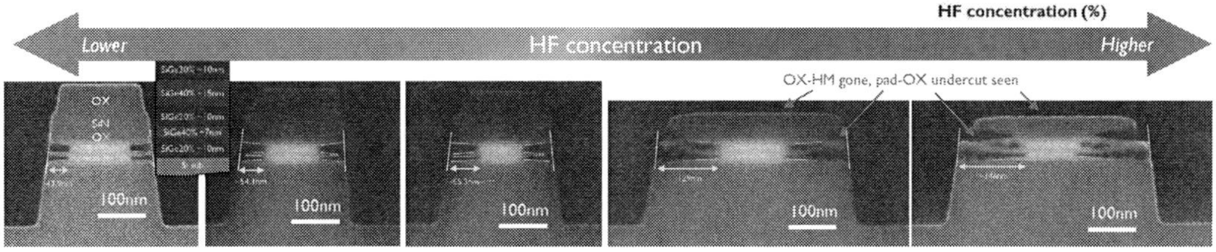

imec With HF Pre-clean

Selective etch SiGe40% vs. SiGe20% by FPM+ (HF/HCl/H_2O_2/DIW)

Impact of **H_2O_2 dilution**

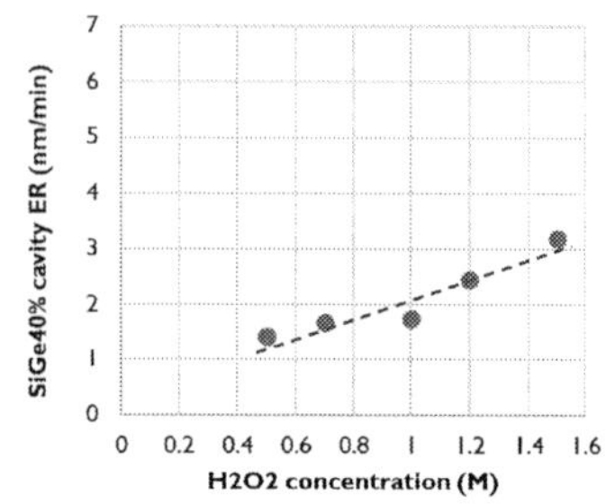

- Higher H_2O_2 conc, higher SiGe40% ER, but poorer selectivity to SiGe20%
- Lower H_2O_2 conc, better selectivity towards SiGe20%

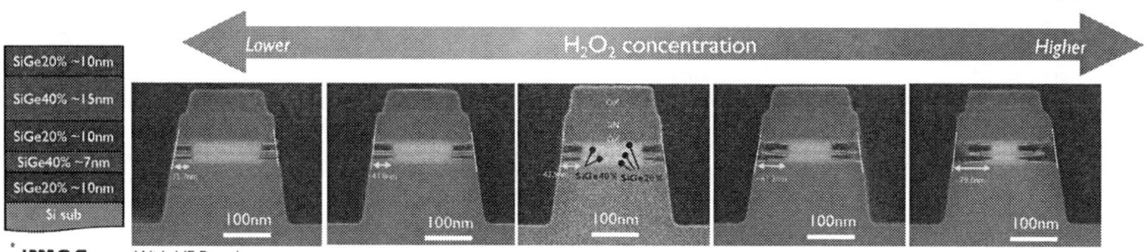

imec

With HF Pre-clean

Selective etch SiGe40% vs. **SiGe15%** by FPM+ (HF/HCl/H_2O_2/DIW)

Impact of **H_2O_2 dilution**

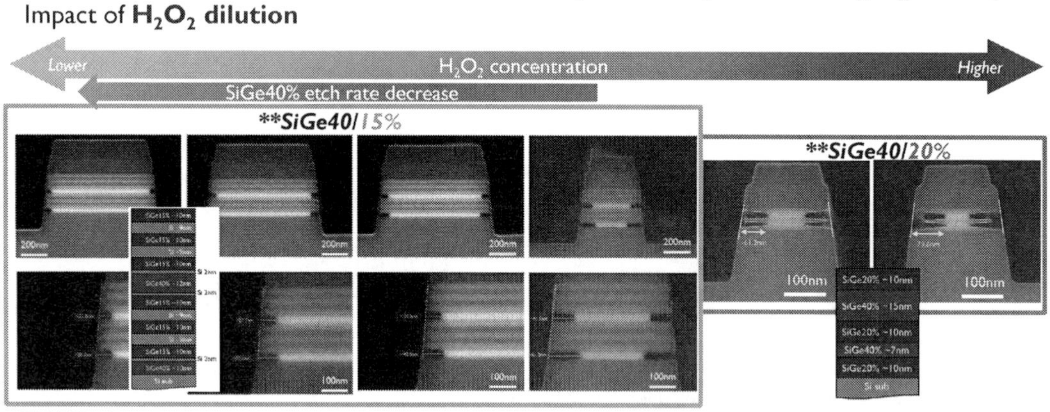

With HF Pre-clean

- Trade-off between SiGe40% etch rate and SiGe15% selectivity observed

imec

Selective etch SiGe40% vs. **SiGe15%** inference

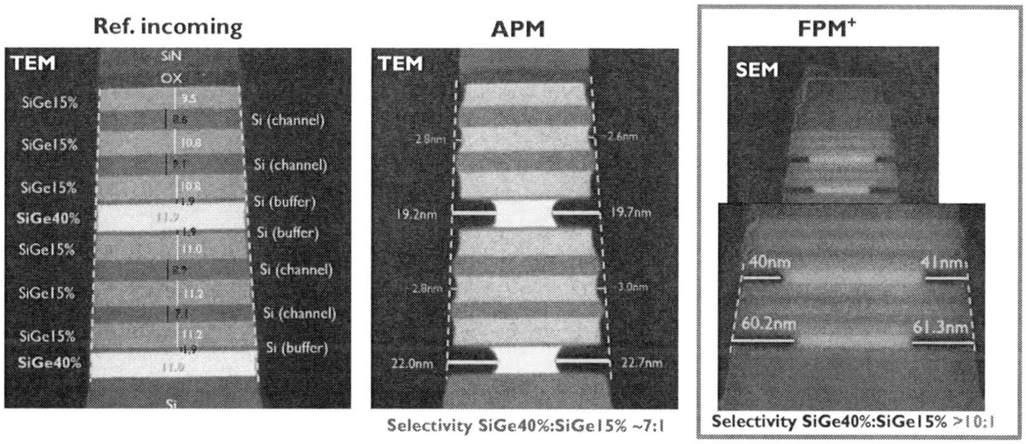

- FPM⁺ shows better selectivity towards SiGe15% compared to APM
- Opportunity of wet formulations or dry etch for further selectivity improvement

imec

SiGe selective etch opportunities

Monolithic CFET

- Opportunities of wet formulations and dry etch for SiGe selective etch

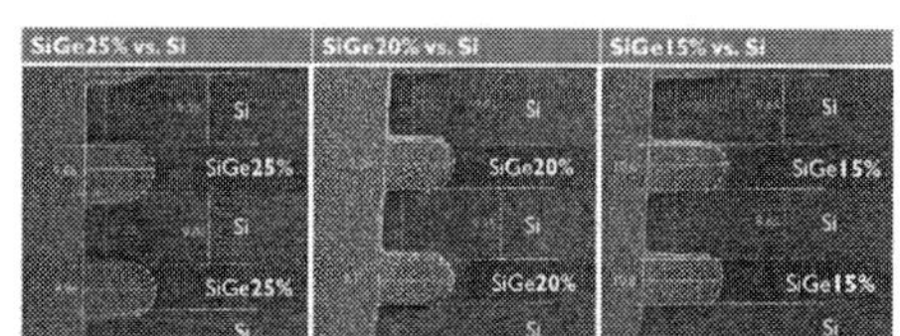

Y. Oniki et al. (imec)
SPCC 2020

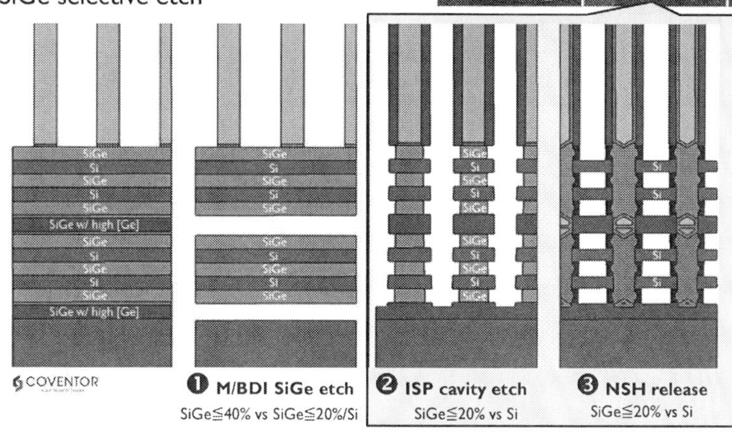

imec

Summary

Summary

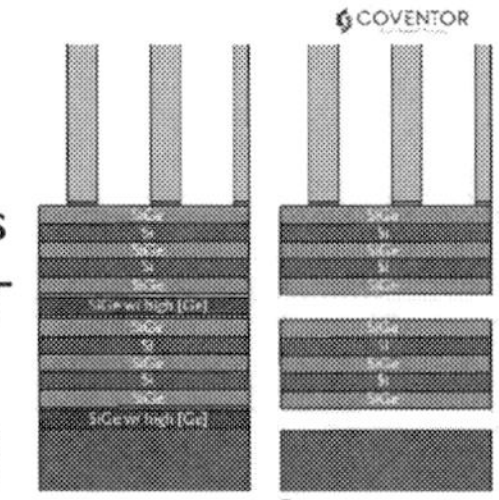

- Logic device scaling continues with new GAA device architectures
- Dielectric isolations (BDI/MDIs) are required for monolithic CFET
- Sacrificial SiGe layers w/ higher [Ge] to be replaced by dielectric materials → **need for SiGe selective etch High vs Low [Ge]**
- SiGe40% selective etch vs. SiGe≦20%/Si by commodity chemicals
  - APM shows poor selectivity to SiGe20%
  - FPM selectivity to SiGe20% and OX improved with the addition of HCl (FPM^+)
  - FPM^+ with lower HF and H_2O_2 concentrations selectively etches SiGe40% vs. SiGe≦20%
- Opportunity of wet formulations or dry etch for further selectivity improvement

imec

imec
embracing a better life
CONFIDENTIAL

Nanosheet RMG work-function metal patterning towards CFET

Ju-Geng Lai, Yusuke Oniki and Efrain Altamirano-Sánchez
imec, Kapeldreef 75, Leuven, Belgium
Kenneth.Lai@imec.be

Overview

- Challenge for nanosheet WFM patterning towards CFET
- Experimental: preparation of test structures
- pWFM TiN etching evaluation
  - RMG SOC wet chemical compatibility
  - TiN etch in nanosheets with HPM
  - SOC/TiN undercut by HPM and APM
- nWFM TiAlC etching evaluation
  - HPM and APM ER evaluation for TiN/TiAlC blanket films
  - TiN/TiAlC etch in nanosheets and undercut with HPM and APM
- Summary

Challenges for Nanosheet WFM patterning

Concern: N/P boundary (NPB) control

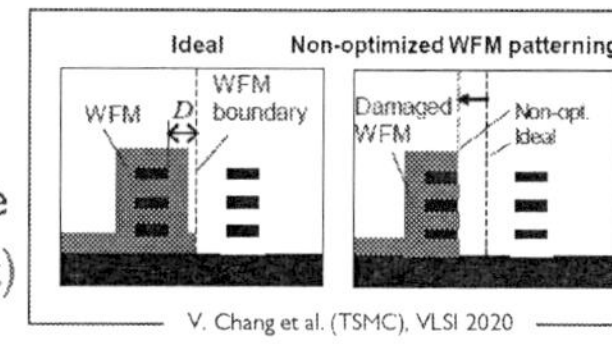

- To avoid mask gap-fill in nanosheets with pinch-off metal gate
- Concern on the WFM lateral etch under the mask (undercut)
  - The covered devices will be damaged in the worst case
- WFM etch selectivity between ① **in nanosheets** and ② **under the mask** to be assessed

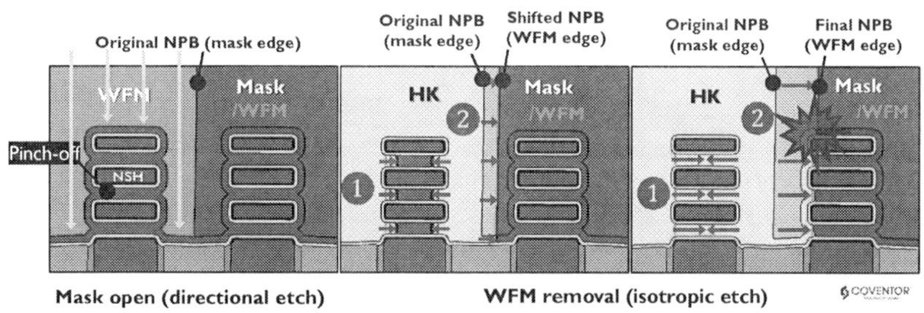

imec

CFET top/bottom WFM patterning

Monolithic CFET

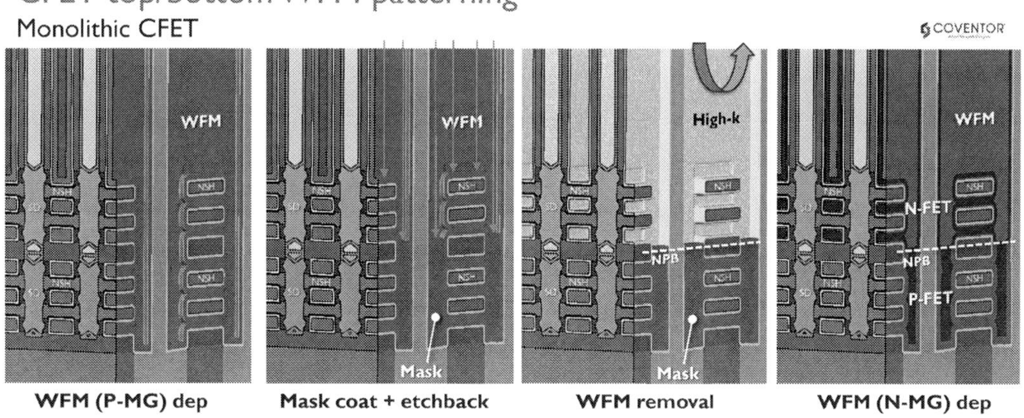

- CFET N/P boundary defined by mask etchback NU + **WFM undercut**

imec

Experimental: preparation of test structures

1. WFM wet etch between NSHs

- NSH Si/SiGe stack epitaxy
- NSH patterning & STI etch
- Dry strip and clean
- SiGe recess
- IL & HK deposition
- WFM fill

2. WFM wet etch under SOC

- IL/HK deposition
- WFM deposition
- SOC/SOG HM coating
- Lithography
- SOC/SOG open
- SOG removal

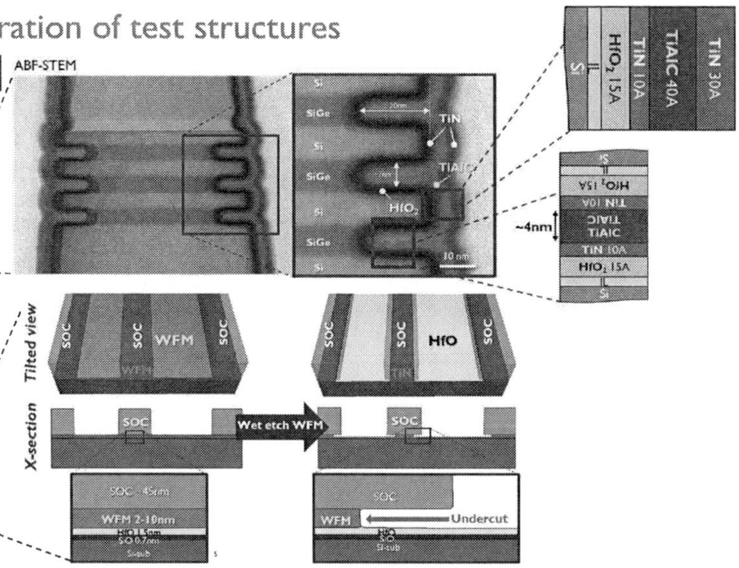

imec

pWFM TiN etching evaluation

RMG SOC wet chemical compatibility
Patterning mask

- imec RMG SOC HM is compatible with APM and HPM

imec

TiN etch in nanosheets with HPM
pWFM patterning

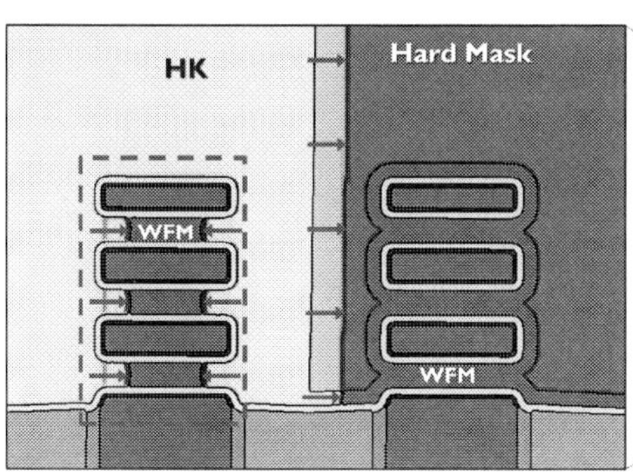

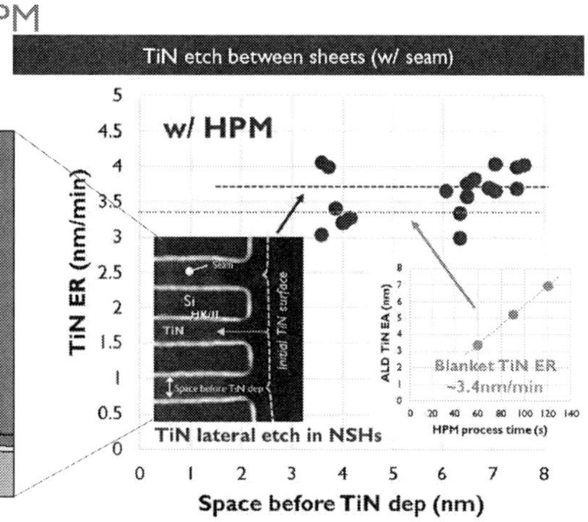

- TiN ER independent from sheet space = **Preferential etching along the seam**

imec

SOC/TiN undercut by HPM (1:1:8) 50°C

TiN thickness dependency

- Negligible undercut seen in the first 5min
- Undercut increased w/ TiN THK and etch time

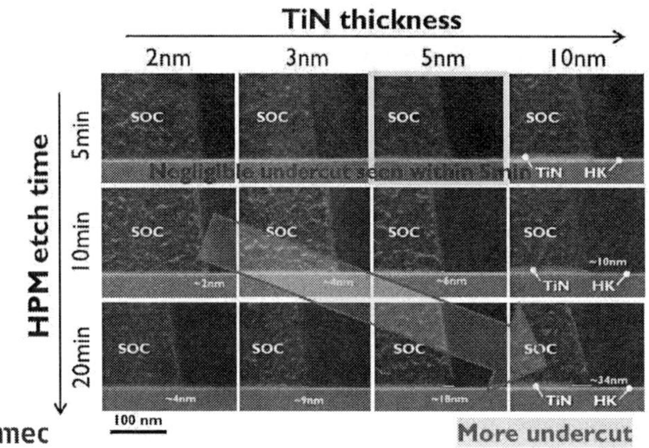

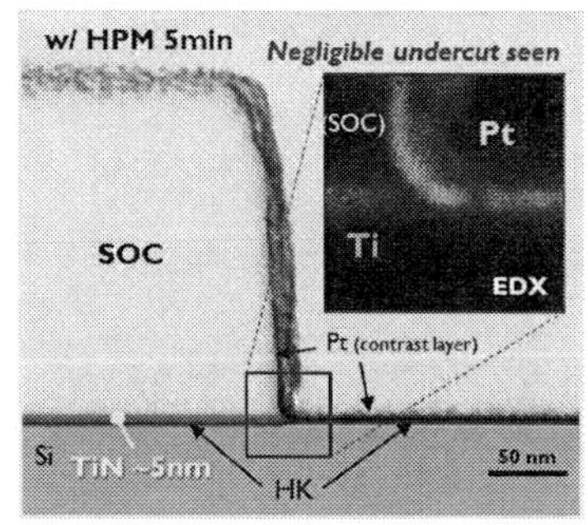

imec

SOC/TiN undercut by HPM (1:1:8) 50°C

TiN thickness dependency

- Undercut can be minimized with thinner WFMs and shorter etch time.
- TiN undercut rate shows lower than the ER on blanket.

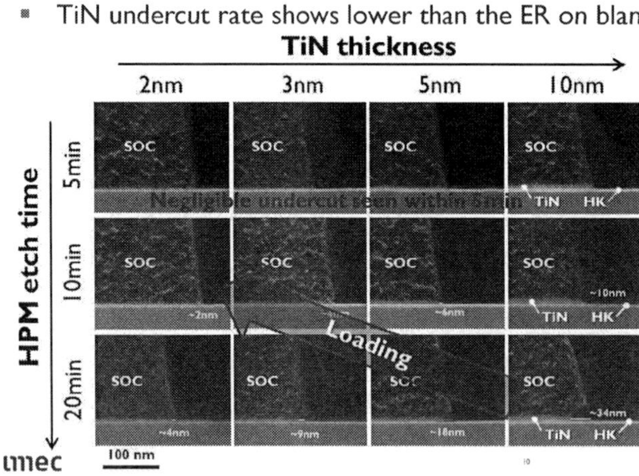

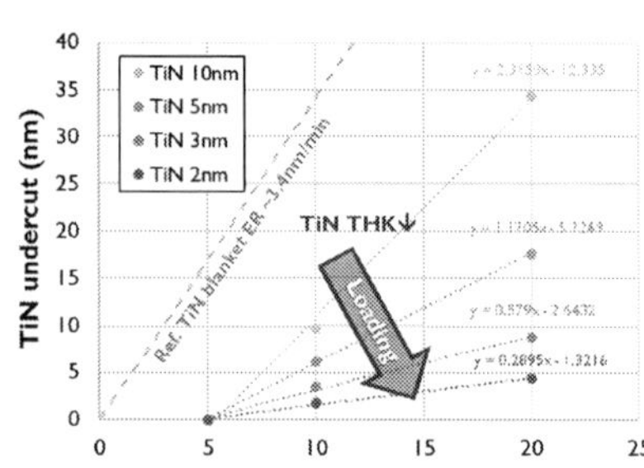

imec

Forksheet WFM patterning

Dual WFM patterning

- **Forksheet dual WFM with ~17nm N/P separation demonstrated**
  - **5nm TiN** (sheet-sheet space after HK dep ~6nm) removed by HPM
  - Negligible NPB undercut seen thank to the incubation and loading effect

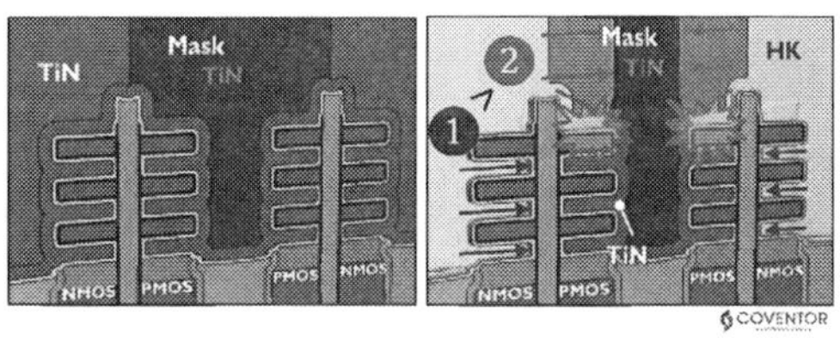

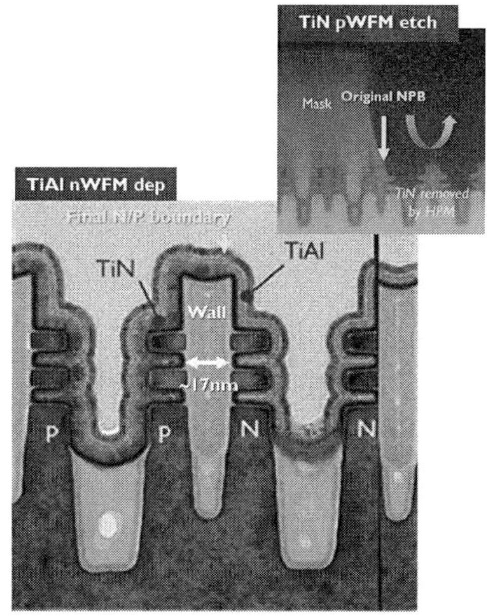

imec

SOC/TiN undercut with APM

SOC adhesion issue

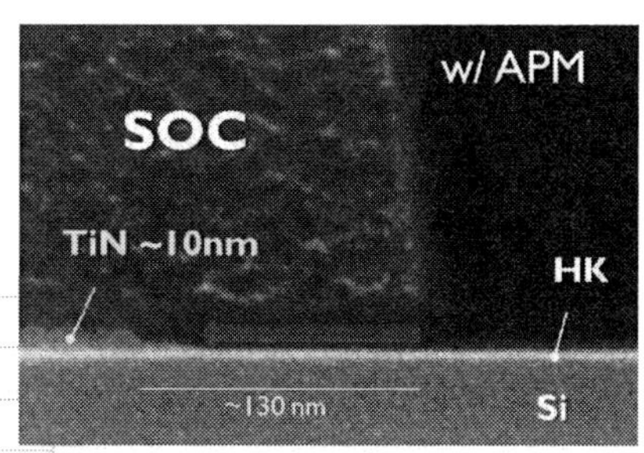

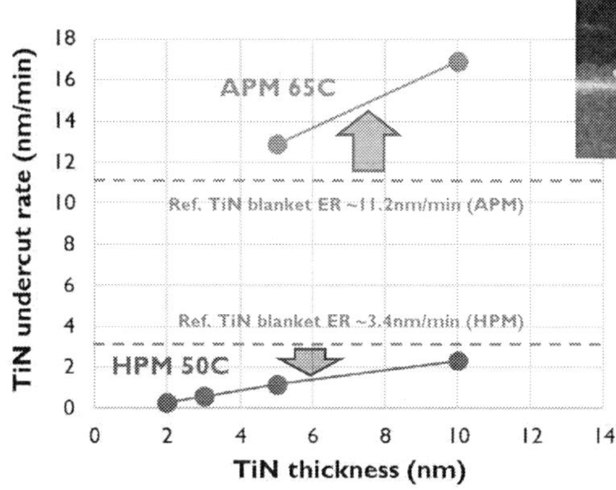

TiN etch with APM (1:4:20) 65°C

- Higher undercut rate w.r.t. blanket TiN etch
- SOC/TiN interface preferentially etched
  - Suspect APM convert TiN surface from hydrophobic (HMDS priming) to hydrophilic resulted in weaker adhesion between SOC/TiN interface.
  - Seam between SOC/TiN interface assisted TiN etch.

imec

nWFM TiAlC etching evaluation

HPM and APM ER evaluation for TiN/TiAlC blanket films

HPM vs APM

TiN blanket wet ER

- HPM 50°C: ~3.4nm/min
- APM 50°C: ~9nm/min

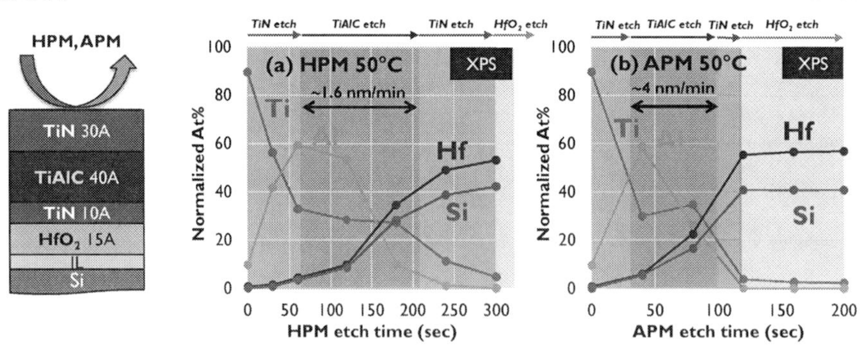

- TiN/TiAlC/TiN etched over HK by HPM and APM
- TiAlC ER roughly estimated as ~1.6nm/min (HPM) and ~4nm/min (APM)

imec

TiAlC nWFM wet etch
HPM

- Sidewall layers fully removed in 300s (consistent with blanket)
- TiN/TiAlC in ~20nm depth cavities fully removed in extra 300s (seam assisted etch?)

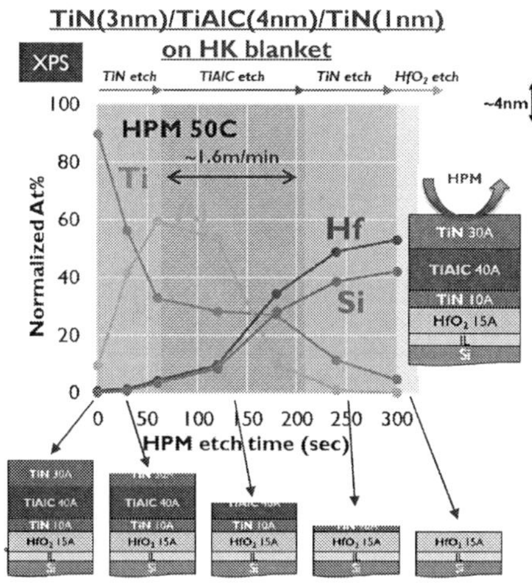

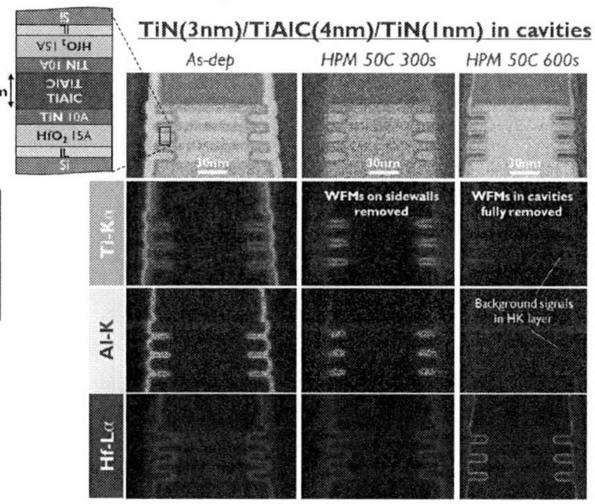

TiN vs. TiN/TiAlC/TiN undercut by HPM
TiAlC thickness dependency

- Slightly lower ER for TiAlC w.r.t. TiN (consistent with blanket ER)

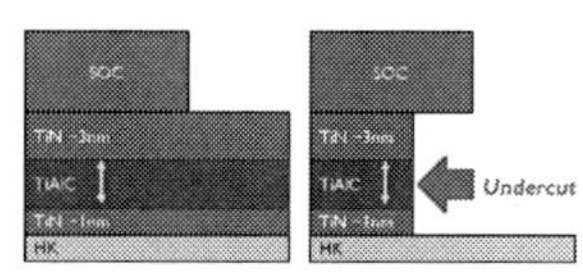

HPM (1:1:8) 50°C ER on blanket
- TiN: 3.4nm/min
- TiAlC: 1.6nm/min

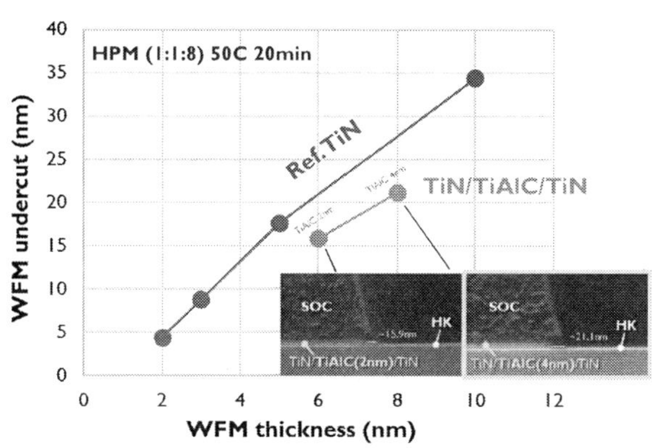

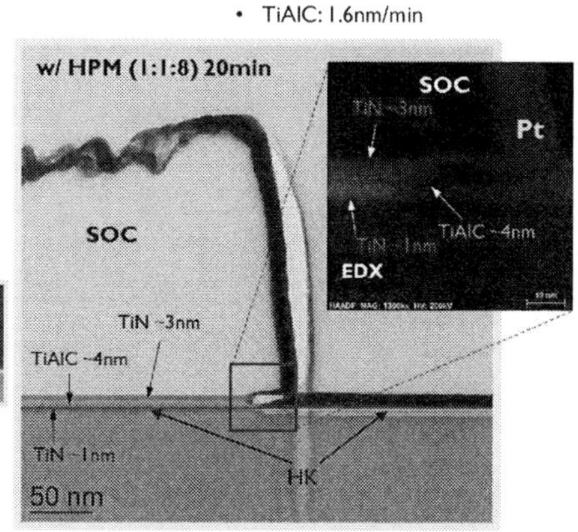

imec

TiN/TiAlC/TiN undercut by HPM vs. APM

SOC adhesion issue

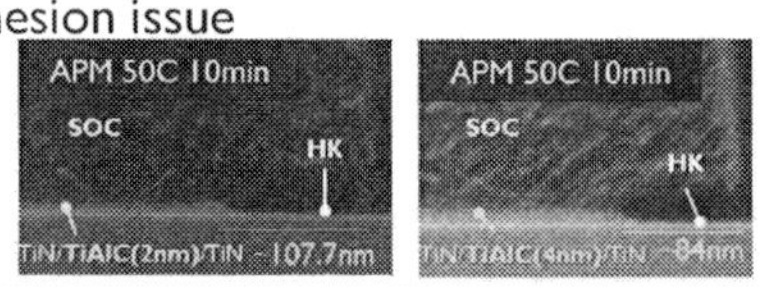

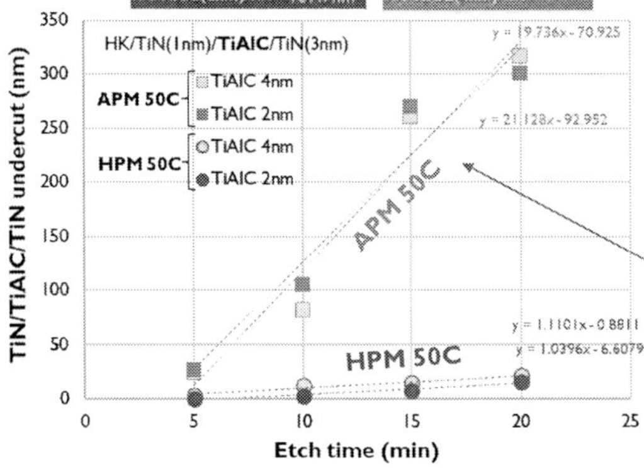

TiAlC blanket ER

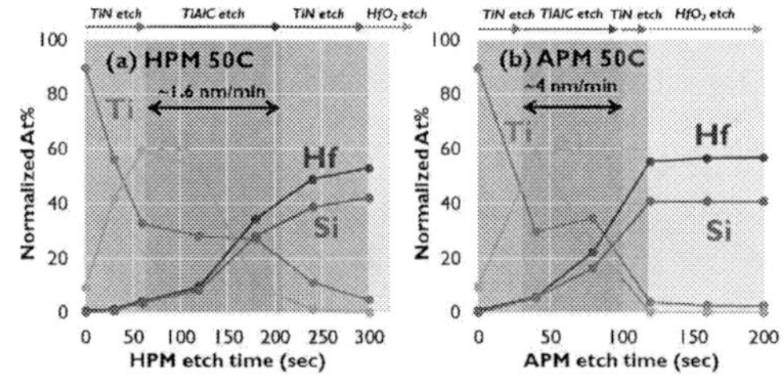

SOC/TiN/TiAl/TiN etch with APM (1:4:20) 50C

- Extremely high undercut rate with APM than HPM and the ER on blanket.
- The same issue found on SOC/TiN (pWFM undercut)

Summary

Summary

Nanosheet RMG workfunction metal patterning towards CFET

- Fast WFM etching between nanosheets = **seam assisted etch**
- WFM lateral etching under SOC can be minimized with thinner WFMs = (incubation +) **loading effect**
- Sufficient process window of the WFM etching in sheets vs. under SOC seen on the forksheet architecture demonstrated
- Poor compatibility of imec RMG SOC/WFM interfaces with APM → need for alternative SOC materials and/or pre treatment iso HMDS

imec

imec

embracing a better life

JLFG
COMMUNICATIONS

Water and Other Chemicals

Environmental Concerns for Semiconductor Processing

Dr. Julia Goldstein
Founder, JLFG Communications
Author, *Material Value* and *Beyond the Green Team*

JLFG

Julia L F Goldstein, PhD

- Julia@jlfgoldstein.com
- 408-761-3272
- https://jlfgcommunications.com
- https://juliagoldsteinauthor.com

JLFG

Sustainability 101 Series, 3DInCites

1. Greenhouse gas emissions – Definitions and scopes
2. Sustainability reporting –Standards and trends
3. Circular economy, part I – What is zero waste?
4. The product lifecycle – Sustainability and the supply chain
5. **Chemicals of concern – Moving beyond RoHS**
6. Water management – Global problem, local solutions
7. Circular economy, part II – Improving e-waste

JLFG

Cleaning: A Necessary Evil?

- Need to strip photoresists
- Residues cause defects
- More layers, finer features
- Common chemicals are toxic
- Challenge: make cleaning safer, maintain performance

JLFG
COMMUNICATIONS

Toxic Cleaning Chemicals: NMP

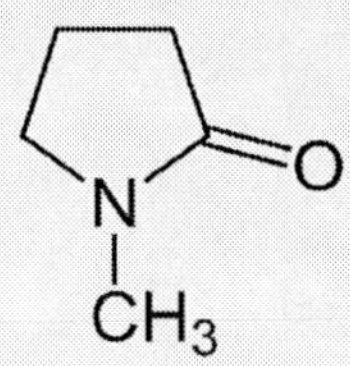

- N-methyl pyrrolidone or 1-methyl-2-pyrrolidone
- "Mutagenic effects have occurred in microorganisms."
- "Experiments have shown reproductive toxicity effects on laboratory animals."
- EPA proposed a ban in 2017
- European Chemicals Agency restricted use since May 2020

JLFG
COMMUNICATIONS

Toxic Cleaning Chemicals: NMP

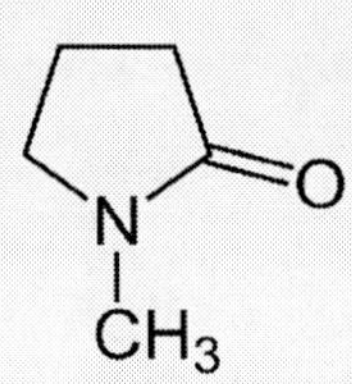

Substance	Water	NMP
Appearance	Clear, colorless liquid	Clear, colorless liquid
Boiling point	100 °C	201 °C
Health hazard	0 (none)	2 (hazardous)
Fire hazard	0 (none)	2 (flash point below 38 °C)

JLFG
COMMUNICATIONS

Toxic Cleaning Chemicals: TMAH

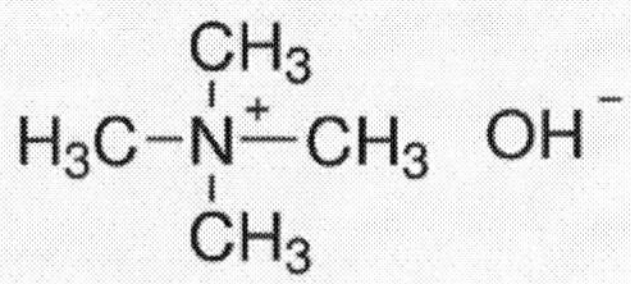

- Tetramethylammonium hydroxide
- No metal ions
- "Acute dermal toxicity;" causes skin burns and damages the central nervous system
- "Fatal if swallowed or in contact with skin"

JLFG
COMMUNICATIONS

Two Approaches to Improve Sustainability

Replace offending chemicals

Increase the concentration

JLFG
COMMUNICATIONS

Safer Choice Guidelines

SAFER CHOICE
Meets U.S. EPA Safer Product Standards™
epa.gov/saferchoice

Functional Classes

- Surfactants
- **Solvents**
- Defoamers
- Additives

JLFG
COMMUNICATIONS

Does not Pass Safer Choice Criteria

Can be Considered for Safer Choice Criteria

Of Concern	**Presumptively of Concern**	**Insufficiently** characterized	**Presumptively Low Concern**	**Low Concern**
Test data demonstrating *Concern*	Structural analogy* to a chemical of *Concern*	No testing available and lack of structural analogy to a tested chemical	Structural analogy* to a chemical of *Low Concern*	Test data demonstrating *Low Concern*

*Can also include metabolic or mechanistic analogy.

Carcinogenicity, neurotoxicity

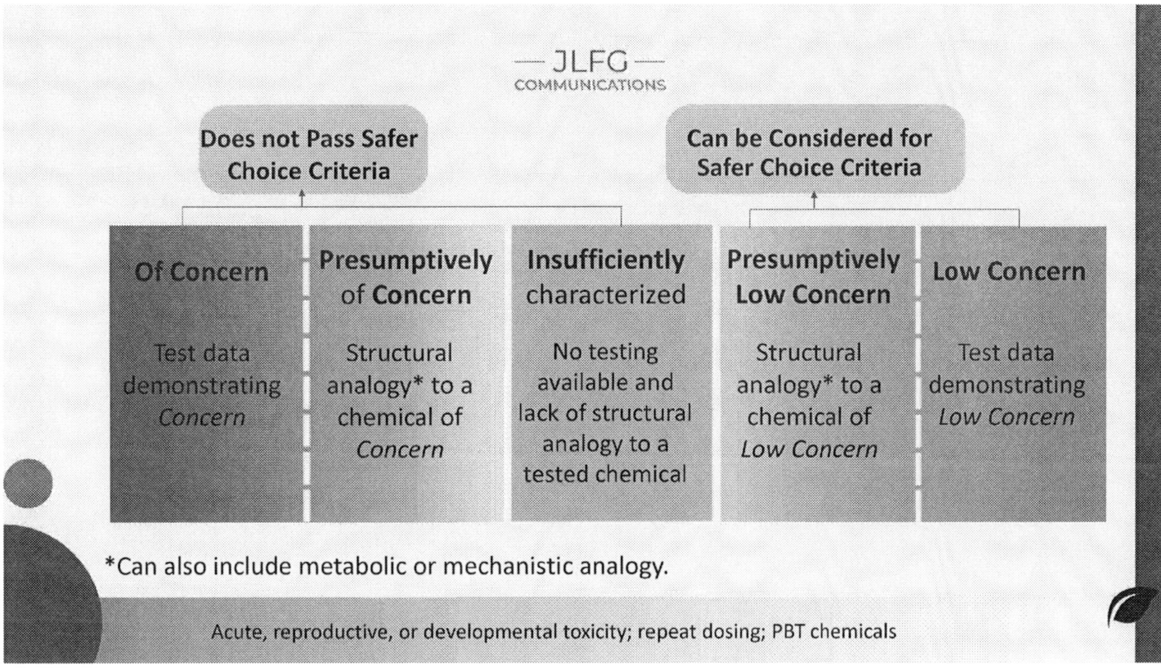
JLFG
COMMUNICATIONS
Does not Pass Safer Choice Criteria
Can be Considered for Safer Choice Criteria
Of Concern
Test data demonstrating *Concern*
Presumptively of Concern
Structural analogy* to a chemical of *Concern*
Insufficiently characterized
No testing available and lack of structural analogy to a tested chemical
Presumptively Low Concern
Structural analogy* to a chemical of *Low Concern*
Low Concern
Test data demonstrating *Low Concern*
*Can also include metabolic or mechanistic analogy.
Acute, reproductive, or developmental toxicity; repeat dosing; PBT chemicals

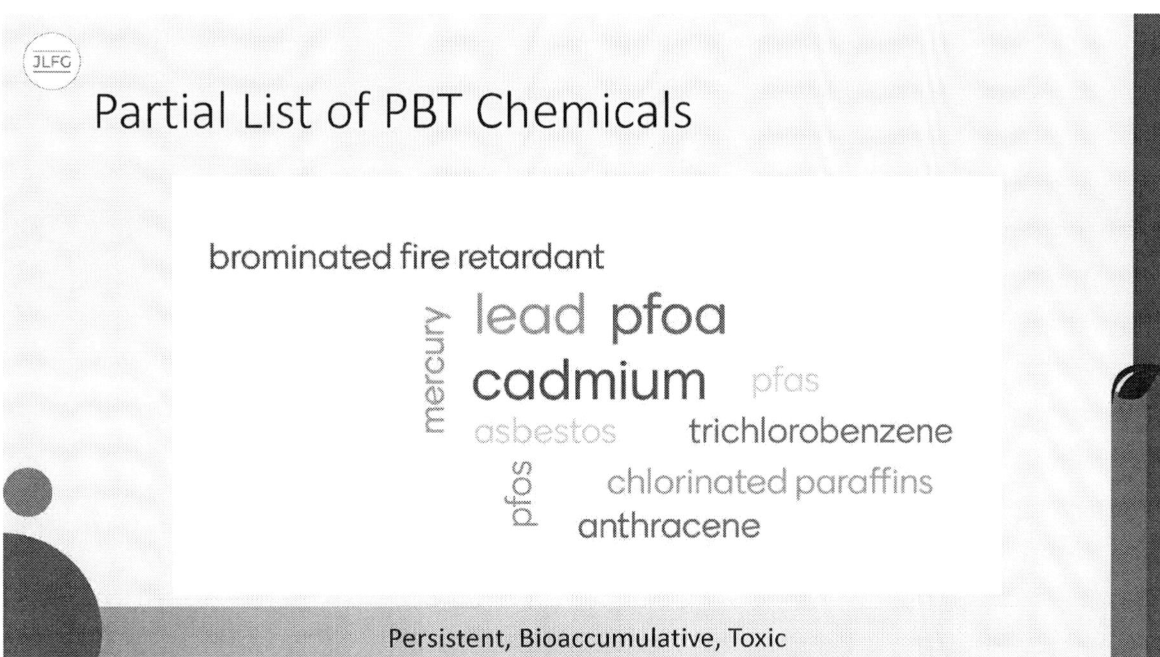
JLFG
Partial List of PBT Chemicals
brominated fire retardant
mercury
lead
pfoa
cadmium
pfas
asbestos
trichlorobenzene
pfos
chlorinated paraffins
anthracene
Persistent, Bioaccumulative, Toxic

JLFG COMMUNICATIONS

MSDS (SDS)

- Chemical name
- Ingredient listing
- Statement about carcinogens
- Safe handling and storage practices
- Physical and chemical properties

NMP, Sisco Research Lab:

"Do not let this chemical enter the environment"

"Readily biodegradable"

JLFG COMMUNICATIONS

NFPA Rating

Useful for firefighters and hazmat crews

Limited for engineers and product designers

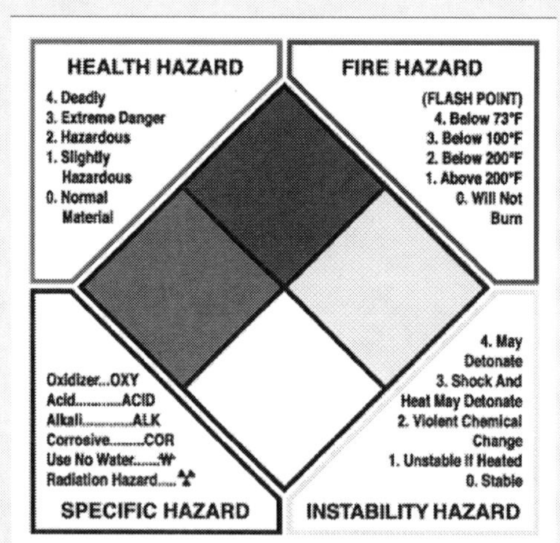

Residual Solvent Classification

Residual Solvent Class	Description
Class 1 (avoid)	Known or strongly suspected carcinogens, ozone-depleting chemicals
Class 2 (limit)	Possible neurotoxicity or teratogenicity, significant but reversible toxicity
Class 3 (preferred)	Low toxic potential, no set exposure limit

"Safer" Options: DMSO

- Dimethyl sulfoxide
- NFPA rating the same as for NMP
- Residual solvents class 3 (NMP class 2)

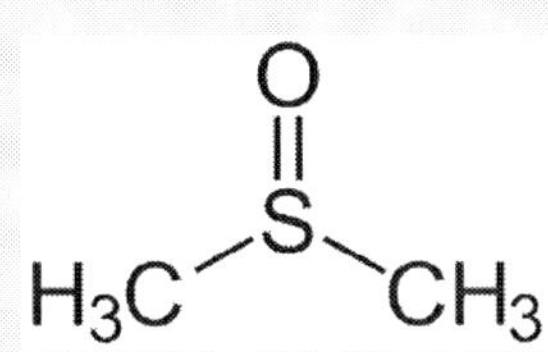

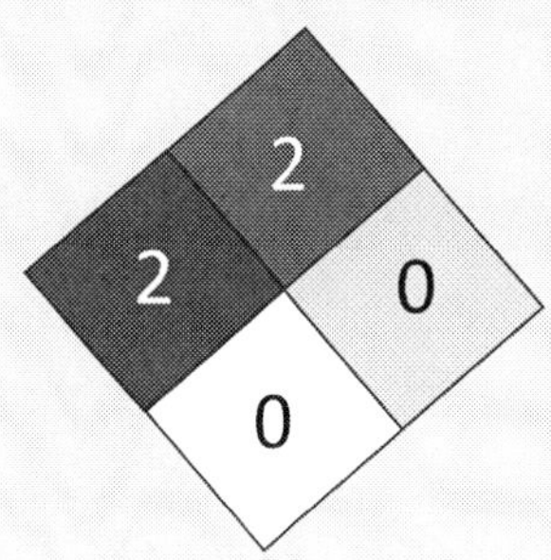

"There are no long-term toxicity or carcinogenic studies for many of the solvents in class 3…they are less toxic in acute or short-term studies."

— JLFG —
COMMUNICATIONS

"Safer" Options: DMSO

- Another clear, colorless liquid
- "Mutagenic effects in mammalian somatic cells"
- "Teratogenic effects in animal experiments"
- "According to the results of tests of biodegradability, this product is not readily biodegradable."

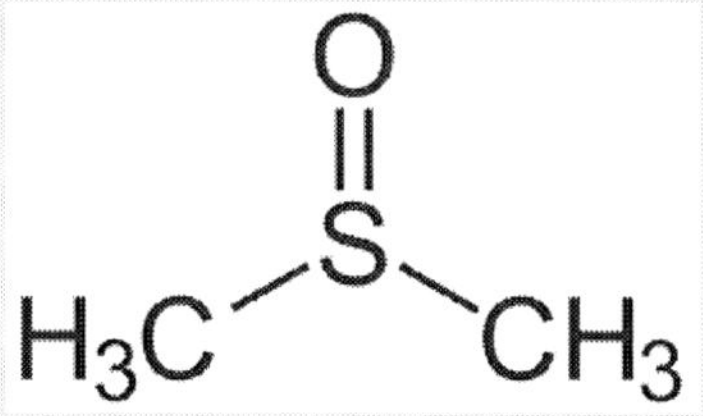

JLFG

How to Evaluate Replacements?

- SDS not adequate
- Safer choice doesn't cover industrial chemicals
- Restrictions: RoHS, REACH
- ChemSec SIN list: https://sinlist.chemsec.org/
- Scivera selection/screening tool: https://www.scivera.com/sciveralens/

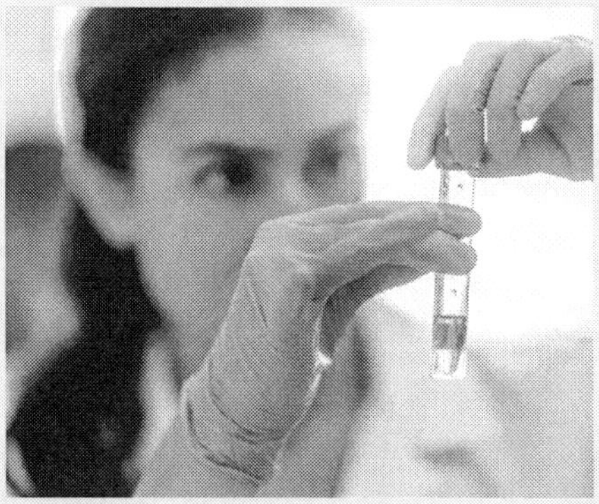

JLFG

Benefits of Concentrated Chemicals

REDUCED PACKAGING

LOWER TRANSPORTATION-RELATED EMISSIONS

DILUTE ON-SITE TO PRECISE CONCENTRATION

JLFG COMMUNICATIONS

On-Site Dilution

Greater dilution rates:

- Minimize chemical consumption
- Reduce hazardous waste generation
- Can be just as effective

JLFG

Example: APM Dilution

AMMONIUM HYDROXIDE/ HYDROGEN PEROXIDE/ WATER SOLUTION

"ENVIRONMENTALLY CONSCIOUS WET CLEANING PROCESS"

$NH_4OH/H_2O_2/H_2O$ RATIO 1:2:40

JLFG

Ideal Replacement Chemical

- Highly effective at removing residues
- Not toxic, carcinogenic, mutagenic, or teratogenic
- Non-volatile
- Non-flammable
- Readily available in concentrated form for on-site dilution

JLFG
COMMUNICATIONS
Thank you!
Julia@jlfgoldstein.com
Jlfgcommunications.com
Juliagoldsteinauthor.com
Free PDF of Material Value available at jlfgcommunications.com/bookstore through October 31.
Beyond the Green Team is coming out November 1.
MATERIAL VALUE
Julia L F Goldstein, PhD
BEYOND THE GREEN TEAM
Julia L F Goldstein, PhD

AUTHOR INDEX

Surface Preparation and Cleaning Conference (SPCC)
c/o Mark Thirsk
Linx Consulting-PO Box 384
Mendon, MA 01756-0384
USA

ISBN 978-1-7138-6333-5

CURRAN ASSOCIATES INC.
proceedings.com